AUTHORS DIGEST

THE WORLD'S GREAT STORIES IN BRIEF, PREPARED BY A STAFF OF LITERARY EXPERTS, WITH THE ASSISTANCE OF MANY LIVING NOVELISTS

ROSSITER JOHNSON, Ph.D., LL.D.
EDITOR-IN-CHIEF

ISSUED UNDER THE AUSPICES OF THE

AUTHORS PRESS

AUTHORS DIGEST

AUTHORS PRESS

"This mustard-pot, here, is the startin'-point of our system"
(*Colonel Carter of Cartersville*, p. 303)

Hand-colored photogravure on French Plate Paper after an original painting made for this edition by S. A. Moss

AUTHORS DIGEST

VOLUME XV

WALTER SCOTT
TO
LAURENCE STERNE

Issued under the auspices of the
AUTHORS PRESS

CONTENTS

CONTENTS

WALTER SCOTT

(Scotland, 1771–1832)

KENILWORTH (1821)

That peculiar faculty possessed by Walter Scott of transporting his readers to the Middle Ages and making them feel at home in Gothic castles and amid scenes of long-gone chivalry, is particularly displayed in *Kenilworth*. Scott considered that he had been most happy in drawing the character of Elizabeth. Whatever history may say of her, the Elizabeth of *Kenilworth* is the Elizabeth whom the world knows to-day. Scott was led to write the story by the sad old ballad of "Cumnor Hall," in which the story of Amy Robsart is told; and his success in depicting the character of Queen Mary Stuart in *The Abbot* made him wish to draw the character of her rival. *Kenilworth* is considered by many as second only to *Ivanhoe*.

 BRIGHT sun rose on the day when Dudley, Earl of Leicester, was to receive his royal mistress, the lioness of the Tudors, in his lordly Castle of Kenilworth. The reigning favorite of the Queen, rich, handsome, and noble, he stood so high in the royal sun that the world confidently expected to see his Earl's coronet changed for the crown-matrimonial of England. He had commanded masks and wondrous pageants for the entertainment of Elizabeth, who was approaching from Warwick.

Among the noisy throng that filled all the highways leading to the castle rode a horseman in the garb of a serving-man of the upper class. By his side on a palfrey rode a lady young and beautiful, whose exquisite grace of form could not be concealed by her plain russet riding-habit. Fatigue and anxiety showed on her face. It was evident that she kept her saddle only by an extreme effort of will.

The two travelers were about to be denied admittance to the castle when a boy, dressed as a devil in preparation for his part in one of the masks, assured the warder that they were mem-

bers of his own troupe.   The boy had recognized in the serving-
man a former farrier of the Vale of White Horse, Wayland Smith.
As soon as they were inside the walls he asked the man what had
brought him to Kenilworth and who the lady was.   "Beshrew
me, Dickie Sludge," answered the man, "thou art so sharp and
curious, e'en find out for thyself."   The lad went off vowing
that it was a poor return.

Wayland whispered to the first servant he met and was shown
with his charge into an apartment in Mervin's Tower.   There
was writing material in the room, and the lady wrote a letter
which she gave to her attendant, saying: "Good Master Wayland, whom God has sent to aid me in my need, convey this at
once to the Earl of Leicester."

"I will find Master Tressilian first," thought Wayland Smith
as he left the tower.   "He, belike, is the best judge of whether
this letter should be delivered."

Wayland was Tressilian's servant.   He had been sent to
obtain news of Amy, daughter of old Sir Hugh Robsart
of Devonshire, who, as Tressilian believed, was being kept
a virtual prisoner in Cumnor Hall, near Oxford, whither she
had eloped with Richard Varney, Leicester's master of the
horse.

In behalf of her father, Tressilian had presented a petition to
the Queen regarding her.   In full court Varney had acknowledged that he had eloped with Amy, and had asserted that she
was now his wife and living at Cumnor.   Tressilian, Varney
said, had been brought up with Amy and was to have married
her.   Hence his jealousy and his accusations.   When Tressilian
replied hotly Varney retorted, and there was mention of swords;
but Elizabeth broke in: "Look you, sirs, the first man that talks
of drawing sword except for me or England I will bracelet him
wrist and ankle.   Varney, bring your wife without fail to Kenilworth, whither we go.   On your peril be it.   I will look into this
matter there."

At Cumnor Wayland had obtained secret speech with Amy.
He found that Varney had been before him and had told her
something that had left her in distress and fear.   She begged
the representative of Tressilian to assist her in flight.   They
eluded the watchfulness of wicked old Anthony Foster, who was

virtually her jailer, and made for Kenilworth, where she declared she could find protection.

Wayland did not meet Tressilian. The latter entered the castle by a postern gate and went straight to his apartments. As Amy sat there now, anxiously waiting for an answer to her letter, the door opened and Tressilian stood before her. Their astonishment was mutual. When she found that she was in Tressilian's apartments she asked that he resign them to her for a time and assured him that she was now near one who was bound to protect her.

"Ah, Amy," replied Tressilian, "your looks belie your words. You need aid and protection, and you shall have it. Lean on my arm and I will take you to the very presence of the Queen. She will do justice."

"No! No!" exclaimed Amy. Frantically she begged him to promise that for twenty-four hours he would take no steps in her behalf. At the end of that time, if she had not received justice, he might do as he thought best.

Sorrowfully Tressilian quit the apartment — leaving her alone, forsaken, distressed. Even in her depth of trouble Amy Robsart was beautiful. Her dark-brown hair, her hazel eyes shaded by long lashes and overarched by exquisitely penciled brows, her pale but regular features, as well as the dazzling white of her teeth and the creamy texture of her skin, would have drawn all eyes even in the brilliant throng of beauties that graced the court of Elizabeth.

In the outer court of the castle Tressilian encountered Wayland, who told him what had taken place and of the letter with which Amy had entrusted him. "Deliver it at once," said Tressilian. "Perhaps she thinks the Earl will use his influence with his villainous dependant," he thought.

Wayland departed to find the Earl. He had not gone far before he discovered that he had lost the letter.

"I am now in a fine scrape," thought he. "I wish I were well out of this castle. I will fly." As if in answer to his thoughts he was accosted by Michael Lambourne, a dissipated servant of Varney, who demanded to know his business in the castle, and getting no satisfactory reply, took him to a postern gate and put him forth.

Queen Elizabeth entered the Castle of Kenilworth amid a splendor of which the memory has lingered to this day in legend and ballad. The great castle, rising in the center of long lines of sweeping walls, with its stately towers ornamented with turrets and platforms at every point of defense, with banners streaming from all its walls and a forest of gay crests and waving plumes disposed on terraces and battlements, formed of itself a wonderful picture that was only a hint of the princely hospitality within.

In the evening the Queen held her court in the great hall, her throne surrounded by such famous gentlemen as the grave Burleigh, the gay and aspiring Raleigh, and those others who "filled the spacious time of great Elizabeth with sounds that echo still." The favorite Earl, Leicester, appeared the most magnificent and courtly of that glittering throng. His haughty bearing and manly person set off his splendid costume to advantage. He looked the great prince—worthy indeed to be what none doubted he was about to become, the sharer of the throne.

The Queen gazed on him with an expression not to be misunderstood and beckoned him close to her side.

Among the shining court was one in sober, dull garb—Tressilian, still dressed in his traveling clothes, distraught and gloomy. "Who is yonder clownish fellow?" asked the Queen, whose quick eye had detected the unfortunate Cornishman.

"A poet, may it please your Grace," said Raleigh.

"I judged so, from his slovenly attire. And pray what is his name? But I remember; it is Master Tressilian, the Menelaus of our Devonshire romance. Which reminds us that we have a duty to perform that concerns us both as woman and as Queen. Pray where is the Paris of our tale—my lord of Leicester's man —Farnham, or whatever his name is?"

Raleigh, who disliked Varney and loved Tressilian, pointed out Leicester's master of the horse. The Queen turned a keen eye on Leicester; and though an involuntary tremor came over him, he bowed low in token of his readiness to receive her commands. "It is the matter of Varney and Tressilian of which we speak; is the lady in presence, my lord?"

His answer was ready: "Gracious Madam, she is not."

Elizabeth bent her brows. "Our orders were strict and imperative."

Here Varney stepped forward and fell on one knee. "Your Majesty," said he, "here are attestations from a learned physician who is well known to my lord of Leicester and from a devout Protestant, one Anthony Foster, the gentleman in whose house the lady is now residing, which will show that only severe illness has caused her to disobey the commands of your Grace."

"Under your Majesty's favor," cried Tressilian, forgetting in part his promise to Amy, "these certificates speak not the truth!"

"How!" exclaimed the Queen. "Do you impeach my lord of Leicester's veracity? He stands guaranty for his man. But you shall have a fair hearing."

Tressilian became confused, and stammered some incoherent fragments of sentences which were cut short by Elizabeth with: "Well, well, Master Tressilian, this matter is ended. We will do something to reconcile old Sir Hugh Robsart to this marriage"; and peremptorily she dismissed the Cornishman from the presence.

Meantime, Amy in her tower waited in vain for any result from her letter to Leicester. Night came and still there was no answer and no Leicester. It was an hour after midnight when physical exhaustion proved too strong for love, for grief, even for uncertainty; and she sank into a lethargic repose.

The sun was streaming through the lattice when she awoke and recollected with a sense of giddy agony where she was. There came a sound at her door. She threw it open to see standing there, not Leicester or Wayland, but Michael Lambourne, Varney's follower, who had carried his debauchery over into the morning, and hearing from the domestics that an unknown lady was concealed in Tressilian's apartment had taken it into his befuddled brain to investigate.

The warder who had charge of the tower came running at Amy's cry of fear. A struggle began between him and the drunken man, during which Amy, terrified, slipped from the room and ran out into a courtyard of the castle, which had been fitted up as a pleasance.

The people of the castle were just beginning to stir in preparation for the hunt which was to be held that day, and Amy, to avoid observation, entered a grotto and retired to its farther end.

It chanced that one of the earliest of the huntress train who appeared from her chamber in full array for the chase was England's virgin Queen. Hardly had she crossed the threshold of her room when the Earl of Leicester was by her side and proposed that she should view the pleasance. To this new scene they walked, the ladies in attendance following at a discreet distance, while the noble Dudley pressed his suit as forwardly as was fitting when a subject sought the hand of his sovereign.

"No, Dudley," said Elizabeth. "I must be the mother of my people—the bride of England. Were it otherwise—oh, my lord, delay the chase—delay it for an hour and give me time to think. And—leave me meantime, my lord—I must be alone. Let no one intrude. Go—but not far away."

Her agitation, her denial of his wishes, which was not, after all, a denial, gave Leicester every reason to hope that at the end of her self-communing Elizabeth would raise him to the dizzy height at which he aimed. Retiring, he gave orders to the attendants that the Queen was not to be disturbed.

Elizabeth entered the nearest grotto, her head bowed in deep thought. Suddenly she became aware of a figure seated beside an alabaster column. It was the unfortunate Amy, who recognized the Queen at once in the stately figure approaching her. At first Elizabeth thought that she beheld one of the performers in the pageants, who had been placed in different situations to surprise her with their homage. "How now, fair nymph of this grotto," said the Queen. "Art thou spellbound and struck dumb by some wicked enchanter? We can reverse the charm and bid thee speak."

Clasping her hands, Amy dropped on her knees and looked up into the face of Elizabeth with such a mixture of agony and fear that the Queen was impressed. "What wouldst thou have, damsel?" she asked.

"Your protection, Madam," replied Amy. "I beseech, I implore your protection against one Varney. I was his prisoner. He practised on my life and I broke forth to—to—"

"Thou shalt have my protection, damsel!" cried the Queen.

"We will sift this matter to the uttermost. So thou art she who did deceive thy old father, Sir Hugh Robsart, who cheated Master Tressilian and married this Varney?"

Amy sprang to her feet. "No!" she cried. "No! As there is a God above me I am not the sordid wretch you take me for. I am not the wife of that contemptible villain."

"Why, God ha' mercy, woman," returned the Queen. "I see thou canst talk fast enough when the theme likes thee. Now tell me, Madam," she continued, the impulse of curiosity now added to her other motives, "tell me, woman—for by God's day I will know—whose wife or whose paramour art thou? Speak and speedily. Thou hadst better dally with a lioness than with Elizabeth."

Amy uttered a cry of despair and then murmured: "The Earl of Leicester knows all."

"The Earl of Leicester!" cried the Queen. "Woman, art thou set upon this? The noblest-hearted, the truest gentleman in England! But were he the right hand of our trust, or something yet dearer, thou shalt have thy hearing in his presence. Come with me—instantly."

Grasping the trembling girl by the arm, she dragged her forth, and with long strides hurried from the grotto to where Leicester stood surrounded by a group of lords and ladies. "Where is my lord of Leicester?" cried the Queen, looking in her fury more than ever like the daughter of Henry. "Stand forth, my lord of Leicester. Knowest thou this woman?"

As if some mighty hand bent him to earth Leicester kneeled down before Elizabeth and prostrated his brow to the marble flagstone on which she stood.

"By God's light," exclaimed the Queen, "false lord, thou shalt answer me or thou diest! My lord of Shrewsbury, you are Marshal of England. Attach him of high treason."

The nobles stood aghast. Amy, throwing herself before the furious Queen and embracing her knees, cried out: "He is guiltless, Madam. He is guiltless!"

"Why, minion," replied Elizabeth, "didst thou not say he was privy to thy whole history?"

"If I did," replied Amy, "I foully belied him. I believe he was never privy to a thought that would harm me."

"Woman," answered the Queen, "I will know who has set thee on to this or my wrath—and the wrath of kings is a flaming fire—shall wither and consume thee like a weed in a furnace."

As the Queen uttered this threat Leicester, who had risen to his feet, raised his head with dignity and was stepping forward to speak when Varney rushed into the presence with every mark of disorder on his face and apparel.

"Pardon, my liege," cried Varney, "let thy vengeance fall where it is due, but spare my noble and innocent patron."

Uttering a faint scream at the sight of Varney, Amy besought the Queen to order her to be confined in the lowest dungeon of the castle, but to spare her the sight of "that most shameless and unutterable villain. I shall go mad if I look upon him longer," cried Amy.

"Beshrew me, but I think thou art distraught already," answered the Queen. "My lord Hundson, see that this poor lady is safely bestowed."

Turning to Varney, she added, as Amy was led away: "And you, sir, speak and explain these riddles."

"Your Majesty's eye has already detected the cruel malady which afflicts my poor lady," answered Varney. "Master Foster, in whose charge I left her, has but just arrived to inform me of her escape, which she managed with the art peculiar to many who are afflicted with her malady. May I have your Grace's permission to take charge of my afflicted lady?"

"We will have our physician examine her first," replied the Queen, and smiling again on Leicester she led the way into the castle.

"This storm came like a levanter in the Mediterranean," whispered Sir Nicholas Blount into Raleigh's ear. "*Varium et mutabile,*" answered Raleigh in the same tone.

The Queen's physician soon reported that Amy would answer none of his questions, but sat with her head in her hands staring straight before her. He judged she was suffering from a form of mental disease known as hypochondria.

"Let her be given into the care of her husband," said Elizabeth, "and let us hear no more of this."

Leicester retired to his room, where he was sought by Varney. The two held a long and earnest conversation lasting over an hour. Soon after it a horse-litter drew up in front of the tower and the unhappy woman, in spite of her screams and struggles, was forced into it. Varney with Foster and two attendants was in waiting and the party started at a trot from the castle and took the road to Cumnor Hall.

"Varney has carried away his crazy wife," the courtiers said.

In the court circle that night Leicester bent a look of rage upon Tressilian; but it was not noticed by the Cornishman, who, at the first opportunity, whispered to the Earl: "My lord, I desire some instant conference with you. My tongue has been bound by a promise for four-and-twenty hours. The time is now passed and I now do your lordship the justice to address myself first to you."

"And what does Master Edmund Tressilian require at my hand?" said Leicester in a voice quivering with suppressed rage.

"Justice, my lord."

"All men are entitled to that—you especially so; and be assured you shall have it."

"Shall I await you in your chamber?"

"No, let us meet under the free cope of heaven."

Wondering at the manner of the Earl, Tressilian followed him out into the pleasance. As they passed out, the Earl saw Michael Lambourne, the drunken follower of Varney, mounting his horse. "Here, sirrah!" cried Leicester. "I require a messenger to your master. See that you deliver this packet into his own hands without fail." Lambourne took the packet, and rode off.

Once in the pleasance the Earl turned to Tressilian and said: "The task of chastising you is fitter for a hangman's scourge than the sword of a nobleman, but—villain, draw and defend yourself!"

Tressilian was overcome by amazed surprise. It gave way to resentment, and though somewhat inferior in skill to Leicester his sword gave such a good account of itself that the combat was well maintained for some space without advantage to either party. Suddenly the noise of men advancing hastily was heard and a voice said: "The jackanapes was right; they are tilting here."

"We are interrupted," said Leicester. "We will find a time and place."

On these terms they parted and succeeded in reaching the great hall again without detection.

Next morning, as soon as Leicester saw the Queen deeply engaged in conversation with Lord Burleigh, he made a sign to Tressilian and the two quitted the presence unobserved. Horses were awaiting in an obscure place, and they rode forth from the castle to a glen, where they again drew their swords and stood with blades opposed. After a short but furious combat Tressilian was disarmed and at the mercy of his adversary. With rage in his face, the Earl shortened his sword to run his antagonist through, when his arm was seized by a boy, who cried out to him to desist. Shaking him off, the Earl turned to Tressilian and said: "Confess thy villainy to me and prepare for death."

"I have no villainy toward thee to confess," answered Tressilian.

"Die a liar, as thou hast lived!" cried the Earl; but the boy, now clinging to his knees, besought him to hear what he had to say.

"My folly! My folly!" cried the boy, "has been the cause of these bloody quarrels between you two and of much more evil, I fear." It was Dickie Sludge, the boy who had greeted Wayland Smith and Amy on their arrival at Kenilworth. He now confessed that he had stolen from Wayland a packet addressed to Leicester. This packet he now handed the Earl. Impressed by the earnestness of the boy's manner, Leicester paused in his passion, opened the letter and read it. When he had finished he turned to Tressilian and said: "Take my sword and run it through my heart, as I was about to run it through yours." So saying, he handed the letter to Tressilian.

It was the missive Amy had despatched to Leicester. In it she told how Varney had come to her at Cumnor Hall and declared that by the Earl's command she must pose for a while as Varney's wife. Varney had not only told her this, but had deeply insulted her by infamous proposals, so that she had driven him from her presence. The letter further told how a poisoned drink made at Varney's order by an astrologer whom Leicester maintained at Cumnor, one Alasco, had been given her and that she would have died had she not been supplied with an antidote by Wayland. She had fled to Kenilworth, she said, and besought Leicester by their mutual love to come to her and do her justice.

"The villains!" cried the Earl. "That villain, Varney! She is even now in his power."

"But I trust in God," said Tressilian, "with no commands of fatal import."

"No, no!" replied the Earl. "I said something in madness, but I recalled it by a trusty messenger. She is, she must be, safe."

"My lord," replied Tressilian, "my quarrel with you is ended; but I have now a quarrel with the seducer of Amy Robsart."

"The seducer of Amy!" cried the Earl. "Say her husband! Her misguided, blinded, unworthy husband. She is as surely Countess of Leicester as I am belted Earl." Then he explained that he had wished to keep his marriage secret for a while until he could find some fitting manner to break the news to Elizabeth, whose anger he feared. Several times he had been on the point of avowing it, when Varney had found some way of preventing him and of inducing him to postpone the disclosure which would have meant his ruin.

When the Queen had ordered that Amy be brought to Kenilworth he had sent Varney to her to ask her to assume illness, and, if sought out and questioned, not to deny that she was Varney's wife. Other than this he had not ordered nor countenanced. When he learned of Amy's presence at Kenilworth Varney had told him that Tressilian was still Amy's lover and was beloved by her in return. He brought proof that she had lodged in Tressilian's apartment and also that Tressilian had visited her at Cumnor and besought her to fly with him. Hence his anger with Tressilian and the words half consenting to the death of the Countess with which he had left Varney—words which he had unsaid in the letter he had despatched by Lambourne.

Now, when Leicester found that Varney had sought to dishonor Amy, and, fearful that she would tell all to her husband, had attempted her life, he fathomed the depths of his follower's rascality and gave ready credence to the protestations of Tressilian that what he had done in behalf of the Countess he had done as the representative of her father alone. Tressilian admitted that he had loved her and always would, but that he was too well assured his love was not returned to speak more of it to Amy.

"Oh, fatal ambition that has enveloped me in these toils!" cried Leicester. "And, oh, villain Varney, who whispered poison in my ear and robbed me of my honor!" And he thought: "I must have been mad when I pressed my suit yesterday with the Queen." "Come," said he suddenly, "we will to the Queen. I will make the only reparation possible, and then for Cumnor to beg forgiveness of Amy."

Leicester reached the castle in advance of Tressilian, and when the Cornishman entered the great hall he found it filled with astonished courtiers, who gathered in whispering groups, ever and anon turning their eyes to the door which led into the Queen's withdrawing-room. Raleigh pointed to the door. Tressilian knocked and was instantly admitted.

He found himself in the presence of Elizabeth, who was walking to and fro in violent agitation, which two or three of her most sage councilors vainly attempted to calm. Before the empty chair of state from which she had started knelt Leicester, his arms crossed and his eyes bent on the ground. The Earl's sword was unbuckled and lay on the ground before him, while beside him stood Lord Shrewsbury, Marshal of England.

"Ho, sir!" cried the Queen, sweeping up to Tressilian and stamping her foot after the manner of her father, Henry VIII. "You knew of this pretty business. You are an accomplice in this deception. Art dumb, sirrah? Thou knewest of this affair, didst thou not?"

"Not, gracious Madam, that this poor lady was Countess of Leicester," replied Tressilian.

"Nor shall anyone know her for such!" cried the Queen. "I say Dame Amy Dudley, and well if she have not cause to write herself widow of the traitor, Robert Dudley."

Leicester ventured to say that Tressilian was guiltless of any wrong, and Elizabeth turned on the disgraced Earl the torrent of her invective.

"Thou doubly false—thou doubly forsworn, whose villainy has made me ridiculous in the eyes of my subjects and odious to myself! Oh, I could tear my eyes out for their blindness!"

Burleigh, watching a favorable opportunity, took the Queen by the hand and led her into a recess, where he spoke to her in that soothing and fatherly way which his long service and venerable years gave him the privilege of using. From her talk with Burleigh, Elizabeth returned to the anxious company calm and regal—every inch a Queen. The slighted and jealous woman had disappeared and in her place stood England's sovereign.

"My lord of Shrewsbury," she said, "we discharge you of your trust. My lord of Leicester, rise and take your sword." Leicester ventured to try some cajoling flatteries and protestations in a low voice to the Queen. She cried:

"Speak up, my lord, so that all may hear. What ho! My lords, come and hear the news. My lord of Leicester's stolen marriage has, it seems, cost me a husband and England a king. Is not this too insolent and ridiculous? His lordship, it seems, is patriarchal in his tastes—one wife was not enough and he designed for us the honor of his left hand. I could be angry with this fellow, yet methinks I can most pity him as I could a child, whose bubble of soap has burst in his hands. Master Tressilian, you and Raleigh shall go at once to Cumnor and bring hither the Countess of Leicester. Her husband will stay here, where we purpose to spend some days more as his guest."

As fast as horses could be urged, Raleigh and Tressilian sped toward the place of Amy's captivity, Tressilian explaining the situation to Raleigh as they rode. By command of the Queen, they had along two armed servants and an officer charged to arrest Foster, Varney, and the astrologer Alasco.

Meantime Amy and her captors had been nearing Cumnor. About midnight Varney heard the sound of a horse hard ridden coming up from the rear. Ordering the others to press on, he lingered behind to see who might be following him. Presently up rode Michael Lambourne and delivered the letter of the Earl, at the same time, for he was partially drunk, saying to Varney that he shrewdly suspected his game was up and that Leicester had written him to forego all designs against the Countess.

Varney at once sounded him on his willingness to help "remove that obstacle," pointing to the litter ahead. Lambourne replied insolently and declared he would expose Varney and all his treachery.

The two were alone. Lambourne knew too much. Varney felt sure the letter contained a revocation of the words the Earl had said upon their parting. There was but one way. Quick as lightning he drew his pistol and shot Lambourne through the head. Then, rifling his pockets to make it appear that he had been killed by highwaymen, Varney put spurs to his horse and rejoined his companions.

At Cumnor, Amy, weeping, trembling, and praying for mercy, was placed in the chamber usually occupied by Anthony Foster, as being more secure than the apartments formerly occupied by her. The stairs leading to this chamber gave on a narrow wooden gallery, which was so arranged that by pulling a rope the wooden floor dropped down, precipitating whoever stood on it into the abyss of the cellars under the hall. Foster had contrived this as a precaution against thieves who, attracted by his reputation for wealth, might try to gain entrance into his chamber.

Now the rope which usually led into the chamber was led outside and hung down by the stairs. "Varney," said Foster, "I will not lay hands on the lady. It were a sin. But by pulling this rope the supports of the gallery are removed."

"Ah, Anthony, thou saint!" replied Varney, "and when one steps upon the gallery the gallery falls. I see. The unfortunate Countess dies the victim of her own haste and disobedience. For I doubt not you have warned her not to leave the chamber?"

"I have," replied Foster.

"Well," answered Varney, "by this letter I see my lord relents. But I never received this letter, my good Anthony. You understand? The bearer of it lies dead upon the road—highwaymen, most likely. That woman yonder dead, Leicester becomes King, and thou and I prosper in his rise. I will build his greatness for him in spite of his own weakness."

Pulling the rope which removed the supports of the gallery, Varney went outside into the courtyard and gave an imitation of the low, long whistle with which Leicester was wont to announce his arrival at Cumnor to Amy. The next instant the door of the Countess's apartment opened upon the balcony, and in the same moment the trap-door gave way. There was a rushing sound—a heavy fall—a faint groan, and all was over.

While the murderers were yet in consultation Tressilian and Raleigh broke in upon them and found with horror that they were too late. Varney, being apprehended, took poison, and so escaped the gallows. Alasco made his escape safely, while Foster, fleeing to a remote part of the hall, was never again seen alive. Years afterward a skeleton, believed to be his, was found in a secret room lying on a chest of gold. A spring lock had caught and held him there to die from slow starvation.

Leicester, after some years of disgrace, was restored finally to the Queen's favor. Tressilian embarked with Raleigh for Virginia, where he ended his days.

THE FORTUNES OF NIGEL (1822)

The scene of this story is in and around London in the reign of James I, or about 1620. It is a vigorous and truthful picture of the time, showing in its details how careful a study the author had made in everything pertaining to the city and court of London. None of Scott's historical portraits is more faithful or more justly drawn than his picture of King James, if we may believe contemporary evidence; and his account of Alsatia, the cant name for Whitefriars, the district between Fleet Street and the Thames, which possessed certain privileges of sanctuary derived from the old convent of the Carmelites or White Friars, surpasses that of Ben Jonson or Shadwell. George Heriot, the King's goldsmith and banker, was a veritable personage, the founder of Heriot's Hospital in Edinburgh.

NIGEL OLIFAUNT, Lord Glenvarloch, whose estates in Scotland were heavily mortgaged on account of moneys supplied to the royal exchequer, was in London in hope of obtaining from the King some relief from his necessities. He was living, attended by one servant, in poor lodgings on Paul's Wharf, in the house of John Christie, a ship-chandler. His single follower, Richard or Richie Moniplies, son of Mungo Moniplies, flesher, of Edinburgh, was so poorly clad that he was taunted by the London apprentices, and when he resented their flings at his costume, was so severely handled that he was carried into the shop of Master David Ramsay, maker of watches and horologes to his Majesty. The wounded man was brought in by Ramsay's two apprentices, Jenkin Vincent, called by his associates, Jin Vin, and Francis Tunstall, who had aided the weaker side in the fray.

David Ramsay was conversing at the time with a man whose costume, though grave, was richer than usual—hose of black velvet slashed with purple silk, a doublet of purple cloth, and over it a short cloak of black velvet, adorned with silver buttons and filigree. In his belt, in place of sword or dagger, he wore an ordinary table-knife and a silver case for writing materials.

He seemed firm in health, though advanced in years, and the air of respectability which his dress announced was well supported by his clear eye, ruddy cheek, and gray hair.

This gentleman, who was none other than Master George Heriot, jeweler and banker to King James, took an interest in Richie when he found that he was a fellow-countryman; he questioned him closely, and was greatly surprised to hear that his master was the young Lord Glenvarloch.

"You one of Lord Glenvarloch's followers, and in such a condition?" he exclaimed.

"Troth, and I am all the followers he has; and blythe wad I be if he were muckle better aff than I am."

"I have seen his father with four gentlemen and ten lackeys at his heels," said Master George, "rustling in their laces and velvets. The good old house of Glenvarloch, that stood by king and country five hundred years! Where does your master lodge?"

"Right anent the mickle kirk yonder, wi' a decent man, John Christie. And your honor will mind we pass only by our family name of Mr. Nigel Olifaunt, as keeping ourselves retired for the present."

"It is wisely done," said the citizen, slipping a piece of money into Richie's hand. "I will find out your lodgings. Now hasten home, and get into no more affrays."

On the following day Master Heriot called on Lord Glenvarloch and offered him his services to get his matters before the King. He surprised the young man by his intimate knowledge of court intrigues, and told him that though the King was disposed to hold the scales of justice even, there were those around him who could throw without detection their own selfish wishes and interests into the scale. "You, my lord, are already a sufferer by this, and without your knowing it."

He then told him that the mortgage on his father's lands, due ostensibly to Peregrine Peterson, was really in the interest of the Lord Chancellor of Scotland, who hoped to get possession of the estate himself, or perhaps to gratify a still more powerful third party. "But I think I can serve you in this matter. Let me take your supplication," he continued. "I will have it suitably engrossed, and will see that it reaches the King's hand."

Lord Nigel thanked him for his friendly mediation in his be-half and accepted an invitation to dine with him. In leaving, the goldsmith pressed on him a small loan of money, which Lord Nigel accepted under the hope that his efforts in his be-half would soon enable him to repay the amount.

Master Heriot sought an early interview with King James and presented to him Lord Glenvarloch's petition, which he explained was a debt due from the treasury for money advanced in great state emergency, about the time of the Raid of Ruthven.

"I mind the thing weel," said King James, "and there was never siller mair welcome to a born prince. But what need he dun us for it, man? We aught him the siller, and will pay him wi' our convenience. We are not *in meditatione fugæ*, to be arrested thus peremptorily."

"Alas! an it please your Majesty," said the goldsmith, "it is the poor young nobleman's extreme necessity, and not his will, that makes him importunate."

"But wherefore comes he not to court, Heriot? Is he comely—presentable in the presence?"

"None more so, but—"

"Aye, I understand ye—puir lad—puir lad! Hark ye, let him have twa hundred pounds and—here, take these rubies in pledge till I gie ye back the siller out o' the next subsidy."

When Lord Nigel went to dine with George Heriot he found among the guests David Ramsay and his daughter Margaret, Heriot's goddaughter, about twenty years old, very pretty, very demure, and with bright black eyes that ever and anon contradicted the expression of sobriety to which silence, reserve, and a plain costume had condemned her. At dinner Nigel was seated between Mistress Margaret and Aunt Judith, an elderly matron who did the honors of Master Heriot's table.

When the rest of the company had taken their departure, Master Heriot asked the Lord of Glenvarloch to remain to prayers. As the clergyman was about to begin, Nigel was sur-prised to see enter a beautiful woman, whose face was so pale that she might almost pass for an apparition. Her long black hair fell over her shoulders without decoration or ornament; and her dress, white and of the simplest fashion, hid all her person but throat, face, and hands.

When this singular figure entered she cast her eyes on Nigel and paused. Aunt Judith took her by the hand, but her eyes continued to rest on him with an expression of melancholy by which he felt strangely affected. When the service closed she arose before any of the rest, bent one knee to Heriot, who seemed to bless her with his hand on her head, and went slowly out, once more turning her eyes on Nigel with so fixed a gaze that his own fell.

Lord Glenvarloch was duly presented at court by Master Heriot and was well received by King James, who tested his scholarship by talking with him in Latin. But when the young lord presented his petition, the King replied: "To our secretary with that gear, my lord—to our secretary with that gear! Ye are welcome to London, but as ye seem an acute and learned youth, I advise ye to turn your neb northward and settle yoursell for a while at Saint Andrew's, and we will be right glad to hear that you prosper in your studies."

Nigel would have retreated at this rebuff from the royal presence, but Lord Huntinglen, who stood near, checked him and interceded for Lord Glenvarloch.

"By my soul, my lord, this is strange," said James. "Ye are pleading for the son of your enemy."

"Who *was* my enemy till your Majesty made him my friend," answered Lord Huntinglen.

"Spoken with a true Christian spirit," said the King. "In plain troth, I had promised George Heriot to be good to the lad. But Steenie and Baby Charles cannot abide him, neither can your own son, my lord; and so, methinks, he had better go down to Scotland before he comes to ill luck by them."

"My son, an it please your Majesty, shall not direct my doings, nor any wild-headed young man of them all."

"Why, neither shall they mine," replied the King. "I will do what I will, like a free king."

"Your Majesty will then grant me my boon?"

"Ay, marry, will I," said James, looking over the petition, and then writing an order on the Scottish Exchequer for the sum in question. "There—there, take the sign-manual, and away with you and this young fellow. I wonder Steenie and Baby Charles have not broken in on us before now."

As Lord Huntinglen passed through the anteroom with Nigel, the Duke of Buckingham, the favorite whom the King called Steenie, was coming in. There was an angry flush on his brow as he touched his cap to Huntinglen, but when he saw Heriot he unbonneted and swept his beaver and plume to the floor, with a profound air of mock respect. Heriot returned his greeting simply and said: "Too much courtesy, my lord Duke, is often the reverse of kindness."

"I only meant by my homage, sir," said the Duke, "to claim your protection—your patronage. You are become, I understand, a solicitor of suits—a fautor of court suitors who chance to be penniless. Have the goodness to prefer me to the knowledge of the high-born nobleman who is honored and advantaged by your patronage."

"That shall be *my* task," said Lord Huntinglen, with emphasis. "My lord Duke, I desire you to know Nigel Olifaunt, Lord Glenvarloch, representative of one of the most ancient and powerful baronial houses in Scotland. Lord Glenvarloch, I present you to his Grace the Duke of Buckingham, representative of Sir George Villiers, knight, of Brookesby, in the county of Leicester."

The Duke colored as he bowed scornfully to Lord Glenvarloch—a courtesy which the other returned haughtily and with restrained indignation.

"We know each other, then," said the Duke, after a pause; "and you know me, my lord, for your enemy."

"I thank you for your plainness, my lord Duke," replied Nigel; "an open enemy is better than a hollow friend."

Lord Huntinglen soon after this introduced Nigel to his son, Lord Dalgarno, whose countenance Nigel observed closely to see whether he could trace any sign of the enmity at which the King had hinted. But Lord Dalgarno received him with an open frankness and courtesy that at once won Nigel's heart. Dalgarno congratulated his new friend on the extraordinary success of his suit, saying:

"Men think of you—talk of you—ask each other, 'Who is this young Scottish lord, who has stepped so high in a single day?' The only question now is how high and how far you may push your fortune."

Nigel responded that it was his intention to return to Scotland as soon as his business was settled, and that he hoped to do something for his vassals, as his ancestors had done.

At this Lord Dalgarno burst into a fit of laughter which Nigel would have resented but for his sense of obligation to Dalgarno's father.

"I crave your pardon, my dear Lord Glenvarloch, but I cannot but laugh that you should think of throwing your cards on the table when the game is in your hands—oh, gad! Swouns, I shall never survive the idea! But where lodge you? I must be your guide to certain enchanted lands which you will scarce discover without chart and pilot."

"I will meet you in Paul's," said Nigel, embarrassed at the question, "at any hour you are pleased to name."

"Oh, you would be private. Nay, fear not me. I will be no intruder."

But the very next morning Dalgarno presented himself at his apartment, saying, as he glanced at Dame Nelly, John Christie's pretty wife: "Not a word—not a single word. I know now why you ride at anchor here; but I can keep counsel—so pretty a hostess would recommend worse quarters."

In vain Lord Glenvarloch protested against the insinuation. "Make no words of the matter," said Dalgarno. "I shall not cross your walk; there is game enough in the forest, and I can strike a doe for myself."

He put Lord Glenvarloch's gallantry on so respectable a footing that Nigel ceased to try to undeceive him. Dalgarno then proceeded in a tone of easy familiarity, trying to impress upon Nigel that he was mistaken in his opinion of the Duke of Buckingham; that though the Duke was sometimes impatient, he had a hundred noble and fiery qualities. "He means not all he says in such passing heats. I can do more with him than most of those around him. You shall go visit him with me, and you will see how you shall be received."

But Nigel would not make any submission to the Duke, and kept away from court. Lord Dalgarno introduced him to gambling-houses, playhouses, and other resorts of the gallants of the time, until Richie Moniplies, tired of his new life, decided to leave Lord Glenvarloch's service. When his master asked why he wished to go Richie gave him a moral lecture and told him that he was the talk of the town, and that even his sworn brother, Lord Dalgarno, ridiculed him. "As I am about to leave you," said Richie, "it is proper that ye suld know the truth, that ye may consider the snares to which your youth and innocence may be exposed, when aulder and doucer heads are withdrawn from beside you."

Richie had hardly departed when Nigel's new landlord—for he had removed to better quarters—handed him a note, saying it had been left at the door by a woman. Nigel opened it and read:

"You are trusting to an unhonest friend, and diminishing an honest reputation. Your friend, Lord Dalgarno, is utterly false to you, and doth but seek to mar your fortune. The kind countenance he shows to you is more dangerous than the Prince's frown. Beware of both."

Nigel at first exclaimed: "A vile calumny!" Then, disturbed at his own reflections, he went to walk in the Park. He had not gone far when he met Prince Charles and his train, among them Buckingham and Dalgarno. The Prince bowed coldly, but Buckingham frowned, and Dalgarno passed with his eyes on the ground. Nigel, now thoroughly incensed, quarreled with Dalgarno, when he met him soon after, called him a villain, and drew his rapier.

"Are you mad?" asked Dalgarno. "We are in the precincts of the court."

"The better," answered Glenvarloch; "I will cleanse them from a calumniator and a coward." He then struck him with the flat of the sword.

The cry went up: "Keep the peace—swords drawn in the Park! What ho! guards! yeomen rangers!"

As people collected, Dalgarno hastened away, saying: "You shall dearly abye this insult."

An elderly man came up to Lord Glenvarloch and said: "This is a Star Chamber business, young man, and may cost you your right hand. Go into Whitefriars for sanctuary, till you can make friends or leave the city."

Lord Glenvarloch, convinced that, in his impatient passion, he had put himself in a dangerous predicament, hastened to take his advice.

Whitefriars, adjacent to the Temple, then well known by the cant name of Alsatia, had the privilege of a sanctuary, and the place abounded with desperadoes—bankrupts, ruined gamesters, duelists, bravos, homicides — all leagued together to maintain the immunities of their asylum. After Nigel had been properly introduced to Duke Hildebrod, grand protector of the liberties of Alsatia, and had paid his dues, he was duly installed in an apartment in the house of a usurer called Trapbois, or "Golden Trapbois" from his reputed wealth, who lived alone with his daughter Martha.

Lord Glenvarloch had been settled in the house of Trapbois three days when Margaret Ramsay went early one morning to George Heriot's in Lombard Street and asked to see the Lady Hermione. The Lady Hermione, the pale-faced beauty who had excited Nigel's curiosity at prayers after the dinner at the goldsmith's, sent for Margaret to come to her apartments. Margaret, who had often seen Lady Hermione when visiting her godfather, entered at once upon her errand, begging to see and talk with her alone, whereupon Monna Paula, her attendant, was dismissed to the antechamber.

"You will be angry with me," said Margaret, "so will my godfather; but I cannot help it; *he* must be rescued."

"*He!*" repeated the lady with emphasis. "To whom, maiden, have you rashly attached yourself?—rashly, I fear it must be."

"It is the young Scottish Lord Glenvarloch, madam," answered Margaret, in a modest but firm tone.

"The young Lord of Glenvarloch! Maiden, you are distracted in your wits."

"I knew you would say so, madam; but I repeat to you again that I have fixed my affections on this young nobleman."

"There is infinite folly in what you say. But what is there in this Scottish lord that can rivet what concerns him so closely in your fancy?"

"He is unfortunate, madam, and surrounded by snares. The Lord Dalgarno—"

"Here, Monna Paula—Monna Paula!" cried Lady Hermione, interrupting her. "I must seek her—I will return instantly."

She returned in a few moments, and asked: "How was the name of this man?"

"Lord Dalgarno, the wickedest man who lives. Under pretense of friendship, he has entered into a conspiracy to ruin him."

"But by what means," asked the lady, "have you become possessed of the secret views of a man so cautious as Lord Dalgarno—as villains in general are?"

While Margaret declined to tell where she obtained her information, she satisfied Lady Hermione that she knew all the facts, and that it was in her power to aid Glenvarloch and baffle Dalgarno if she had a certain sum of money. The result was that Lady Hermione entrusted her with two hundred pieces to secure Lord Glenvarloch's escape.

Meanwhile Nigel, who, under the name of Grahame, had settled himself in the miser's house, was aroused one night by a woman's shriek. Jumping up hastily, he seized his sword and pistols and ran down to the usurer's apartment. Martha, his hostess, was struggling with two men, one of whom was about to strike her with a long knife when Nigel shot him dead. The other ruffian, after firing a pistol without effect, leaped from the window and escaped.

"Oh! my father—my poor father!" cried Martha. "I knew it would come to this, and all along of the cursed gold! They have murdered him!"

The body of old Trapbois lay on the floor, strangled with a scarf or sash which had been wound tightly around his neck. When Duke Hildebrod came, attended by a number of persons armed with firelocks and halberds, Martha showed him the sash, and asked whether he did not know who had worn it.

"I must needs say I have seen Captain Peppercull wear one of such a fashion," replied Hildebrod. "If it is he, he will be far by this time. But be patient, and we will have him."

"They who help me in my revenge," said Martha, "shall share my means."

"Enough said," replied Hildebrod. "Master Grahame, here is one seeking you."

A waterman approached and taking Nigel aside, informed him that the Lord Chief Justice had issued a warrant for his

arrest, and that a party of musketeers would come in the morning to take him. "If you would give the bloodhounds the
slip," he continued, "my wherry will await you at the Temple
Stairs at five o'clock to-morrow morning."

"I will be ready," replied Nigel.   "Come hither to carry my
baggage."

When Martha Trapbois heard that her guest was to leave
Whitefriars, she said: "I will go with you."

"Go with me? What can I do for you? I might, indeed,
take you to some friend."

"Friend!" she exclaimed, "I have no friend; but I have
that will purchase many. Come with me."

She led the way to her father's room, pushed aside the heavy
bedstead, and raising a trap-door disclosed a small steel-bound
chest, so heavy that Nigel had to exert his strength to raise it.
"Take it to your room," she said; "it must pass as part of your
baggage. I will be ready when the waterman calls."

Nigel tore down a part of the hanging, which he corded
around the chest to conceal its appearance, and arranged his own
baggage for departure; and when day broke they were on their
way down the Thames. As Martha Trapbois had no plans
beyond escaping from Alsatia, Nigel landed her at Paul's Wharf,
and giving her a letter of recommendation to John Christie,
engaged two porters to carry her chest thither.

When Lord Glenvarloch learned that the unknown person
who had sent the waterman had given orders that he be put on
board the *Royal Thistle*, about to sail for Scotland, he objected
and insisted on being set ashore at Greenwich, where he heard
the court then was. Determined to get speech with the King,
he entered the Park just in time to aid his Majesty slay a deer;
but when the King, who had taken him for one of his train, recognized Glenvarloch, he began to shout: "Hillo, ho—here, here
—Steenie, Steenie!"

The Duke of Buckingham galloped up, crying: "What is it?"

"What is it?" repeated the King. "It is treason, for what
I ken. Your dear dad and gossip might have been murdered,
for what you care."

"Murdered! Secure the villain!" exclaimed the Duke.
"By Heaven, it is Olifaunt himself."

Lord Glenvarloch was rudely seized, and being found to be heavily armed, was sent to the Tower. He had been hardly an hour in confinement when the warder came to inform him that he was to have the company and attendance of another prisoner, and without any explanation a boy was shoved in and the door bolted behind him. Lord Glenvarloch did what he could to cheer up the lad, but he burst into a flood of tears and, drawing his cloak around him, consigned himself apparently to sleep in a chair.

Glenvarloch, tired of his efforts to console him, was walking up and down when another visitor, John Christie, was brought in. Nigel offered him his hand, but Christie drew back and demanded to know what had become of his wife.

"Has Dame Nelly left you?" asked Nigel; "and, if she has, do you ask her of me? By my faith as a Christian, my honor as a gentleman, if aught amiss has chanced with your wife I know nothing of it."

But Christie would not listen and went away unconvinced. Shortly afterward another visitor was announced, and George Heriot came in. Nigel, glad to see him, for the goldsmith had been absent in Paris some time, extended his hand to him, but Heriot drew back with formal courtesy and bowed.

"You are displeased with me, Master Heriot," said Lord Glenvarloch, reddening. "Speak out, and frankly—what I cannot deny I will at least confess."

Master Heriot then enumerated his delinquencies: First, the abduction of Nelly Christie; second, the murder in Alsatia, and the fate of Martha Trapbois, last known to have been in his company with a very large sum of money; and last, the matter of the money loan to pay the mortgage on his estates. The creditors, alarmed at Glenvarloch's present circumstances, were pressing for a settlement of the debt. "But," said Heriot, "if you will entrust to me the warrant under the sign-manual, I may be able to recover the money for you."

Lord Glenvarloch sent for his casket, which had been sealed when he was arrested, and searched for the warrant, but all in vain.

"I thought and expected nothing better," said Heriot bitterly. "A fair heritage lost, I daresay, on a foul cast at dice or a trick at cards! My lord, your surprise is well played."

This new suspicion drove Nigel to the very extremity of his patience, and after a few hasty exclamations he relapsed into a proud and sullen silence.

"Your story, my lord," said Heriot, "is as worthy of belief as this masking mummer here." And with this he took hold of the supposed page's cloak, led him out to the middle of the apartment, and somewhat unceremoniously uncovered his face, revealing the countenance of his own goddaughter, Margaret Ramsay.

"How comes it, minion, that I find you in so shameless a dress and so unworthy a situation? Speak, or I will—"

"Master Heriot," said Lord Glenvarloch, "whatever right you may have over this maiden elsewhere, in my apartment she is under my protection."

"A proper protector! Come—come, lady light o' love, how in Heaven's name came you here?"

"Sir, since I must speak, I went to Greenwich this morning with Monna Paula, to present a petition to the King on the part of Lady Hermione. Monna Paula was frightened and I put on this dress to give her courage."

"Mercy-a-gad!" exclaimed Heriot, "is she in the dance too? Could she not have waited my return?"

Master Heriot then questioned his goddaughter closely concerning her interview with the King, and finally took her away, saying, as he bade Glenvarloch good-by, that he did not think altogether so harshly of him as his hasty speech would imply. As they went out Nigel could not help thinking that Margaret Ramsay was one of the prettiest young women he had ever beheld; and his obeisance to her was so marked as to bring color to her cheeks.

Whatever Master Heriot may have thought of Margaret's interview with royalty, it was not without its effect on the fortunes of both Dalgarno and Glenvarloch, for Margaret had seized the occasion to say also a good word for the latter. The Lady Hermione's petition, which was accompanied with incontrovertible proofs, set forth that Lord Dalgarno had married her in Spain and deserted her, asserting that the marriage was

no marriage, and then had basely attempted to sell her to one
of his comrades. The King was incensed when he learned the
facts, and sending for Lord Huntinglen told the unhappy father
that his son was a villain; and that it was the opinion of the
council that Lord Dalgarno should amend his wrong by wedding the lady.

Lord Huntinglen stood for a moment immovable as he heard
of his son's disgrace, then sank on the floor with a groan.

The King, moved to sympathy for his old friend, said: "Be
patient, man—be patient! The council, and Baby Charles,
and Steenie may a' gang to the deevil; he shall not marry her
since it moves you so deeply."

"He shall marry her, by God!" answered the Earl, endeavoring to recover his composure. "I pray your Majesty's pardon,
but he shall marry her were she the veriest courtesan in all
Spain."

An hour later, in the royal chapel, in the presence of King
James, Prince Charles, the Duke of Buckingham, and others,
the Bishop of Winchester married Lord Dalgarno and Erminia
Pauletti, daughter of the late Giovanni Pauletti of the noble
house of Sansovino, Genoa, and of the no less noble Lady Maud
Olifaunt, of the house of Glenvarloch. The Lady Hermione,
or Erminia Pauletti, who was attended by Monna Paula, was
colorless and half fainting during the ceremony, and her responses were expressed only by inclinations of the head; but
those of Dalgarno were loud and in a tone of levity and scorn.
When it was over, he asked haughtily how this fair Lady Dalgarno was to be bestowed. "Is she to be sent to the harem of
my lord Duke, or is she—"

"Hold thy base ribald tongue!" said his father. "The Lady
Dalgarno shall remain as a widow in my house."

"But for one single circumstance, nothing could have bribed
me to take that woman's hand; it gives me power of vengeance
over the family of Glenvarloch."

"How is that?" asked the King. "What does he mean,
Jingling Georgie?"

"This friendly citizen, my liege," said Dalgarno, "hath
used a sum belonging to my lady, and now, thank Heaven, to
me, in acquiring a certain mortgage on the lands of Glenvarloch.

If this be not redeemed by to-morrow noon, I shall come into possession of these demesnes."

But this was not to be. Before the hour appointed Richie Moniplies, attended by two porters bearing money-bags, appeared at the scrivener's and took up the mortgages. As Richie passed out he was met by Lord Dalgarno, who, recognizing him, gave him a message for Lord Glenvarloch—that, if he were of the same mind as yesterday, he could find him on the morrow, at four in the afternoon, at Camlet Moat in Enfield Chase.

Dalgarno was very angry with the scrivener when he found that the mortgage had been paid, but ordered the gold to be sent to his house, to be taken with him to Scotland on the morrow. He had hardly gone when Captain Colepepper came in to borrow some money. The scrivener, who was a scoundrel, and had been implicated in the attempted robbery which ended in the death of old Trapbois, told him that the bags of gold belonged to Lord Dalgarno, who was to take them to Scotland, and suggested that they might easily be intercepted.

On the following day Lord Dalgarno waited at the appointed hour for the coming of Lord Glenvarloch. Part of his following had gone on, but with him was his page Lutin, in charge of a horse with the money, and a gaily dressed lady whom he called Nelly. The couple were sitting near a mound called the Camlet Moat, when Dalgarno saw horsemen coming down the lane. The next instant he fell dead with a bullet through his brain.

Richie Moniplies, who had got wind of Colepepper's proposed attack on Lord Dalgarno, had secured three trusty fellows and followed, in hope of circumventing the scoundrels. He might have succeeded if he had not found in one of the glades of the forest a man sitting under a tree and groaning so bitterly that the party stopped to ask whether he were hurt. He answered that he was an unhappy man whose wife had been carried off by a villain; and Richie was astonished to recognize in him John Christie.

The two or three minutes lost in mounting Christie behind one of the riders might have saved Dalgarno's life, for the shot that killed him was fired just before they reached the scene.

The robbers were surprised at their work and Colepepper was killed by Moniplies, but Lutin escaped with the treasure.

Lord Glenvarloch was pardoned by the King and shortly afterward, with the full approbation of his Majesty, who had become greatly interested in the pretty Peg-a-Ramsay, as he called her, and had labored hard to establish her descent from the Dalwolseys, was married to Margaret Ramsay. After the marriage in St. Paul's the King attended the bridal banquet at Master Heriot's, where he laid aside for the time his regal dignity. While he was enjoying himself Heriot came and whispered to him and, at a nod from the King, the door opened and, to the surprise of Lord Glenvarloch, Richie Moniplies, gorgeously attired in a superb brocaded suit, entered with Martha Trapbois on his arm.

"What the de'il!" exclaimed the King. "Body of our regal selves! It is a corpse that has run off with the mortcloth!"

"May I sifflicate your Majesty to be gracious to her?" said Richie. "She is my ain wedded wife; and she has brought me fifty thousand pounds of good siller, that has enabled me to pleasure your Majesty and other folk."

"But how the de'il did ye come by her, man?"

"She is the captive of my bow and spear," said Richie. "There was a convention that she should wed me when I should avenge her father's death."

"I pray you, peace!" said Martha. "Let us do what we came for. I call all to witness that I restore to Lord Glenvarloch his ransomed lordship, as well as this other paper, which also is his."

The King, who was beside Lord Glenvarloch, exclaimed: "Body of ourselves, it is our royal sign-manual for the money. How came you by it, Mistress Bride?"

Martha declined to tell until commanded by the King, and then briefly explained that her father had taken it from Lord Glenvarloch's casket, and that she had found it after his death. As to her marriage, she said: "I chose this man because he was my protector when I was desolate. He is truly honest, and I may thank God that I have come by no worse."

"That is sae sensibly said," replied the King, "that, by my

soul, I'll try whether I canna make him better. Kneel down, Richie."

Richie obeyed, and King James, touching him on the shoulder with his rapier, said:

"Rise up, Sir Richard Moniplies of Castle Collop! Now, my lords and lieges, let us to dinner, for the cock-a-leikie is cooling."

PEVERIL OF THE PEAK (1823)

The plot of this story, the longest of the *Waverley Novels*, and one of the most complicated in characters and incidents of the author's works, turns on the alleged conspiracy of the Roman Catholics to murder Charles II and establish Catholicism in England, commonly called the Popish Plot. The scenes are laid chiefly at Martindale Castle, near the Peak of Derbyshire, from which the cavalier family of Peveril derived its supplementary name; Moultrassie Hall, two miles distant, the seat of Major Bridgenorth, an old Parliamentary soldier; the Isle of Man, where the Countess of Derby exercised regal powers, and London. The time is 1678. The story is prefaced by an introductory letter from the Rev. Dr. Jonas Dryasdust, of York, to Captain Clutterbuck.

SIR GEOFFREY PEVERIL, or Peveril of the Peak as he was commonly called, was a High Churchman who had fought for the King in the Civil Wars, and had suffered by fine and sequestration when his seat of Martindale Castle fell before the cannon of Cromwell; but no fear for his person or his property deterred him from joining the Earl of Derby before the fatal engagement in Wiggan Lane. He escaped from that field to join Charles II, was at the final defeat of Worcester, where he was captured, and would have met the fate of the Earl of Derby but for the intercession of a Mr. Bridgenorth, who had influence in the councils of Oliver.

Bridgenorth, a zealous Presbyterian, lived at Moultrassie Hall, about two miles from the castle, and a companionship, if not an intimacy, sprang up between the two families. The Major had not only saved Sir Geoffrey's life, but had obtained him permission to compound for his estate on easy terms, and when the knight was obliged to sell a considerable portion of his patrimony had become the purchaser at a larger price than any Cavalier had been able to obtain.

Major Bridgenorth, eminently successful in worldly affairs, was visited by severe afflictions in his family. Between the breaking out of the Civil War and the Restoration he lost six

children; and in 1658, when his wife bore him a daughter, it was at the cost of her life. Lady Peveril, who brought him news that he was once more a father, communicated also the intelligence that he was no longer a husband. Major Bridgenorth's grief assumed the form of a sullen stupor from which nothing could arouse him. Lady Peveril tried to place in his arms the infant whose birth had cost him so dear, conjuring him to remember that Alice still lived in the child she had left to his paternal care. He almost threw the babe into Lady Peveril's arms, saying: "Take the unhappy child away, and let me only know when I shall wear black for her."

"I will take her for a season," said Lady Peveril. "The little Alice shall share the nursery of our Julian, until it shall be pleasure and not pain for you to look on her."

Thus it happened that Alice Bridgenorth and Julian Peveril, the only child of Sir Geoffrey and Lady Peveril, were brought up together. When Alice was in her second year, Major Bridgenorth first saw his daughter. He caught her in his arms, and when he saw the tint of ruddy health in her complexion he pressed her to his heart.

"Praise be to God in the first instance," he said, "and next, thanks to you, Madam, who have been His instrument."

"I suppose Julian must lose his playfellow now," said Lady Peveril.

"God forbid my girl should ever come to Moultrassie," said Bridgenorth. "It has been the grave of her race. I will seek for her some other place of abode."

"That you shall not, Major Bridgenorth," answered the lady. "If she goes not to her father's house, she shall not quit mine. I hope you will come here frequently to visit her."

The time of the King's restoration brought Sir Geoffrey and Major Bridgenorth somewhat nearer in politics, for the latter was a Presbyterian and not averse to a monarchy. So the two families lived on amicable terms, and Bridgenorth even took part in the celebration of the King's return at the castle. But shortly after this, on a visit to Martindale of the Countess of Derby, a cousin of Lady Peveril, Bridgenorth overheard a conversation between the two ladies in which the Countess, who claimed the rights of royalty in the Isle of Man, told how William Christian had been executed for treason by her orders.

Bridgenorth was furious when he heard this, for Christian was the brother of his deceased wife.

"Cruel murderess!" he cried, "I can bear witness that William Christian was the only barrier between thee and the wrath of the Commons of England; and but for his earnest remonstrances thou hadst suffered the penalty of thy malignancy, even like the wicked wife of Ahab. Charlotte, Countess of Derby, I attach thee of the crime of which thou hast made thy boast."

"I shall not obey your arrest," said the Countess, composedly. "What have your English laws to do with my acts of justice? Am I not Queen in Man as well as Countess of Derby? What right can you assert over me?"

"Major Bridgenorth," said Lady Peveril, "I tell you that I will not permit any violence against this honorable lady within my husband's castle."

"You will find yourself unable to prevent me from executing my duty, madam," said Bridgenorth. "I am a magistrate and act by authority."

Bridgenorth placed himself between them and the door, but Lady Peveril called on her steward, Whitaker, and bade him arm three men and attend her.

"How mean you, madam?" said Bridgenorth. "I thought myself under a friendly roof."

"You are so, Master Bridgenorth," said Lady Peveril calmly, "but it is a roof that must not be violated by the outrage of one friend against another."

Bridgenorth would have gone out when Whitaker and his men appeared, and half drew his sword in anger; but Lady Peveril ordered him disarmed, and said: "Do not take it to heart, Master Bridgenorth, that you are detained for a few hours, until the Countess of Derby can have nothing to fear from your pursuit."

When Sir Geoffrey, who had been absent, returned, he hastened to see Bridgenorth, but he had escaped. Fearful that he would return with force enough to take the Countess, he advised her instant departure, saying that he would take her safely to

Vale Royal, though the sheriff stopped the way with a whole *posse comitatus.*

The Countess of Derby, under escort of Sir Geoffrey and a well-armed party, set out on her journey, but was overtaken by Bridgenorth accompanied by eight or ten men, one of whom was armed with a warrant. Sir Geoffrey, bidding the Countess ride on, drew up his men across the road and called to Bridgenorth to halt.

"Make way, Sir Geoffrey Peveril," said Bridgenorth, "or you will compel me to do that I may be sorry for. I am in this matter the avenger of the blood of one of the Lord's saints, and I will follow the chase while Heaven grants me an arm to make my way."

"You shall make no way here but at your peril," said Sir Geoffrey. And when a pursuivant rode forward and showed his warrant, the knight tore it in two. Major Bridgenorth put his hand on his pistol-holster and Sir Geoffrey closed with him, seized him by the collar, and unhorsed him with much violence. Sir Geoffrey sprang from the saddle and aided Bridgenorth to rise.

"Come, neighbor Bridgenorth, get up," said he. "I trust you have had no hurt in this mad affray? I was loath to lay hand on you, man, till you plucked out your petronel."

But Bridgenorth shook himself free, mounted his horse with a sullen and dejected air, and rode away. Sir Geoffrey looked after him and said: "Now there goes a man who would have been a right honest fellow had he not been a Presbyterian."

Shortly afterward Lady Peveril received a long letter from Bridgenorth, announcing his departure, and thanking her for all she had done for Alice. He also begged her to pardon him for enticing from her service Deborah Debbitch, whose nurture, instructed by Lady Peveril, was indispensable to the health of his child. Sir Geoffrey, on reading this epistle, jumped to the conclusion that Bridgenorth would marry Deborah.

"It is the true end of a dissenter," he said, "to marry his own or somebody else's maid-servant. Go look to Julian. Will the boy never have done crying for lack of that little sprout of a Roundhead? But we shall have little Alice back with us in two or three days, and all will be well again."

But Alice came not again. Major Bridgenorth left Moultrassie Hall in the care of a housekeeper and departed, with his daughter and Deborah, none knew whither, though some said to foreign lands and some to New England.

Julian was sent soon afterward to the Isle of Man, to share the education of the young Earl of Derby. In time he became a gallant and accomplished youth, traveled on the Continent with the Earl, and, after a visit to Martindale Castle, went to live, as a guest of the Countess, at the Castle of Rushin, in the Isle of Man. One day, when fishing in a little valley, he was accosted by Deborah Debbitch, who was walking with Alice. As both Julian and Alice had been under her charge at Martindale Castle, Deborah was delighted with the opportunity to talk about former times, and the two young persons easily renewed their old acquaintance. Julian had left home when too young to know of his father's quarrel with Bridgenorth, and he now listened with interest and surprise to Deborah's account of it. His imagination caught fire at the singular story, and, notwithstanding the prudent remonstrances of Dame Deborah, he persuaded himself that Heaven had designed Alice and him for each other, in spite of every obstacle that passion or prejudice could raise betwixt them. When, after many stolen interviews, he declared his love, he said:

"It is the will of Heaven that in our affection should be quenched the discord of our parents. What else could lead those who parted infants on the hills of Derbyshire to meet thus in the valleys of Man?"

"We have done wrong, Julian, very wrong. We never should have met. Farewell, and forget that we ever have seen each other."

"This evil is not remediless," said Julian. "I will go to my father—I will use the intercession of my mother—they have no other child—and they must consent, or lose him forever."

Julian was not long left in doubt of his father's opinion of Bridgenorth, for the old knight characterized him as that "base, dishonorable Presbyterian fellow, Bridgenorth—I would as lief think of a toad."

And when Julian casually spoke to his mother of the Bridgenorths, she conjured him never to mention the name, especially in his father's presence.

When Julian returned to Man, and Alice discovered, through much questioning, the result of his visit to his parents, she again forbade him to come to the house.

"You come hither in spite of my earnest request. Is this honorable? Is it fair? Is it kind? Let me once more entreat you to absent yourself from this place—till—till—"

"Till when, Alice? Let me conjure you to name a date—to fix a term—to say till *when*!"

"Till you can bear to think of me only as a friend and sister."

"That is a sentence of eternal banishment," said Julian. "But tell me where your father is, and leave the rest to me."

"Do not attempt to see him, I charge you," said Alice. "He is already a man of sorrows, and I would not add to them."

"I will watch for his arrival," answered Julian, "and he shall answer to me on the subject of my suit."

"Then demand that answer now," said a voice, as the door opened, "for here stands Ralph Bridgenorth."

After the first surprise was over, Bridgenorth sent Alice to her chamber, and motioning Julian to a seat, took one himself. To his inquiries, Julian responded that what he had to say respected both his daughter's happiness and his own.

"I must understand you," said Bridgenorth, "even as carnal men understand each other on the matters of this world. You are attached to my daughter by the cords of love; I have long known this."

"You, Master Bridgenorth?" exclaimed Peveril—"*you* have long known it? May I not hope, then, that it has not met your disapprobation?"

"In some respects, certainly not. But be not so hasty as to presume that all you may desire in this matter can be either easily or speedily accomplished."

"I foresee, indeed, difficulties," answered Julian, "but they are such as I trust to remove. My father is generous; my mother is candid and liberal. They loved you once; I trust they will love you again. I will be the mediator betwixt you."

Bridgenorth responded in general terms that to forgive human wrongs was Christlike, but that we had no commission to forgive those done to the cause of religion and of liberty; nor have we a right to shake hands with those who have poured forth the blood of our brethren. With this he looked at the picture of William Christian on the wall and was silent a few moments. When he spoke again it was vaguely and enigmatically.

"There are mighty designs afloat, and men are called to make their choice betwixt God and Baal. The ancient superstition—the abomination of our fathers—is raising its head and flinging abroad its snares, under the protection of the princes of the earth. But true English hearts wait but a signal to rise as one man, and show the kings of the earth that they have combined in vain! We will cast their cords from us; the cup of their abominations we will not taste."

"You speak in darkness, Master Bridgenorth," said Julian.

"Well, enough for the present. To-day this is thy habitation. Thou shalt be to me for this day as the child of her without whom my house had been extinct."

At dinner Peveril found himself between Alice and her father, but Alice was mute and most of the talking was done by Bridgenorth, who had traveled much on the Continent and had been even in New England. When they parted at nightfall Bridgenorth said:

"The patriarch bought his beloved by fourteen years' hard service to her father, Laban. But he that would wed my daughter must serve, in comparison, but a few days, though in matters of such mighty import that they shall seem as the service of many years. Reply not now, but go, and peace be with you."

When Julian returned to Castle Rushin he found that the Countess, in consequence of news received during the day, had removed to Holm-Peel, a stronger castle about eight miles across the island. The next day he learned from the Earl that the enmity against the Catholics had resulted in the pretended discovery of a plot to dethrone the King and restore the ancient religion; that his mother, the Countess, and her confessor, Aldrick the Jesuit, were mentioned in connection with it; and that Edward Christian, brother of the William who had been put to death by the Countess, was even now in the island with secret and severe orders. With him was a prick-eared rogue called

Bridgenorth, brother-in-law to the deceased, and the two had already formed a considerable party in the island, rendering it unsafe to remain at Castle Rushin.

A little later Julian received a billet, signed with the initials "A. B.," saying: "Meet me at noon at Goddard Crovan's Stone, with as much secrecy as you may."

As he was descending the steps leading to the entrance of the castle, to keep this appointment, he was intercepted by Fenella, the Countess's mute train-bearer, an exquisitely formed little creature in a green silk tunic. Her face was darker than the usual hue of Europeans, and her eyes were more than ordinarily alert and acute, because it was only by sight that she obtained information of what passed around her. Many were the tales circulated concerning the Countess's elf, as she was called, and it was currently said that her deafness and dumbness were only toward those of this world, and that she had been heard talking, singing, and laughing elfishly with the invisibles of her own race.

Fenella frowned, shook her head, and pointed backward as Julian tried to pass her, and when he persisted she wrote on her tablet: "There is danger around the Countess, but there is much more in your own purpose." To his surprise, she then sketched hastily Goddard Crovan's Stone, with a male and a female figure beside it.

When he gazed on this with surprise, wondering how she had obtained her information, she slowly and sternly shook her head as if to forbid the meeting she had sketched, and when he shook her off and went on his way she uttered an elfish screech, stamped her foot, and shook her clenched fist at him.

Julian found Alice awaiting him at the stone. She explained that she had asked this interview to beg him to break off all intercourse with her family and return to his parents, or, what was safer, go to the Continent till better days came to England. "Farewell then, Julian, and take my solemn advice: Shun my father; you cannot walk in his paths and be true to gratitude and honor. What he doth from pure and honorable motives you cannot aid him in, except upon the suggestion of a silly and interested passion, at variance with all the engagements you have formed at coming into life."

While Julian was protesting strongly against this view

Major Bridgenorth stepped from behind a copse and confronted them. He signed to his daughter to withdraw.

"I obey you, father," said Alice, "but you do me injustice if you suspect me capable of betraying your secrets. That you are walking in a dangerous path I well know; but you do it with your eyes open, and are actuated by motives of which you can estimate the worth and value. My sole wish was that this young man should not enter blindfold on the same perils; and I had a right to warn him, since the feelings by which he is hoodwinked had a direct reference to me."

"'Tis well, minion," said her father, "retire and let me complete what you have begun."

"Julian," said Alice, as she turned away, "farewell, and caution!"

"A true specimen of womankind," said Bridgenorth, looking after her, "who would give up the cause of nations rather than endanger a hair of her lover's head."

Bridgenorth then entered into a long disquisition on the political affairs of the kingdom, and especially on the secret but rapid strides of Rome to erect her Dagon of idolatry in the land. Julian listened in silence to dark hints of a coming storm, much of which was a riddle to him, but when he had an opportunity to reply he warned Bridgenorth of the danger he incurred in remaining in the island.

"Take a hint from me," he said. "You are here on an errand dangerous to the lord of the island. Be warned, and depart in time."

"We part then, my son, but not in anger," said Bridgenorth. "For my daughter, forbear every thought of seeing her, save through me. I accept not thy suit, neither do I reject it; only this I intimate to thee, that he who would be my son must first show himself the true and loving child of his oppressed and deluded country. Farewell! Thou shalt hear of me sooner than thou thinkest for."

On his return to Holm-Peel Julian was entrusted by the Countess with despatches for London, and set out immediately and secretly, intending to call on the way at Martindale Castle to see his parents. He landed at Liverpool, where he bought a horse and began his journey to Derbyshire. He was followed by a stranger, who called himself Richard Ganlesse, but who was in reality Edward Christian. Arrived at Martindale Castle, he found everything in confusion and a party of armed men in possession. The sound of voices drawing him to the sitting-room, he found there his father with his arms pinioned behind him, guarded by two fellows, his mother near by as pale as death, with her eyes fixed sorrowfully on her husband, and other men at the table writing. Regardless of the inequality of the contest, Julian attacked the men guarding his father, but a third seized on his collar and attempted to master his sword. Julian drew a pistol and fired full in his face. He staggered back and showed, as he sank into a chair, the face of Bridgenorth black-ened with powder. A cry of astonishment escaped from Julian, and he was easily disarmed and secured.

"Young man," said Bridgenorth coolly, "you have reason to bless God, who has saved you from the commission of a great crime."

"Bless the devil, ye crop-eared knave!" exclaimed Sir Geoffrey, "for nothing less than the father of all fanatics saved your brains."

"Sir Geoffrey," said Major Bridgenorth, "I have already told you that with you I will hold no argument, for to you I am not accountable for my actions. I am a magistrate, and I exe-cute a warrant addressed to me by the first authority in the state."

The result was that Sir Geoffrey and Lady Peveril were sent up to London in their own coach, but Julian was taken in charge by Bridgenorth, who argued that it was safer to keep him back lest he should attempt a rescue, promising to bring him to London himself.

Julian, after giving his parole, was taken by Bridgenorth to Moultrassie Hall, where Alice hailed the return of her father from his perilous visit to the castle. Major Bridgenorth turned his cold gray eyes on her and Julian as they saluted each other, and said:

"There are those within who should not know that ye have been acquainted. Wherefore be wise, and be as strangers to each other."

When Julian demanded of Bridgenorth why he was in custody, he was told that he was accused of abetting the foul, bloody, and heathenish plot for the establishment of Popery, the murder of the King, and the massacre of all true Protestants.

"They lie like villains," said Peveril, "who hold me accessory to any plot either against the King, the nation, or the state of religion."

"Julian Peveril—why should I conceal it from thee?—my heart yearns for thee as a woman's for her first-born. To thee I will give, at the expense of my own reputation, means of escape to Liverpool and a secure passage from the kingdom."

"Major Bridgenorth," said Julian, "my father is in danger, my mother in sorrow; I am their only child—their only hope; I will aid them or I will perish with them."

"Perish then in thy obstinacy," said Bridgenorth, leaving the room.

But that night the retainers of Sir Geoffrey attacked Moultrassie Hall, and but for Julian would have burned it. Julian himself was released and soon afterward followed his parents to London.

Edward Christian, the brother of Major Bridgenorth's wife and uncle of Alice, who had various aliases, was a villain. In order to secure influence at court, he had determined that his niece should supplant the Duchess of Portsmouth in the favor of the King, and to insure this he brought her to London and placed her in charge of Mistress Chiffinch, whose reputed husband acted as pander to Charles. To insure his ends Christian sought the Duke of Buckingham, who had been thwarted in some of his schemes by the Duchess of Portsmouth, and was willing to see her supplanted. He asked Christian to show him the beauty, but Christian declined, saying:

"If this maiden become a prince's favorite, rank gilds the shame and the sin. But to any under Majesty she must not vail topsail."

"Most profligate and damnable villain!" said the Duke, as Christian departed. "I will find this girl out in spite of them, and judge whether their scheme is likely to be successful. If so, she shall be mine—mine entirely, before she becomes the King's; and I will command her who is to guide Charles."

Meanwhile Julian Peveril, arrived in London, went to deliver one of the letters entrusted to him by the Countess of Derby, when he met the dumb girl Fenella, who beckoned him to follow her. Supposing that she would lead him to the Countess of Derby, who he conjectured had come to town, he followed her into the park, where they came upon a group of gentlemen and some attendants. Julian recognized in the foremost one, dressed in plain black velvet, the person of King Charles, and would have retired; but Fenella began to dance to the music of a flageolet, played by one of the attendants, with a grace and agility that astonished Julian, who knew her limitations. The King, who seemed pleased, said to him: "Friend, we thank thee for the pleasure of this morning." Julian, thus addressed, kneeled and tried to explain that his Majesty had mistaken his character.

"And who art thou, then, my friend, and who is this dancing nymph?" asked Charles.

"The young person is a retainer of the Countess Dowager of Derby, so please your Majesty, and I am—"

"Hold—hold!" said the King, "this is a dance to another tune. Hark thee, friend, do thou and the young woman follow Empson. Empson, carry them—hark in thy ear."

Peveril tried to explain the situation, but the King cut short his apology, saying:

"Now, a plague on him who can take no hint. Follow Empson, and wait till we send for you."

With no alternative, Julian did as he was ordered, and he and Fenella were taken to the house of Mistress Chiffinch, whither the King soon followed. Mistress Chiffinch appeared embarrassed at the coming of the King, and coughed loudly as if to give warning to someone in the next room. She was evidently heard, for the door suddenly opened and Alice Bridgenorth rushed in, pursued by the Duke of Buckingham. Alice exclaimed:

"I remain no longer here, madam. I leave instantly a house where I am exposed to company I detest, and to solicitations I despise."

Mistress Chiffinch implored her, in broken whispers, to be silent, saying: "The King—the King!"

"If I am in the King's presence," said Alice, "it is the better.

It is his Majesty's duty to protect me, and on his protection I throw myself."

The King angrily chided Buckingham, who, however, succeeded in fooling him as usual, and Charles suggested to Julian that he should cause his female companion to dance. This gave Julian an opportunity to explain who he was and what had brought him to London.

"Body of me," said the King, "you a son of Sir Geoffrey Peveril, the old Worcester man? I remember him well. Is he not dead, or very sick at least?"

"He has been imprisoned, your Majesty, on account of alleged accession to this plot."

The King avowed his sympathy, but declared his inability to interfere, as he himself would certainly be declared an accessory.

Julian gave to the King the packet of papers that the Countess of Derby had entrusted to him, and was dismissed. As he was about to depart Alice announced her determination to accompany him, and notwithstanding the efforts of the Duke and of Mistress Chiffinch to detain her, she went out with Julian, followed by Fenella. Julian, half leading, half supporting Alice, reached St. James's Street before it occurred to him that he did not know whither to go. While he was hesitating Fenella plucked him by the cloak and imperatively motioned to him to leave Alice and follow her. Alice clung to his arm, and this, to Julian's embarrassment, increased the passion of Fenella. To add to his anxiety, he observed that they were followed by two gallants, who finally opposed his way and obliged him to take notice of their insults. He told Alice to await him at Hungerford Stairs, near which they were, and attacked them. The crowd, which speedily gathered, permitted only one to oppose him, and Julian soon ran him through the body. On looking for Alice he learned that she had been handed into a boat, which had gone up the river; and he was seeking a boat to follow, when he was arrested for wounding a gentleman belonging to the household of the Duke of Buckingham, and consigned to prison.

The trial of Sir Geoffrey and Julian resulted in an acquittal, and they were discharged from custody. As they passed down the street they were attacked by the crowd, who called them

Papist cutthroats, and were forced to take refuge in a house, which proved to be the lodging of Major Bridgenorth, who welcomed them to its shelter and hospitality.

"Odzooks," said the old Cavalier, "had I known it was thy house, man, I would sooner had my heart's blood run down the kennel than my foot should have crossed thy threshold."

"I forgive your inveteracy," said Bridgenorth, "on account of your prejudices."

"My dearest father," said Julian, "you know not this gentleman, and do him injustice. My own obligations to him are many; and I am sure when you come to know them—"

"I hope I shall die ere that moment come," said Sir Geoffrey.

But the good old knight had to take back his rash words. The Countess of Derby came to London, and after much private conversation with Julian explained to the King how Major Bridgenorth, about to leave England forever, had acquired strong possession over the domains of Peveril, but desired to restore them to their ancient owners with much fair land besides, conditionally that Julian should receive them as the dowry of his only child and heir.

"By my faith," said the King, "she must be a foul-favored wench indeed if Julian requires to be pressed to accept her on such fair conditions."

"They love each other like lovers of the last age," said the Countess, "but the knight likes not the Roundhead alliance."

"Our royal recommendation shall put that to rights," said the King. "Sir Geoffrey Peveril will not refuse our recommendation when it comes to make him amends for all his losses."

Four weeks later the bells of Martindale-Moultrassie were ringing for the union of the families from whose estates it takes its compound name.

Edward Christian was pardoned by the King on condition of his leaving England forever. With him went Fenella, who proved to be his own daughter, and who, believing herself to be the child of the slain William Christian, had personated a mute and taken service with the Countess of Derby to aid Edward in securing vengeance.

QUENTIN DURWARD (1823)

This is a tale of France in the fifteenth century, in which King Louis XI and Charles, Duke of Burgundy, figure among the chief characters. The hero, Quentin Durward, is a young Scotchman, who goes to France to seek his fortune and becomes a member of the royal bodyguard of Scottish Archers. The heroine is the Countess Isabelle de Croye, a ward of the Duke of Burgundy, who with her aunt, the Countess Hameline, has sought refuge at the court of France. The scenes are chiefly at Plessis-les-Tours, Péronne, and Liège. The delineations of Louis XI and Charles the Bold are among the most graphic and forceful in fiction; and the character of the King, in the dramatic version of the story, was one of Sir Henry Irving's most successful personations.

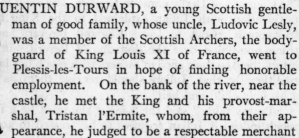QUENTIN DURWARD, a young Scottish gentleman of good family, whose uncle, Ludovic Lesly, was a member of the Scottish Archers, the bodyguard of King Louis XI of France, went to Plessis-les-Tours in hope of finding honorable employment. On the bank of the river, near the castle, he met the King and his provost-marshal, Tristan l'Ermite, whom, from their appearance, he judged to be a respectable merchant and a butcher. The King, who called himself Maître Pierre, amused at the youthful inexperience and Scottish boastfulness of Quentin, took him to an inn near the castle and entertained him with the best the place afforded. While they were at table, a beautiful young girl with long black tressses bound with a chaplet of ivy leaves came in with a platter on which was a saucer of dried prunes and a richly chased goblet.

"How now, Jacqueline," said Maître Pierre, "did I not desire that Dame Perette should bring what I wanted? *Pasques-dieu!* Is she too good to serve me?"

"My kinswoman is ill at ease," said Jacqueline, " and keeps her chamber."

"She keeps it *alone*, I hope?" replied Maître Pierre, with emphasis. "I am none of those upon whom feigned disorders pass for apologies."

46

Jacqueline turned pale and even tottered, for Maître Pierre's voice and looks were unpleasing, and had an effect both sinister and alarming.

"I blame not thee, Jacqueline," he continued; "thou art too young to be—what it is pity to think thou must be one day—a false and treacherous thing, like the rest of thy giddy sex. Here is a Scottish cavalier will tell you the same."

Jacqueline looked for an instant on the stranger, with a glance that appeared to Durward a pathetic appeal for support and sympathy. He relieved her of her burden and with a blush offered the cup and trencher to Maître Pierre.

"You are a foolish young man," said Maître Pierre, "and know as little of women as of princes. Thou mayst withdraw, Jacqueline. I will tell thy negligent kinswoman she does ill to expose thee to be gazed on unnecessarily."

"I trust you will not be displeased with my kinswoman, since—"

"*Pasques-dieu!*" said Maître Pierre, interrupting her, "do you bandy words with me, you brat, or stay you to gaze on the youngster here? Begone; his services will suffice me."

Jacqueline obeyed; and Quentin was so much interested that he complied mechanically when Maître Pierre, in the tone of one accustomed to be obeyed, said:

"Place that tray beside me. That is a beautiful creature." Then, looking steadily and firmly at Quentin: "A lovely girl to be the servant of an auberge? You are noble, you say?"

"I surely am," replied Quentin, "if fifteen descents can make me so. But do not constrain yourself on that account. I have always been taught it is the duty of the young to assist the more aged."

"An excellent maxim, young man," said Maître Pierre, taking a purse from his bosom and filling the goblet more than half full of silver pieces. "Remain in this hostelry until you see your kinsman, whom I will cause to be acquainted with your coming."

When Quentin was about to excuse himself from accepting a stranger's liberality, Maître Pierre, bending on him his dark brows and assuming a dignified air, said, in a tone of authority: "No reply, young man, but do what you are commanded."

Shortly afterward Quentin received a visit from his uncle, Ludovic Lesly, commonly known as Le Balafré from a scar on his face, a member of the Scottish Archers, who welcomed him and asked him numerous questions about Scotland, from which he had not heard in a long time. Le Balafré overcame his scruples about taking service under the King, and took him to Lord Crawford, commander of the Guard, and Quentin was soon clad in the gorgeous uniform of the Archers. When next the Guard were ordered to duty in the presence-chamber, Quentin attended his uncle, and he nearly dropped his weapon when he recognized in King Louis the Maître Pierre with whom he had been so familiar.

When the King saw him he walked straight to him and, smiling, said to Lesly: "Balafré, your kinsman is a fair youth, though a fiery. We love to cherish such spirits, and mean to make more than ever we did of the brave men who are around us. Let the year, day, hour, and minute of your nephew's birth be written down and given to Oliver Dain."

Shortly after this the Princess Joan, with the ladies of her suite, entered. She was pale, thin, and sickly, her form bent to one side, and visibly lame. The King, who loved her not, destined her for the bride of the Duke of Orleans, the heir apparent to the throne, who, however, shuddered as he touched her hand. The King was about to set out for the hunt, when the Comte de Crèvecœur, envoy of the Duke of Burgundy, arrived and demanded an immediate audience.

The Count, contrary to the usage among envoys of friendly powers, entered fully armed in superb Milan armor, preceded by a herald bearing his letters of credence, and followed by a page carrying his helmet. After a few preliminaries, the Count, entreating forgiveness for appearing thus, said: "Although it is only the voice of Philip Crèvecœur de Cordès that speaks, the words he utters must be those of his gracious lord and sovereign the Duke of Burgundy."

"What has Crèvecœur to say in the words of Burgundy?" said Louis, with dignity. "Yet hold—remember that in this presence Philip Crèvecœur de Cordès speaks to his sovereign's sovereign."

The Count presented a written schedule of wrongs alleged

to have been committed by the King's officers on the subjects of Burgundy, for which redress was demanded. The Duke also demanded that the King should cease his secret and under-hand dealings with his towns of Ghent, Liège, and Malines; and lastly, that the King send back to his dominions, under a secure safeguard, the persons of Isabelle, Countess of Croye, and her relative and guardian the Countess Hameline; the said Countess Isabelle, ward of the said Duke of Burgundy, having fled from his dominions and being maintained in secret by the King of France.

"You did well, Count de Crèvecœur," said Louis scornfully, "to begin your embassy at an early hour, for if it be your purpose to call me to account for the flight of every vassal from your master's dominions, the bead-roll may last till sunset. Who can affirm that these ladies are in my dominions? Who can assert, if they are in France, that their place of retirement is within my knowledge? Since thy sole errand here seems to be for purposes of insult, we will send someone in our name to the Duke of Burgundy—convinced that thou hast exceeded thy commission."

"On the contrary," said Crèvecœur, "I have not yet ac-quitted myself of it. Hearken, Louis of Valois, King of France." He then, after reciting the titles and dignities of the Duke of Bur-gundy, renounced in his name all allegiance and fealty toward the crown of France, and defied the King as a prince and as a man. With this he drew the gauntlet off his right hand and flung it on the floor.

While Dunois, Orleans, Lord Crawford, and others con-tended who should lift the gauntlet, some cried: "Strike him down! Cut him to pieces! Comes he here to insult the King of France?"

But the King appeased the tumult by exclaiming in a voice that overawed all: "Silence, my lieges! lay not a hand on the man nor on the gage. My lord cardinal—my Lord Bishop of Auxerre—it is your holy office to make peace among princes. Do you lift the gauntlet, and remonstrate with Count Crèvecœur on the sin he has committed, in thus forcing us to bring the mis-eries of war upon his kingdom and that of his neighbor."

Under this appeal, Cardinal Balne took up the gauntlet and

followed Crèvecœur. In a few minutes he returned and reported that the Count had consented to stay twenty-four hours,
and in the mean while to receive again his gage of defiance.

"See that he be nobly attended and cared for at our charge,"
said the King. "Such a servant is a jewel in a prince's crown.
Twenty-four hours! Skilfully employed, it may be worth a
year in the hand of incapable agents. To horse—to horse, my
gallant lords! To the forest! Now for your boar-spears."

In the chase Quentin Durward had the good fortune to save
the King's life by spearing a boar when Louis made a false stroke
and fell before the infuriated animal. The King, after cutting
the boar's throat, looked up and said:

"Is it thou, my young Scot? Maître Pierre owes thee as
good entertainment as he gave thee at the Fleur-de-Lys. Why
dost thou not speak?"

Quentin was shrewd and answered in a few well-chosen
words, craving pardon for the rustic boldness with which he had
conducted himself when ignorant of the stranger's high rank.

"Tush! man," said the King; "I forgive thy sauciness for
thy spirit. Help me to my horse. I like thee, and will do thee
good. Build on no man's favor but mine—not even on thine
uncle's or Lord Crawford's; and say nothing of thy timely aid
in this matter of the boar."

Quentin had hardly reached his quarters when he was visited
by Oliver Dain, originally the King's barber and later a trusted
counselor, called also Mauvais or Diable, who entered with a
humble and modest look, and announced that his Majesty had
selected him to execute a piece of duty this afternoon.

"Selected *him*?" said Balafré, in great surprise. "Selected
me, I suppose you mean?"

"I mean as I speak," replied the barber in a decided tone.
"Bring with you a harquebuss, young gentleman, for you are
to mount sentinel."

"But," said Balafré, "my nephew is only an esquire, serving
under my lance."

"Pardon me," answered Oliver, "the King sent for the register and enrolled him among the guard."

Quentin followed Master Oliver out of the barrack, his
uncle looking after him with wonder and curiosity. Oliver led

him through a maze of stairs and passages to a latticed gallery called Roland's Gallery, and bade him keep good watch until he received further orders. In time the King came to him and explained that he was to dine in strict privacy with the Cardinal Balne and the Count de Crèvecœur, and that something might happen, for the devil is most busy when foes meet on terms of truce. When the King stopped, with a gloomy look, Quentin ventured to ask what his duty was to be in these circumstances.

"To keep watch at the beauffet," said Louis; "and if there be treason, to shoot the traitor dead."

"Treason, sire!" exclaimed Quentin. "But it is my duty, your Majesty's life being endangered."

"Certainly—I mean it no otherwise. When I say, '*Ecosse, en avant*,' shoot Crèvecœur dead."

Louis then led his young Life Guardsman, whom he seemed to have taken into special favor, to a vaulted chamber, where a table was spread, and posted him behind the beauffet, saying: "Remember the word, *Ecosse, en avant*."

Quentin kept his position until the dinner was over, when the King dismissed his guests and called the Archer from his place of concealment.

"Thy watch is not yet over. Follow me," he said, and led the way again to the Hall of Roland. "Take notice," he added imperatively, "thou hast never left this post; let that be thine answer to thy kinsman and comrades. To bind the recollection on thy memory, I give thee this gold chain. And now attend. No man, save Oliver or I myself, enters here this evening; but ladies will come hither. You may answer if they address you, but your answer must be brief. But hearken to what they say; if thou hearest aught, retain it in thy memory until it is communicated to me, and then forget it. Now I think better of it, pass for a Scottish recruit who hath not yet acquired our language. So, thou wilt not answer. You understand me. Be wary, and thou hast a friend."

After the King's departure the first to enter the hall was the Princess Joan, who was soon followed by two ladies, in the younger of whom Quentin recognized the maiden who had served Maître Pierre at the inn. As Quentin rendered to this beauty and her companion the same homage he had just paid

to the royal princess, he thought the young lady colored slightly
and seemed embarrassed. The Princess Joan received the two
courteously and entered into conversation with them, which
had not lasted more than fifteen minutes when a man in a riding-
cloak entered.

Quentin interposed between him and the ladies, and requested him to retire instantly.

"By whose command?" asked the stranger contemptuously.

"By that of the King, which I am placed here to enforce."

"Not against Louis of Orléans," said the Duke, dropping
his cloak.

"Your Highness," replied Quentin, "is too great to be withstood by me. I trust your Highness will bear me witness I have
done the duty of my post, so far as your will permitted."

"You shall have no blame, young soldier," said Orléans;
and passing on he joined the ladies. But, instead of paying
court to the Princess, he gave most of his discourse to the Countess Isabelle de Croye, to whom his attentions, which gave visible pain to Joan, appeared to be disagreeable. The Princess,
seeming about to faint, the Duke summoned her attendants
from an adjoining room, and the King, hearing the bustle,
entered, and gave a keen look around.

"You here, my fair cousin?" he exclaimed. Then, turning
to Quentin, added sternly: "Had you not charge?"

"Forgive the young man, sire," said the Duke; " he did not
neglect his duty. I was informed that the Princess was in this
gallery."

After bowing the ladies to their apartment the King returned
to Quentin, and said:

"Thou hast done foul wrong, and deservest to die. What
hadst thou to do with dukes or princesses? What with anything but my order?"

"So please your Majesty, what could I do?"

"What couldst thou do?" asked the King scornfully. "Thou
shouldst have leveled thy piece, and if the presumptuous rebel
did not retire on the instant he should have died within this
very hall! Begone to thy quarters. Send Oliver to me. As
thou dost value thy life, be not so loose of thy tongue as thou
hast been slack of thy hand."

When Oliver came the King upbraided him for having advised him to receive the two Countesses who had offended the Duke of Burgundy, who was on the eve of closing an alliance against him with Edward of England.

"I know not what to do. I dare not wed this beauty to one of my subjects; I dare not return her to Burgundy; I dare not transmit her to England or Germany, where she is likely to become the prize of someone more apt to unite with Burgundy than with France, and more ready to discourage than encourage the honest malcontents in Ghent and Liège. Cannot thy fertile brain devise some scheme?"

Oliver, after a long pause, said: "The husband likely to answer your Majesty's views must unite various qualities—a friend to your Majesty, an enemy to Burgundy, of policy enough to conciliate the Gauntois and Liègeois, of valor enough to defend his dominions against the power of Duke Charles, of noble birth, and of excellent and virtuous character."

"Nay, Oliver, I leaned not so very much on character. Since I myself must suggest someone, why not William de la Marck?"

"De la Marck! The Wild Boar of Ardennes is the most notorious robber and murderer on the frontiers, excommunicated by the Pope for a thousand crimes."

"We will have him released from the sentence, friend Oliver. Holy Church is merciful."

"He hath the face and form, as well as the heart, of a Flemish butcher. She never will accept him."

"His mode of wooing, if I mistake him not," said Louis, "will render it difficult for her to make a choice. I must determine the Ladies of Croye for a speedy and secret flight. Thou must find means to let William de la Marck know of their motions, and let him choose his own time and place to push his suit."

"To whom will your Majesty entrust so important a charge?" asked Oliver.

"To one who has neither kin nor interest in France—in a word, I design to employ the young Scot."

In accordance with this plan, Quentin Durward was ordered to set out at midnight to escort the two ladies to Liège, where

they were to be entrusted to the care of the Bishop Henry of
Bourbon.   The ladies and a maid were mounted on palfreys,
and two sumpter mules carried their baggage.   To guard these
Quentin had but three men, but he saw with pleasure that they
were fully armed and bore long lances.   A guide, entrusted
with the passwords, led the party through the defenses of the
castle and onward until daybreak, when he had orders to leave
them to other guidance.   When they had been in the saddle
several hours, they were overtaken by two knights in armor of
polished steel, but showing no device, one of whom called out to
Quentin:

"Sir squire, give place; we come to relieve you of a charge
which is above your rank and condition.   Leave these ladies
in our care, who are fitter to wait upon them, especially as we
know that in yours they are little better than captives."

Quentin replied that he was in discharge of a duty imposed
by his sovereign, and that the ladies preferred to abide under
his protection.

"Out, sirrah!" exclaimed one of the knights; "will you, a
wandering beggar, put yourself in resistance against belted
knights?"

"If there be difference of rank between us," said Quentin,
"your discourtesy has done it away."

With this Quentin, calling upon one of his men to aid him,
rode forward to meet their attack.   His companion, run through
the eye with a lance, fell dead, but his own lance, striking his
antagonist fair in the breast, hurled him to the ground.   Quentin dismounted and ran to his fallen antagonist, but the other
knight anticipated him, and bestriding his friend, exclaimed:
"In the name of God, good fellow, get thee gone with thy woman's ware.   They have caused mischief enough this morning."

"I will first learn whom I have had to do with," said Quentin.

"That shalt thou never live to know or to tell," answered
the knight.   "If we were fools for interrupting your passage, we
have had the worst, for thou hast done more evil than thou and
thy whole band could repay."

But Quentin drew his sword and advanced on him, and the
duel was at its hottest when a large party of horse rode up, crying: "Hold, in the King's name!"

Both paused, and Quentin saw with surprise that his captain, Lord Crawford, was at the head of the party.

"Crawford," said Quentin's antagonist, hastily giving up his sword, "I render myself, but, for God's sake, save the Duke of Orleans."

"What? The Duke of Orleans! How came this, in the name of the foul fiend?"

"Ask no questions," said Dunois, for it was he, "it was all my fault. See, he stirs."

Quentin, meanwhile, stood like one planet-struck. He had unhorsed the first prince of the blood in France, and had measured swords with her best champion, the famous Dunois. The result was that when the Duke of Orleans came to himself he and Dunois were carried away by Crawford, who had orders to deliver them at the Castle of Loches, and Quentin rode onward with his charges toward Liège. When the Countess Hameline heard the names of the two knights, she remarked:

"This young gentleman did his devoir bravely and well; but methinks 'tis pity that he did not succumb with honor, since his ill-advised gallantry has stood betwixt us and these princely rescuers."

"Madam," replied the Countess Isabelle in a displeased tone, "but that I know you jest, I would say your speech is ungrateful to our brave defender. For my part, I beg that he will accept my grateful thanks. Holy Virgin, he is wounded! he bleeds!" she exclaimed, as she saw blood streaming down Quentin's face. "Dismount, sir, and let your wound be bound up."

In spite of all he could say of the slightness of his wound, Quentin was obliged to dismount and remove his helmet, while the ladies washed his wound, stanched the blood, and bound it with the Countess Isabelle's kerchief. This incident seemed intended by Fate to complete the mysterious communication between two young people who, though far different in rank and fortune, strongly resembled each other in youth, beauty, and the romantic tenderness of an affectionate disposition. From that time on the Countess Isabelle was paramount in Quentin's bosom, while she thought of him with more emotion than of any of the high-born nobles who for two years had besieged her with their adoration. After this Quentin rode beside the ladies, into whose society he seemed to be tacitly adopted.

When Quentin reached the place where his guide was to join him, a gaudily clad Bohemian named Hayraddin Maugrabin appeared, riding a shaggy horse of the country. As he answered all the questions put to him, and was possessed of the password given by the King, Quentin was obliged to accept his guidance. In this way they traveled more than a week, their resting-places chiefly the monasteries. Near one of these Quentin, who suspected and watched his guide, detected him in communication with a follower of William de la Marck, and this decided him to alter the route assigned by his instructions and to follow the left bank of the Maes to Liège, instead of crossing at Namur. The elder lady objected, but the Countess Isabelle gave full and ample permission to change the route, and the next day they arrived safely and were hospitably received by the Bishop in his Castle of Schonwaldt.

Quentin had been in Schonwaldt but four days when the castle was attacked at night by William de la Marck aided by the Liègois, and captured. Aroused from his sleep by a knocking at his door, Quentin was surprised to see his Bohemian guide, who said hastily:

"William de la Marck is here. If you would save the Countess and your own hopes, follow me."

Hayraddin led the way to the women's apartments, where, on a signal from him, two closely veiled women appeared. The Bohemian aided one, while Quentin took the other, and the party succeeded in leaving the castle and reaching a place where horses awaited them.

"I see but two horses," said Quentin.

"You two must ride for Tongres ere the way becomes unsafe. Marthon will abide with the women of our tribe."

"Marthon!" said the Countess. "Is not this my kinswoman?"

"Pardon my deceit," said Hayraddin. "I dared not carry off *both* the ladies of Croye from the Wild Boar of Ardennes."

"Wretch!" said Quentin. "But it is not yet too late. I will back to rescue the Lady Hameline."

"Hameline," whispered the lady, "hangs on thy arm to thank thee for her rescue."

"Ha! How is this?" said Quentin, extricating himself from her hold. "Is the Lady Isabelle then left behind?"

Hayraddin tried to detain him, but the Scot shot back to the castle with the speed of the wind. He had the good fortune to rescue the Syndic Pavillon of Liège, who had fallen and was nearly smothered in his armor. After some search the two found the Countess Isabelle nearly overcome with fright. As Quentin raised her from the ground and pressed her to his bosom, she said: "Is it you, Durward? I thought all had left me to my fate. Do not leave me."

"Never—never!" said Quentin. Then, to the Syndic: "This lady was put under my charge by your ally, the King of France. Aid her, if your city would not lose his favor. Above all, save her from the hands of William de la Marck."

"That will be difficult," said the Syndic.

At Quentin's suggestion, the Countess veiled herself and passed as the Syndic's daughter, while Durward himself acted as his squire, and in this manner they succeeded in passing out of the castle, though not until they had witnessed the murder of the Bishop of Liège and other atrocities at the hands of the Boar of Ardennes. The Countess Isabelle, nearly fainting, was carried in Quentin's arms, her own encircling his neck; thus they reached a boat in the river and soon afterward the house of the worthy Syndic, where all received the utmost attention.

The Countess now determined that her only course was to return to Burgundy, and on the following day she set out, under Quentin's escort, toward their destination. The Syndic having brought news that William de la Marck had sent out riders in search of them, it was deemed best to disguise themselves as peasants and to accept the guidance of one Hans Glover, who knew the country. They were pursued by a party of the Boar's Schwarzreiters, but were rescued by a party under the Count de Crèvecœur and taken to the court of the Duke of Burgundy at Péronne.

The Count, who was a cousin of the Countess Isabelle, looked askance at Quentin when he was presented to him, and asked:

"Pray, my cousin, what has this—this *very* young gentleman done to deserve such intercession at your hands?"

"He has saved my life and honor," said the Countess, reddening with shame and resentment.

"Life and honor!" said the Count. "Methinks it would have been as well, my cousin, if you had not put yourself in the way of lying under such obligations to this very young gentleman."

"My lord Count," said Durward, "lest you should talk of a stranger in slighter terms than you might afterward think becoming, I take leave to tell you that I am Quentin Durward, an archer of the Scottish Body-Guard, in which, as you know, none but gentlemen are enrolled."

"I thank you for your information, and I kiss your hands, seignior archer," said Crèvecœur, in a tone of raillery. "Have the goodness to ride with me to the front."

In the conversation that followed, Crèvecœur questioned Quentin closely in regard to his leaving Plessis-les-Tours in charge of the ladies by orders of King Louis, who, when the Count had been there, had affected ignorance of their movements. Crèvecœur was shocked to hear that Schonwaldt had been taken and the Bishop murdered.

"Did you know of this assault—of this murder? Speak— thou art one of Louis's trusted archers, and it is he that has aimed this painful arrow."

"I know no more of these villainies than you. But what could I do? They were hundreds, and I but one. My only care was to rescue the Countess Isabelle, and in that I was happily successful."

Arrived at Charleroi, the Count left the Countess Isabelle, who was incapable of traveling farther, to the care of the abbess of the Cistercian convent, and, taking Quentin with him, rode on to Péronne, around which the Duke of Burgundy's army lay encamped. To the astonishment of Crèvecœur, and still more so to that of Durward, they were met with news that King Louis was at Péronne, whither he had come attended only by Monsieur d'Orléans and Dunois and a score or two of the Scottish Guard. Crèvecœur was greatly troubled, and expressed the opinion that, in consideration of what had taken place at

Liège, King Louis might as safely have undertaken a pilgrimage to the infernal regions as this ill-timed visit to Péronne.

Crèvecœur was right. When the news of the taking of Schonwaldt and the murder of the bishop reached Charles of Burgundy, he flew into a rage and with difficulty refrained from slaying Louis as he sat at table.

"Treacherous ally! perjured king! dishonored gentleman!" he exclaimed. "Thou art in my power, and I thank God for it."

"Rather thank my folly," said Louis, who quietly retained his seat, while the Duke, with his hand on his sword, refrained from drawing it against one who offered no resistance. "My cousin Orléans—kind Dunois—and you, my trusty Crawford—bring not on ruin and bloodshed by taking offense too hastily. Our cousin the Duke is chafed at the tidings of a near and loving friend, whose slaughter we lament as he does. Therefore stand back, and if it be required yield up your swords, I command you."

The result was that the King was consigned to Earl Herbert's Tower in the Castle of Péronne, while Duke Charles spent several days debating with himself what should be done with him. When at last the Duke's anger was somewhat abated he summoned the nobles of Burgundy to meet in council in the great hall of Herbert's Tower, and invited the presence of the King and his few followers.

While they were in council a herald, dressed in a tabard bearing the arms of the Boar of Ardennes, demanded an audience.

"Who art thou, in the devil's name?" was the greeting he received from Charles.

"I am Rouge Sanglier," answered the herald, "the officer-at-arms of William de la Marck, by the grace of God Prince Bishop of Liège, and, in right of his wife, the Honorable Countess Hameline of Croye, Count of Croye and Lord of Bracquemont."

The herald then made many demands of the Duke, to all of which he answered only by "Ha!" or some similar exclamation, until he demanded the release of the Boar's "worthy and trusty ally, the most Christian King, whose royal person it is rumored that you, Charles of Burgundy, have put under restraint, contrary to your duty as a vassal of the crown of France."

"Now, by Saint George of Burgundy—" said the Duke; but ere he could proceed, Louis arose, and said in a tone of dignity and authority:

"Sirrah herald, carry back notice to the perjured outlaw and murderer, William de la Marck, that the King of France will be presently before Liège, for the purpose of punishing the sacrilegious murderer of his late beloved kinsman, Louis of Bourbon; and that he purposes to gibbet De la Marck alive for the insolence of terming himself his ally."

"And begone," said the Duke. "Yet stay. Let him be scourged till the bones are laid bare. Set the hounds upon him. Come, we will see the sport."

As the council broke up Oliver le Dain whispered to King Louis: "It is the Bohemian, Hayraddin Maugrabin."

"He must die," answered Louis.

"He is a known villain," said Tristan l'Hermite, "and hath slain the King's subjects, robbed churches, deflowered virgins—"

"Enough," said Duke Charles; "he is my royal cousin's property. Now, will you make good your promise and go with me to punish this murdering La Marck and the Liègeois?"

"I will march against them," said Louis, "with the oriflamme displayed."

"And, to put this fair cause of mischief out of the way, will you agree to the Countess Isabelle of Croye wedding with the Duke of Orléans?"

"Fair cousin," said the King, "the Duke is the betrothed bridegroom of my daughter Joan. Be generous, yield up this matter."

But the Duke was obstinate, and the King at last consented, provided that the parties were willing and a dispensation from the Pope were obtained. But the parties proved intractable, the Countess Isabelle saying she preferred a cloister, and the Duke of Orléans, hearing her decision, declining the alliance. Duke Charles was furious, and exclaimed in his anger that he would bestow her hand on anyone that brought him the head of the Boar of Ardennes. "I swear it, by Saint George, by my ducal crown, and by the order that I wear!"

In the battle a few days later, under the walls of Liège, the head of the Boar of Ardennes was actually cut off by Le Balafré, but as Quentin had brought the giant to bay and had nearly overcome him, the prize was awarded to him to the satisfaction of all, not excepting the beautiful Countess of Croye.

ST. RONAN'S WELL (1823)

St. Ronan's Well, the scene of this story, is Inverleithen-upon-Tweed, Peebleshire, Scotland. The time is about 1800, in the reign of George III. The story, which is much involved, met with severe criticism in its day, especially from its English readers, some of whom went so far as to say that its author had committed literary suicide. It has, too, many supernumerary characters who have little or no connection with the main narrative, as Sir Bingo and Lady Binks, Lady Penelope, Mr. Meiklewham, Mr. Winterblossom, Dr. Quackleben, and Captain MacTurk.

THE Mowbrays of St. Ronan's, once a powerful family, became gradually reduced in importance, though of considerable note down to the middle of the seventeenth century, when Sir Reginald Mowbray distinguished himself by the obstinate defense of the castle against Cromwell, in consequence of which the fortress was dismantled and blown up with gunpowder. Sir Reginald, who returned after the Revolution, built a new house, suited to his diminished fortunes, in the village; and the family occupied this until about fifty years before the time of this story, when a casual fire induced the laird of the day to remove to a more pleasant and commodious dwelling three miles away.

The deserted mansion then became an inn, kept at first by a worthy couple, servants and favorites of the Mowbray family, who died reasonably wealthy, leaving behind an only daughter. This daughter, universally known as Meg Dods, though a considerable heiress, had resisted every matrimonial proposal, and ruled her house, in single blessedness, with the despotism of Queen Bess herself.

But in time Meg's house gradually lost its custom. A mineral spring was discovered about a mile and a half from the village, and a speculative builder erected there lodging-houses and shops, and finally a hotel, so that the desertion of the

Mowbray Arms became general. Meg's friends advised her to take down her sign, but she scornfully replied that "her father's door should be open to the road till her father's bairn should be streekit and carried out at it with her feet foremost."

At the opening of this story Meg's principal guest was a young man named Francis Tyrrel, who had been a resident of her house several years before, and whose chief occupation appeared to be fishing and sketching. At the other hotel at St. Ronan's Well, as the spa had been christened, was, among other guests, the Earl of Etherington, from one of the English counties, whose chief amusement was card-playing.

Francis, fifth Earl of Etherington, was very eccentric, having in his make-up, men said, a touch of insanity. But he was, in other respects, a handsome, accomplished man, with an expression somewhat haughty, but singularly pleasing when he chose it, and a favorite with the fair sex. During his travels in France he formed an attachment for a beautiful orphan, Marie de Martigny, whom he was supposed to have married. From this union sprang Francis Tyrrel, as he called himself and was called by his father. The Earl, who appears not to have acknowledged this early marriage, wedded, on his return to England, Ann Bulmer, of Bulmer Hall, and from this union sprang Francis Valentine Bulmer Tyrrel, who, during his father's life, bore the title of Lord Oakendale. Whatever may have been the relations between the Earl and Marie de Martigny, he brought his eldest born from France, and Francis resided in his house and shared, in all respects, the life and education of the younger son, who was usually called Valentine.

Though Valentine regarded his brother's fortunes as standing in direct opposition to his own, he did not dislike him, and when the two were students at the University of Edinburgh they frequently made excursions into the Highlands together. On one of these occasions, when staying at Meg Dods's hostelry, Francis Tyrrel made the acquaintance of Clara Mowbray, daughter of the lord of the domain of St. Ronan's. Clara, then hardly sixteen years old, was a wild and beautiful woodland nymph, simple as a child in all that concerned the world and its ways, and with a lively and natural wit which brought amusement and gaiety wherever she went. She was under no restraint; for her father, a cross, peevish old man, was confined to his chair with the gout, and her only companion, a girl of somewhat inferior caste who served her for company in her rides and strolls, never thought of interfering with her will or pleasure.

Francis and Clara had become betrothed before Valentine knew of their intimacy, and when the elder made his brother his confidant, the latter felt a mischievous satisfaction in forwarding the affair. The Earl had at various times thrown out dark hints of a possibility that the hereditary estate and honors might be transferred to the elder, instead of the younger son; and Valentine foresaw that his father would lose all wish to accomplish this if Francis should commit such an unpardonable act as to ally himself secretly with a Scottish beauty.

Some tattling spy carried the news of the lovers' meetings to old Mowbray, who, greatly incensed at his daughter, prohibited further intercourse; and, in an endeavor to frighten Francis from the neighborhood, began an action against him for poaching. His person was described to all the keepers about Shaw's Castle, as Mowbray's estate was named, and all personal intercourse between the lovers became impossible, except under desperate risks. Francis withdrew to a town called Marchthorn, and maintained intercourse with Clara only by letter.

Valentine then became agent, letter-carrier, and go-between for the parties, employing one Hannah Irwin to aid him. Clara had not been so strictly watched since Francis's removal; her brother was traveling abroad, and the father was confined to his room. Valentine had prevailed on the Rev. Mr. Cargill to marry the two secretly, on the ground that if he declined he might prevent a too successful lover from doing justice to a betrayed maiden. It was therefore settled that the lovers should meet at the old kirk of St. Ronan's at twilight, and go off in a chaise for England as soon as the ceremony was performed.

All was arranged save the actual appointment of the day, when Valentine received a letter from his father which set him to thinking. It was in reply to a letter written by himself, in which casual mention had been made of the family of Mowbray of St. Ronan's, and it charged Valentine to cultivate the acquaintance of Mr. Mowbray as intimately as possible. As a motive for this, the Earl let Valentine into a family secret, that by the last will and testament of his granduncle by the mother's side, Mr. S. Mowbray of Nettlewood, a large and fair estate was bequeathed to the eldest son and heir of the Earl of Etherington, on condition of his forming a matrimonial alliance with a lady of the house of Mowbray of St. Ronan's.

The estates of Nettlewood and Oakendale lay contiguous, and Valentine saw at once that any marriage that helped to bring about the union of these estates would be not only pardoned but welcomed by his father. Moreover, that the very catastrophe which he had arranged as sure to exclude Francis from his father's favor, was likely to become a strong motive for the Earl's placing his rights above his own. Therefore, after much deliberation, Valentine hit upon the plan of substituting himself for his brother and marrying Clara, trusting to his general resemblance to Francis and the dusk to prevent his recognition, and believing that Clara, once within his power, would be prevented by shame from receding.

The marriage ceremony was performed in the presence of Hannah Irwin and Valentine's valet Solmes, and the couple set out in a chaise, but had not proceeded more than a mile when Francis, who in some way had got wind of the fraud, intercepted them. Valentine jumped out of the carriage, but fell under the wheel, and, the horses taking fright, it passed over his body. The next he knew he was stretched on a sick-bed miles away, with Solmes in attendance. To his anxious inquiries he was informed that the young lady had been sent back home and was ill in consequence of her adventure, and that Francis was in the same house with himself, very anxious on his account. In this condition, he acquiesced in Francis's proposal that they should bid adieu to each other and to Clara Mowbray. Valentine hesitated at the latter stipulation, averring that Clara was his wife and he was entitled to claim her as such. But Francis assured him that Clara disowned and detested such an alliance, and as there had been an essential error in the person, such a ceremony never could be accounted binding by the law of any Christian country.

In accepting this arrangement Valentine insisted on but one condition, that Francis should take upon himself the burden of the Earl's displeasure, and should represent the separation of the two as the result of his own work. The consequence was that the old peer went into a towering rage against Francis, and on his death Valentine succeeded to his title and estates. Meanwhile, Francis, who had a small patrimony from his mother, had gone abroad, none knew whither.

Such were the antecedents of the two young men who appeared at St. Ronan's at the time of the beginning of this story, Francis at the Mowbray Arms and the Earl of Etherington at the Well. The Earl of Etherington, a dissipated gambler, became intimate with John Mowbray, the brother of Clara, and the present laird, and allowed him to win money from him at piquet. He then obtained Mowbray's permission to address his sister, explaining to him how the possession of the Nettlewood estate depended on such a marriage. At the intercession of her brother, who was ignorant of any previous relations between his sister and Etherington, Clara agreed to his appearing at the house as Mowbray's guest, but declined to receive him as a suitor. Etherington, who knew of his brother's presence and feared his interference with his schemes, sent to him his friend, Captain Jekyl, to propose a compromise. He offered that, if Francis would permit the marriage to enable him to secure the Nettlewood estate, he would make a previous contract of separation, with suitable provisions for the lady, and stipulations by which the husband should renounce all claim to her society. As an answer to this, Francis asserted that he was in possession of papers, sent to him by his father when on his death-bed, proving his legitimacy and his right to the title of Earl of Etherington, all of which he should produce in due time. He made also a counter-proposal, that he would bind himself under the strongest penalties never to disturb his brother's possession of the earldom and estates, on condition that he would leave Clara Mowbray undisturbed by his marriage suit or other claim; in short, that he would not molest her by his presence, word, letter, or intervention of a third party, and be to her in future as if he did not exist.

When Captain Jekyl laid this counter-proposal before his principal, and announced that Francis Tyrrel would not consent that Miss Mowbray's happiness should be placed in his keeping, the Earl asked:

"And on what grounds? Does he still seek to marry the girl himself?"

"I believe he thinks the circumstances of the case render that impossible," said Jekyl.

"What! then he would play the dog in the manger! He shall find himself mistaken. She has used me like a dog, Jekyl, since I saw you; and, by Jove! I will have her, that I may break her pride and cut him to the liver with the agony of seeing it."

"You are determined, then, to go on with this strange affair?" asked Jekyl.

"On—on—on, my boy! Clara and Nettlewood forever!" answered the Earl. "This brother of hers provokes me, too: he does not do for me half what he might—what he ought to do. He stands on points of honor, forsooth, this broken-down horse-jockey. I can see he wishes to play fast and loose—has some suspicions of my right to my father's titles and estates. I am much tempted to make an example of him. But for the girl— her caprices are so diverting that I sometimes think, out of mere contradiction, I almost love her."

Shortly after this, Mowbray, playing at piquet with Etherington, became the Earl's debtor to an overwhelming amount. Smarting under his losses, and angry at hearing certain rumors about his sister which were in circulation among the gossips at the Well, he went home, after drinking deeply, determined to bring Clara to her senses without delay. He immediately sought his sister, who, seeing his condition, tried to pacify him, but he was deaf to all her efforts, and at last said:

"Clara, what is there which makes you so obstinately reject every proposal of marriage? Is it that you feel yourself unworthy to be the wife of an honest man? Speak out! Evil fame has been busy with your reputation. The fortunes of our house are ruined, but no tongue shall slander its honor. Speak —speak, wretched girl! Why are you silent?"

"Stay at home, brother!" said Clara. "Stay at home, if you regard our house's honor. Stay at home, and let them talk of me as they will, they can hardly say worse of me than I deserve!"

Mowbray set his teeth, clenched his hands, looked on the

ground, as one that forms some horrid resolution, and muttered almost unintelligibly: "It were charity to kill her!"

"Oh! no—no—no!" exclaimed the terrified girl. "Do not
kill me, brother! I have wished for death—thought of death—
prayed for death; but, oh! not a bloody death, nor by your
hand!"

"Fool!" he said, grasping her by the shoulder and pushing
her from him, "who cares for thy worthless life? Live, if thou
canst, and be the hate and scorn of everyone else, as much as
thou art mine!"

"Brother," said Clara, "say you did not mean this! It is
not manly—it is not natural; there are but two of us in the
world!"

"Clara," he said, after a pause of mournful silence, "we must
think what is to be done. Dishonor concealed is not dishonor
in some respects. Dost thou attend to me, wretched girl?"

"Yes, brother—yes, indeed, brother," she hastily replied,
fearful of awakening again his ferocious and ungovernable
temper.

"Thus it must be, then. You must marry this Etherington;
there is no help for it, Clara."

"But, brother—" said the trembling girl.

"Be silent. No refusal or expostulation—that time is gone
by. Fallen as you are, you are still too good for him. Swear
you will not hesitate. Submit to your fate, for it is inevitable."

"I will—submit," answered Clara, in trembling accents, as
she left the room.

She had hardly gone when wheels in the courtyard announced a visitor, and in a few minutes Mr. Peregrine Touchwood, whom Mowbray had met at the Well, entered. After
some preliminaries, Touchwood asked his host if he had ever
heard of one Reginald Scrogie, who, ashamed of the name he
bore, chose to join it to Mowbray, as having a more chivalrous
and gentlemanly twang.

"I have heard of such a person, sir. I believe he regulated
his family settlements upon the idea that his heir was to inter-
marry with our house."

"You may also have heard that this old gentleman had a
son who thought Scrogie sounded as well as Mowbray, and had

no fancy for an imaginary gentility attained by the change of one's natural name."

"I think I have heard from Lord Etherington," said Mowbray, "that old Mr. Scrogie Mowbray had an unfortunate son, who had imbibed low tastes, wandering habits, and singular objects of pursuit, on account of which his father disinherited him."

"It is very true, Mr. Mowbray," proceeded Touchwood; "his father disinherited him because he had the qualities for doubling the estate rather than for squandering it."

"But pray, Mr. Touchwood, what has this Mr. Scrogie, Jr., to do with you or me?"

"It has a great deal to do with me, at least, since I am the very man myself."

"The devil you are!" said Mowbray. "But your name is Touchwood?"

"I got it from an old godfather, and a pretty spell of money with it. He was my grandfather's partner in Touchwood, Scrogie and Company."

"Well, Mr. Touchwood, though you set no value upon your connection with my family, I cannot forget that such a circumstance exists, and I therefore bid you heartily welcome to Shaw's Castle. But what has recalled us to your recollection?"

"Why, I was settled some time at Smyrna, and there I became acquainted with Francis Tyrrel."

"The natural brother of Lord Etherington?"

"So called," answered Touchwood, "but more likely to prove the Earl of Etherington himself, and t'other fine fellow the bastard."

"The devil he is! You surprise me, Mr. Touchwood."

"Thought I should. But the thing is not less certain: the proofs are in our house in London, deposited there by the old Earl, who repented of his roguery to Miss Martigny before he died, but had not courage enough to do his legitimate son justice till the sexton had housed him."

"Good Heaven, sir!" said Mowbray; "and did you know all this while that I was about to bestow the only sister of my house on an impostor?"

"What was my business with that?" asked Touchwood.

"I thought this Bulmer, even when declared illegitimate, might be a reasonably good match for your sister, considering the estate to accompany the union; but now that I have discovered him to be a scoundrel I would not wish any decent girl to marry him."

Mr. Touchwood then, to Mowbray's astonishment, gave a detailed account of Valentine's rascality in substituting himself for Francis at the marriage ceremony performed by Mr. Cargill, and that, to the best of his knowledge and belief, his sister was not otherwise guilty. To prove his assertions, he informed him that Solmes, the Earl's confidential valet, was in his power, he having detected him in a forgery, and was now acting in his pay and under his instructions.

"I wish to God, sir," said Mowbray, "that since you were so kind to interest yourself in affairs so intimately concerning my family, you had been pleased to act with a little more openness toward me. Here have I been for weeks the intimate of a damned scoundrel, whose throat I ought to have cut for his scandalous conduct to my sister. I have been rendering her and myself miserable, and getting myself cheated every night by a swindler, whom you could have unmasked by a single word."

Touchwood smiled and shook his head. "I look upon you, Mr. Mowbray, as a young man spoiled by staying at home and keeping bad company; but I will make it my business, if you will submit yourself to my guidance, to inform your understanding so as to retrieve your estate. Don't answer me, sir; I hate to be answered, and, to tell the truth, it is because Tyrrel has a fancy of answering me that I make you my confidant rather than him."

Mowbray was not so inexperienced as his visitor thought, and while Touchwood talked he plainly saw that he was dealing with an obstinate, capricious old man. He also saw that, as he was wealthy and childless, and disposed, as a sort of relative, to become his friend, it would pay to conciliate him. So, subduing the natural haughtiness of his temper, he answered respectfully that he was willing to submit his own judgment to that of so experienced and sagacious a friend, and invited him to spend the night.

The next morning, when Mowbray thought over the events of the evening before, he became conscious that he had been too harsh with Clara, whom he really loved as much as he was capable of loving anyone. "Yes—oh, yes," he said to himself, "she would naturally think that my knowledge of this mock marriage would render me more eager in the rascal's interest; and she would have judged right, too, for, had he actually been Lord Etherington, I do not see what else she could have done. She may marry the other one now, if the law is not against it; then she has the earldom, Oaklands, and Nettlewood all at once. Gad! we should come in winners, after all. I'll away to Clara instantly, get the truth out of her, and consider what is to be done."

He knocked at his sister's door, but could get no answer. "Clara—dear Clara! Answer me but one word—say but you are well. I frightened you last night; I had been drinking—I was violent—forgive me! Clara—dear Clara! speak but a single word, and you shall remain in your room as long as you please."

But no response came, and when he entered her room he found the bed had not been occupied. "I have terrified her to death," he cried. "She has fled into the woods and perished there!"

As he ran out of the room he met Touchwood, who said: "You are as mad as a *hamako*; sit down and let us consult—"

"Damn you!" cried Mowbray; "if you had behaved like a man of common sense, this would not have happened."

"God forgive me if I have done wrong," said Touchwood. "But may she not have gone to the Well? I will drive thither to see."

"Do—do," said Mowbray. "I thank you—I thank you."

While Touchwood went his way, Mowbray mounted his horse and rode recklessly through the wood and across the ford. As he reached a sequestered spot the sound of a pistol-shot drew him to a little glade, where he saw Lord Etherington, Jekyl, and Captain MacTurk, engaged in pistol-shooting to decide a bet. As he sprang from his horse, dripping wet, Lord Etherington said: "What does this mean, Mr. Mowbray?"

"It means, sir, that you are a rascal and impostor," replied Mowbray.

"That, Mr. Mowbray, is an insult I cannot carry further than this spot," said Etherington. "Mr. Jekyl, you will have the kindness to stand by me in this matter?"

Jekyl assented, and Captain MacTurk offered his services to Mr. Mowbray. The ground was hastily marked out and the principals placed. Lord Etherington's ball grazed Mowbray's forehead at the very second when Mowbray's pierced his heart. He sprang from the ground and fell down a dead man, while Mowbray stood fixed as a pillar of stone.

Meanwhile Clara, after wandering through the wet wood, went to Meg Dods's Inn, whether attracted by a light in the window or in search of Tyrrel, can never be known. Francis Tyrrel was writing in his room when Clara entered, holding a light in her extended hand. Almost impressed with the belief that he saw a vision, he shuddered when she stooped beside him and took his hand.

"Come away," she said in a hurried voice, "my brother follows to kill us both. Come, Tyrrel, let us fly—we shall easily escape him—but I will have no more fighting; we have had too much of that."

"Clara!" exclaimed Tyrrel. "Alas, is it thus you come to me? Stay, do not go. Sit down."

"I must go," she replied—"I am called. Nay, if you will hold me by force, I know I must sit down; but you will not be able to keep me."

A convulsion fit followed, and when Tyrrel aroused the house, Meg Dods found him in a state little less distracted than his unhappy patient. She recognized Clara and with her usual decision at once took measures for her relief. When Tyrrel would have remained beside the bed of the sufferer, she gently led him from the room, saying, "This is nae sight for men folk," and promised to bring him word of her condition every half hour. He had not long to wait, for she passed away before morning. When he looked upon her corpse, and the surgeon tried to explain to him that death was a mercy, as her reason probably would not have returned, he muttered, "My life is spared till I avenge her," and hastened from the house. Touchwood met him at the door.

"Whither would ye?" he said, stopping him.

"For revenge!" said Tyrrel. "Give way, on your peril."

"Vengeance belongs to God," replied the old man. "Mow-bray has met Valentine Bulmer, the titular Earl of Etherington, within this half hour, and killed him on the spot."

"You bring tidings of death to the house of death," answered Tyrrel; "and there is nothing in this world left that I should live for."

REDGAUNTLET: A TALE OF THE EIGHTEENTH CENTURY (1824)

The scene of this story is laid in Scotland, in the reign of George III. The action centers in a Jacobite plot in favor of the Young Pretender, Charles Edward, fostered by the principal representative of the Redgauntlet family. The story is told largely in letters and diaries.

THE house of Redgauntlet was for centuries supposed to lie under a doom which, originating in the killing by Sir Alberick Redgauntlet of his own son, affected the fortunes of the family through many generations, and appeared to render nugatory all its undertakings. The head of the house in 1745, Sir Henry Redgauntlet, was possessed of considerable wealth, and would have retained it if he had listened to his wife; but the influence of his younger brother, who had a restless spirit and great energy, led him to follow the fortunes of the unhappy house of Stuart, and he lost his life on the scaffold, while the brother, Edward Hugh Redgauntlet, was exiled. On this fatal conclusion of the family schemes Lady Redgauntlet fled with her two children, Arthur and Lilias, from the north of England to Devonshire, determined to break off all communication with her late husband's family, and especially with the brother, to whose insane political enthusiasm she attributed Sir Henry's death. Arthur was hardly a twelvemonth old when his father suffered, and Lilias was born after that event. Sir Henry, in the settlement of his affairs, had confided the custody of his children to his brother, notwithstanding the latter's attainder; but the mother, who hated and feared her brother-in-law, determined that they should be brought up free from his influence and as adherents of the reigning dynasty. To secure this end she suppressed the name of Redgauntlet and concealed from her children all knowledge of their uncle.

The uncle, who might have been soothed by an offer of confidence, revolted against the distrustful and suspicious manner in which Lady Darsie Redgauntlet acted toward him, and swore solemnly that he would not submit to such an injury. When the children were two or three years old, the little girl was seized and carried to a boat in waiting, and the boy would have shared her fate if the mother had not held him and aroused the neighborhood by her cries. After this Lady Redgauntlet adopted every precaution her ingenuity could suggest to keep her son's existence concealed from his uncle, and even to hide his identity from himself, for he was brought up under the name of Darsie Latimer. When the boy was six years old he was put under the care of Samuel Griffiths, an eminent banker of London, and a certain clergyman, both of whom were sworn to observe profound secrecy concerning the boy's birth and pretensions until he should attain his majority. The mother died soon afterward, in ignorance of her daughter's fate.

Darsie Latimer was sent by his guardians to Edinburgh, with the understanding that he was to refrain from visiting England until the expiration of his twenty-fifth year, when he was to come into full possession of his property. Meanwhile, his quarterly allowance was sent regularly from London, and there was a tacit understanding that he was to make no inquiries concerning his family before a certain time. In the Edinburgh High School Darsie made the acquaintance of Alan Fairford, the son of an advocate, and formed with him an intimacy that lasted through life. Rather than part with him, he joined him in his law studies and spent a weary season at the Scotch Law Class and a wearier at the Civil, living during the time in Alan's father's house. Alan was kept closely at his studies, but Darsie, with a liberal income and caring little for the law, was free to go and come at pleasure.

Once, when near Dumfries, he walked down to the Solway Firth, where he was amused by watching horsemen hunting salmon with barbed spears. The feats of one, well mounted on a strong, black horse, attracted his special attention. He was a tall man, wearing a sort of fur cap or bonnet, with a short feather in it, and he appeared to hold some sort of authority over the others, directing their movements both by voice and hand.   Darsie lingered on the sands, after most of the riders had gone, looking across at the forbidden shores of England, when the tall man galloped up to him and called out abruptly:

"Soho, brother! you are too late for Bowness to-night—the tide will make presently."

Darsie turned and looked at him without answering, for his unexpected approach, amid the gathering shadows, had something wild and ominous.

"Are you deaf?" he called, "or are you mad?   Are you weary of life?   The sky threatens a blast that will bring in the waves three feet abreast."

Darsie said he was a stranger and ignorant of the way, to which the rider replied: "You will presently be among the quicksands.   There is no time for prating; get up behind me."

As soon as Darsie was seated on the croup of the horse, the rider set off at a gallop for the north shore, where he gave him directions for Shepherd's Bush.   Darsie set out on the path he thought he had pointed out, when the fisherman called him back.

"Stay, young man—you have mistaken the road already.   I wonder your friends should send out such an inconsiderate youth, without someone wiser than himself to care for him.   It is not my custom to open my house to strangers, but your pinch is like to be a smart one; so I must for once give you a night's lodging in my cottage."

At the rider's order, as the sky was rapidly blackening, Darsie again seated himself behind him, and was taken through a steep and rugged glen to a group of cottages beside a brook. They stopped at one of these, and a loud halloo brought to the door a man and a woman, with two large Newfoundland dogs and some terriers.   The woman drew back when she saw a stranger, and as they entered she retreated into a side apartment, whither she was followed by the horseman, after he had motioned Darsie to a seat.   An elderly woman soon entered and spread a table for supper.   She was evidently a menial, but was dressed above her rank, and wore a rosary of black and silver beads, with a cross of silver.

While she was cooking the fish, the man who had taken the horse entered.   He was broad-shouldered and of possibly sixty years, with a hard and harsh countenance and eyes sunk under projecting eyebrows. He gave Darsie an inquisitive and somewhat sinister look, and then set himself to arranging the table, on which he placed silver salt-cellars, a silver lamp, and at the head of the table a silver flagon with armorial bearings, which seemed to Darsie to indicate that he was in the house of a decayed gentleman rather than a fisherman.

When the master of the house returned, he had thrown off his riding-cap and jockey-coat, and appeared in a gray jerkin trimmed with black, and with clean and unsullied linen. His frame was large and sinewy, and his figure and features and his curling chestnut locks showed no touch of time, though he was more than fifty. He took a seat at the head of the table and motioned Darsie to a chair beside him, the two domestics having already taken places at the foot of the table. As Darsie appeared to hesitate, the host observed, with something approaching a sneer:

"Cristal Nixon, say grace; the gentleman expects one."

"If the gentleman is a Whig," growled the old man, "he may please himself with his own mummery. My faith is neither in word nor writ, but in barley bread and brown ale."

"Mabel Moffat," said the host, looking at the old woman, "canst thou ask a blessing upon our victuals?"

The old woman shook her head, kissed the cross on her rosary, and was silent.

"Mabel will say grace for no heretic," said the master of the house, with the same sneer on his brow and in his accent. At the same moment the door opened and the young woman came in. She advanced a few steps, then stopped bashfully, as she caught Darsie's eye upon her, and asked the master of the house whether he had called.

"No," he said, "but it is a shame that a stranger should see a house where not one can or will say a grace. Do thou be our chaplain."

The girl came forward with timid modesty and pronounced the benediction in a silver-toned voice, her cheek coloring just enough to show that she felt some embarrassment. She vanished when she had finished, and Darsie saw her no more.

In the morning Darsie was awakened by his host.

"You sleep sound," said his full deep voice. "Ere five years have rolled over your head your slumbers will be lighter—unless ere then you are wrapped in the sleep that is never broken."

"How!" exclaimed Darsie, "do you know anything of me—of my prospects—of my views in life?"

"Nothing," he answered, with a grim smile. "But come; a brown crust and a draught of milk await you, if you choose to break your fast; but you must make haste."

After eating his frugal breakfast, Darsie was conducted by his host, mounted on his black horse, out of the glen and across an uncultivated tract of downs, until he came in sight of Shepherd's Bush. As the host was pointing the way, they were joined by a rider in Quaker garb, mounted on a sleek, well-kept horse.

"Soho! friend Joshua," said the fisherman, " has the Spirit moved thee and thy righteous brethren to act with some honesty, and pull down yonder tide-nets that keep the fish from coming up the river?"

"Surely, friend, not so," answered Joshua; "thou canst not expect that our own hands should pull down what our own purses established. I prithee seek no quarrel against us, for thou shalt have no wrong at our hand."

"I tell you in fair terms, Joshua Geddes, that you and your partners are using unlawful craft to destroy the fish that make the livelihood of fifty poor families. These nets of yours are unlawful, and we will have them down at all risks and hazards. But hark thee, Joshua, I will put thee in the way of doing one good deed. Here is a stranger youth, whom Heaven has so scantily gifted with brains that he will lose himself unless thou wilt kindly help him. Young gentleman, this pious pattern of primitive simplicity will show thee the way to the Shepherd's Bush."

He then abruptly asked Darsie how long he intended to remain at Shepherd's Bush, and departed, saying: "We may meet again."

Darsie Latimer learned from Joshua Geddes that his host was variously known as the Laird and as Herries of Birrenswork. The good Quaker had heard various stories concerning him, but knew little of him, save that he never before heard of his receiving a stranger in his house.

"He does not," said Darsie, "appear to possess in much abundance the means of exercising hospitality."

"That is to say, friend," remarked Joshua, "that thou hast supped ill and breakfasted worse. If thou wilt accompany me to my tenement, called Mount Sharon, which is nearer by two miles than thy inn, thy youthful appetite will be appeased. What sayest thou?"

Darsie accepted the invitation in the spirit in which it was given, and thus it happened that he became an inmate of the good Quaker's house for several days, Joshua insisting on sending to the inn at Shepherd's Bush for his luggage.

One evening the attack on Geddes's fishing-station, at which the Laird had hinted, was made in earnest by a large number of men. The Quaker, who had an intimation of expected trouble, went down to the station to pass the night, accompanied by Darsie Latimer, who insisted on sharing the danger. Joshua, who did not believe in the use of carnal weapons, threw into a tub of water the pistols that his superintendent had made ready for him, and determined to meet the mob with moral suasion only. But the attacking party, which consisted of more than a hundred men armed with guns, fish-spears, crowbars, and bludgeons, was thoroughly in earnest and refused to listen to any arguments. They set to work to demolish the station, and would have struck down the Quaker but for Darsie, who received the blow intended for him. When Latimer recovered consciousness, it was to find himself with hands and feet bound, lying in a cart which was traveling rapidly over a rough road. His head was oppressed with a dispiriting sickness, his heart seemed on fire, and his limbs were chilled and benumbed with want of circulation. There seemed to be five or six persons about the cart, some on foot, others on horseback, the latter riding in front and acting as guides. Darsie spoke to the men about the cart, saying that he had had no connection with the fishing-station, where he was only a visitor, and offering a substantial reward for his deliverance. While he was speaking, a horseman approached and said in a determined voice:

"Young man, no personal harm is designed to you. If you remain silent and quiet you may reckon on good treatment; but if you tamper with these men I will take such measures for

silencing you as you will remember all the days of your life. I
will remove the belts if you will give me your word of honor that
you will make no attempt to escape."

"*Never!*" replied Darsie, with the energy of despair; "I
will never submit to loss of freedom a moment longer than I am
subjected to it by force."

"Enough," replied the speaker; "then do not complain that
I, who am carrying on an important undertaking, use the only
means in my power to insure its success."

Darsie was carried into England, where in time he discovered
that he was in the hands of Mr. Herries of Berrenswork. That
gentleman explained to him that he had certain rights over him
which, of no legality in Scotland, were revived in England, but
declined to tell what those rights were.

"You must prepare to attend me either as a captive or a
companion," he said, "for I must immediately change my
quarters. If you consent to go as a companion you must give
your parole of honor to attempt no escape; for if you break your
word once pledged, be assured that I will blow your brains out
without scruple."

"I am ignorant of your plans and purposes," said Darsie,
"and cannot but hold them dangerous. I will, therefore,
rather be your prisoner than your confederate."

"That is spoken fairly, and I will impose no unnecessary hardship on you. A horse will be provided for you,
and suitable necessaries; and Cristal Nixon will act as your
valet. If you object to the costume provided for you, your
mode of journeying will be as unpleasant as that which brought
you hither."

The next morning Darsie was required to put on a camlet
riding-skirt, like those worn by country ladies of moderate rank,
and a riding-mask that effectually concealed his features. In
this costume he set out with others and traveled until nearly
noon, when the party, which had avoided villages and houses
on the route, stopped at a large outlying barn, where preparations had been made for their reception. Soon afterward Mr.
Herries, or Redgauntlet as he was properly called, entered with
the young woman who had said grace in Herries's house, and
presented her in these words:

"It is time you two should know each other. Salute Lilias, Darsie."

Latimer was surprised and somewhat confused at this sudden command; but the young lady offered at once her cheek and her hand with perfect ease and frankness, saying:

"Dearest Darsie, how rejoiced I am that we are at last permitted to become acquainted."

Darsie hardly knew what to think of so eager a salute. She was very pretty, and her beautiful brown locks, which escaped in ringlets from under her riding-hat, with the bloom that exercise had brought into her cheek, made her more than usually fascinating.

"How can she," he thought, "look so like an angel, yet be so mere a mortal after all?"

When, after their rest, the party rode on, Redgauntlet, who was obliged to go in advance, left word with Cristal Nixon that the two young persons were to have unreserved communication with each other. Accordingly, when they were permitted to ride together, Darsie said:

"You must think me deficient in gratitude, Miss Lilias, for not sooner thanking you for the interest you appear to take in my affairs."

"*Miss* Lilias!" she exclaimed. "For whom or for what, in Heaven's name, do you take me, that you address me so formally?"

Darsie replied that he believed he had the honor of addressing the niece of Mr. Redgauntlet.

"Surely," she said; "but were it not as easy for you to say, to your own, only sister?"

"My sister!" exclaimed Darsie, starting as if he had received a pistol-shot.

"And you did *not* know it, then?" she asked. "I thought your reception was cold and indifferent!"

A kind and cordial embrace followed, and so light was Darsie's spirit that he really felt more relieved by being quit of embarrassments than disappointed by the vanishing of the day-dreams he had begun to encourage.

"I know so little of our family story," said Darsie, "that I almost doubted that I belonged to the house of Redgauntlet, although the chief of the family intimated as much to me."

"The chief of the family!" said Lilias. "You must know little indeed if you mean my uncle. You yourself, my dear Darsie, are the heir and representative of our ancient house; for our father, Sir Henry Darsie Redgauntlet, who suffered at Carlisle in 1746, was the elder brother. I am surprised that this should be unknown to you, for since my uncle has had you in his power, I never doubted he had communicated to you our whole family history."

"He has left me to learn it from you, Lilias; and from your lips I shall hear it with more pleasure than from his, for I have no reason to be pleased with his conduct toward me."

Lilias then gave him an insight into his uncle's machinations in behalf of the house of Stuart and the claims of the Young Pretender, for the furtherance of which he needed Darsie's authorization as head of the house of Redgauntlet.

"That he never shall obtain," said Darsie; "my principles and my prudence alike forbid such a step."

"But you may temporize," said Lilias. "I entreat you to avoid direct collision with him. To hear you declare against the family of Stuart would either break his heart or drive him to some act of desperation."

They were now approaching the Solway, and presently stopped at the house of one called Father Crackenthorp, not far from a rude pier, near which lay fishing-boats. Redgauntlet came forward and assisted Lilias to dismount, but apparently forgot Darsie, whose situation, encumbered with his female costume, was awkward, especially as his skirt had been secured around his ankles with corking-pins by Nixon, doubtless out of caution to prevent his escape. In endeavoring to dismount Darsie stumbled and would have fallen but for a gentleman who hastened to aid him. As soon as he recovered his footing a glance at the gentleman's face disclosed his friend Alan Fairford. He was about to whisper his identity and caution him to be silent, when Redgauntlet returned hastily, followed by Cristal Nixon.

"I'll relieve you of the charge of this young lady," said Redgauntlet haughtily.

"I had no desire to intrude, sir," replied Alan; "but the lady's situation appeared to require assistance, and—have I not the honor to speak to Mr. Herries of Birrensworth?"

"You are mistaken, sir," said Redgauntlet, turning aside and making a sign to Cristal, who hurried Darsie into the house and locked him in a chamber. But Darsie had now wrought himself up to such a pitch of passion that his uncle's wrath had lost its terrors, and he made such a noise that Redgauntlet came and asked what he wanted.

"I want my liberty," said Darsie, "and to be assured of the safety of my friend, Alan Fairford, whose voice I heard but now."

"Your liberty shall be your own within half an hour, and your friend shall be freed also in due time," said Redgauntlet.

"This does not satisfy me," said Darsie. "I must see my friend instantly. I have heard the clash of swords—I must have ocular demonstration of his safety."

"Arthur—dearest nephew," said Redgauntlet, "drive me not mad! Thine own fate—that of thy house—that of Britain herself, are at this moment in the scales; and you are occupied only about the safety of an insignificant pettifogger!"

"He has sustained injury at your hands, then?" cried Darsie fiercely. "If so, not even our relationship shall protect you."

"Peace, ungrateful and obstinate fool!" said Redgauntlet. "Yet stay. Will you be satisfied if you see this precious friend of yours well and sound, without attempting to speak with him?"

Darsie signified his assent.

"Take my arm, then, and do you, niece Lilias, take the other; and beware, Sir Arthur, how you bear yourself."

Redgauntlet then led him to an apartment where a man stood sentinel at the door, and showed him Alan Fairford and Joshua Geddes within, apparently in deep conversation. Darsie, who did not know that the good Quaker also had engaged in the search for him, longed to speak, but dared not.

"Gentlemen," said his uncle, "I know you are as anxious on Mr. Darsie Latimer's account as he is upon yours. I am commissioned by him to inform you that he is as well as you are, and hopes to meet you soon. Meantime, while I cannot suffer you to be at large, you shall be treated as well as your temporary confinement will permit."

He went out, without waiting to hear their answers, and led Darsie into a small room, where he told him to lay aside his mask and feminine attire, saying: "I restore you to yourself, and trust you will lay aside all feminine thoughts with your costume. Follow me, while Lilias remains here. I will introduce you to those whom I hope to see associated with you in the most glorious cause hand ever drew sword in."

"Uncle," said Darsie, "my person is in your hands; but remember, my will is my own. I will take no step of importance but upon conviction."

"But canst thou be convinced, foolish boy, without hearing and understanding the grounds on which we act?"

So saying, he led Darsie into a large room, where sat or walked to and fro several gentlemen in plain riding-dresses. As Darsie looked round the circle he thought he could discern few traces of that adventurous hope which urges men upon desperate enterprises. His uncle, who did not, or would not, see any marks of depression of spirit among them, went from one to another with cheerful countenance and a warm greeting of welcome. He then made a short and spirited speech, entreating them to come to the aid of their rightful sovereign, concluding with, "Charles Edward is in this country—Charles Edward is in this house! Charles Edward waits your decision, to receive the homage of those who have ever called themselves his loyal liegemen. He that would now turn his coat must do so under the eye of his sovereign."

Shortly afterward Redgauntlet, followed by Sir Richard Glendale, Darsie, and others, led the way to an upper chamber, where the Royal Wanderer was to receive their homage.

Charles Edward arose from his seat and bowed in acceptance of their salutation with a dignified courtesy which converted the wretched room into a place worthy of the occasion. The Prince was in clerical garb, for he had come into the country in the guise of Father Buonaventure, but over it he wore a loose riding-coat, under which were a sword and a pair of pistols.

In the long consultation that followed Charles Edward acceded to all the suggestions of his adherents but one—that he should dismiss a lady who followed his fortunes, and who was believed to have close relations with the Elector of Hanover. This proposal he treated as an impertinence, declining to accept their services under any condition that betrayed his sovereign rights. As he would listen to no compromise, the conference ended in his withdrawal to the upper end of the apartment, while his adherents stood at a distance and conversed in whispers.

Redgauntlet, followed by Darsie, hastened out to provide for the Prince's safety. He sent Nixon to summon Nanty Ewart, the captain of a smuggler in the harbor, and ordered the latter to lie by in readiness for a voyage to Wales or the Hebrides, or perhaps Sweden or Norway. "If you have any cargo, throw it overboard," he added, and Ewart, who was half drunk, replied sullenly: "Ay, ay, sir."

"Go with him, Nixon," said Redgauntlet, "and see that he does his duty."

Ewart went away muttering: "Rebel—Jacobite—I'll make you and your d—d confederates walk the plank—"

"D—d unhandsome terms Redgauntlet used to you, brother," said Nixon.

"Which do you mean?" said Ewart, recollecting himself. "Have I been thinking aloud?"

"Do you know," said Nixon, pausing after each word, "there is one yonder whose head is worth—thirty—thousand—pounds —of sterling money—"

"What of that?" said Ewart quickly.

"In an hour or two these Jacobite gentry will be safe in Carlisle Castle."

"The devil they will!" said Ewart. "And you have been the informer?"

"Yes, I have been ill paid for my service among the Redgauntlets, and have been treated worse than a dog. But I have them in a trap now, Nanty. You see I am frank with you."

"And I will be as frank with you," said the smuggler. "You are a d—d old scoundrel—traitor to the man whose bread you eat! I will back and tell them of their danger."

"Are you stark mad?" said Nixon. "Hear reason—or else hear this!" and he discharged a pistol into Ewart's body.

Nanty staggered, but kept his feet. Then, collecting his

remaining strength, he drew his hanger and, fetching a stroke with both hands, cut Nixon down. A seaman, hearing the pistol-shot, strolled up and found both the men stark dead.

Meanwhile Redgauntlet had hastened back to the conference, to find nothing decided. He had hardly reached the room when Lilias put into his hand a paper which a messenger had brought for Nixon. Redgauntlet read it, dropped it on the floor, and stood gazing on it as if petrified. A bystander picked it up and read: "All is prepared; keep them in play till I come up. You may depend on your reward. C. C."

"Black Colin Campbell, by G—d!" he exclaimed.

A scene of confusion followed. Some slunk from the apartment, and were heard riding away, and some threw themselves at the Prince's feet and begged him to fly. Amid it all, a gentleman plainly dressed in a riding-habit, but without arms except a *couteau-de-chasse*, entered and stood gazing on them, while they looked on him as on the angel of destruction.

"You look coldly on me, gentlemen," he said. "But you guess my errand."

"And are prepared for it, General," said Redgauntlet. "We are not men to be penned up like sheep for slaughter."

"Pshaw! you take it too seriously. Let me speak but one word with you."

"Hear *me*, sir," said the Wanderer, stepping forward. "I am the mark you aim at. I surrender myself willingly, to save these gentlemen's danger."

An exclamation of "Never—never!" broke from the little body of partizans, as they gathered around the Prince.

"Is it to be peace or war, General Campbell?" asked Redgauntlet. "You are a man of honor, and we can trust you."

"I thank you, sir," said the General. "The answer rests with yourself. I am supported by both cavalry and infantry, but my commands are to make no arrests, provided that you all quietly return to your homes."

"What!—all?" exclaimed Sir Richard Glendale; "all, without exception?"

"All, without one single exception," said the General. "If you accept my terms, say so, and make haste."

"Is this real?" asked Redgauntlet. "Am I—are all—are any of these gentlemen at liberty to embark in yonder brig?"

"You, sir—all—all the vessel can contain, are at liberty to embark, uninterrupted by me; but I advise none to go who have not reasons unconnected with this meeting, for this will not be remembered against them."

"Then, gentlemen," said Redgauntlet, "the cause is lost forever!"

While most of the gentlemen rode away, Redgauntlet accompanied the Prince into exile, bidding an affectionate farewell to his nephew and niece, whom he never saw again. Soon afterward Sir Arthur Darsie Redgauntlet came into full possession of his property and rights, and sealed his affection for his friend Alan Fairford by bestowing on him his newly found sister.

THE BETROTHED (1825)

This novel is the first of the *Tales of the Crusaders*, which include also *The Talisman*. The scene is laid in England in the reign of Henry II, near the close of the Second Crusade.

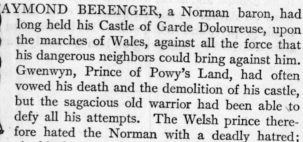RAYMOND BERENGER, a Norman baron, had long held his Castle of Garde Doloureuse, upon the marches of Wales, against all the force that his dangerous neighbors could bring against him. Gwenwyn, Prince of Powy's Land, had often vowed his death and the demolition of his castle, but the sagacious old warrior had been able to defy all his attempts. The Welsh prince therefore hated the Norman with a deadly hatred; and yet, when Archbishop Baldwin preached the Crusade, the two were induced to meet as friends and allies in the cause of the Cross. Gwenwyn accepted an invitation from Raymond to the Garde Doloureuse at Christmas time, and saw the Lady Eveline Berenger, sole child of the châtelain, then aged sixteen, the most beautiful damsel on the Welsh marches.

Gwenwyn was already married; but his bride Brengwain was childless, and as sovereigns marry for lineage, he promptly divorced his wife and consigned her to a nunnery, and on the following Easter sent a delegation to Raymond to ask for the hand of his daughter, not doubting that a Norman baron would be delighted and honored by a proposal to ally his house with that of a sovereign prince. But Raymond Berenger thought otherwise, and in a friendly letter declined the honor, on the ground that the hand of his daughter had been sought in marriage by a noble and potent Lord of the Marches, Hugo de Lacy, Constable of Chester, to whom a favorable answer had been returned.

When Raymond's letter was read to Gwenwyn by Father

88

Einion, his chaplain, the Prince sprang to his feet like a startled lion.

"Priest," he said, "hast thou read that accursed scroll fairly? If thou hast added or diminished one word or one letter, I will have thine eyes so handled that thou shalt never read letter more."

The monk replied, trembling, that he had read it word for word, and while the fury of Gwenwyn seemed too great for utterance, the harp of Cadwallon sounded and the bard sang:

"We wed not with the stranger. Vortigern wedded with the stranger: thence came the first wo upon Britain, and a sword upon her nobles, and a thunderbolt upon her palace. We wed not with the enslaved Saxon: the free and princely stag seeks not for his bride the heifer whose neck the yoke hath worn. We wed not with the rapacious Norman; the noble hound scorns to seek a mate from the herd of ravening wolves. When was it heard that the Cymry, the descendants of Brute, the true children of the soil of fair Britain, were plundered, oppressed, bereft of their birthright, and insulted even in their last retreats—when, but since they stretched their hand in friendship to the stranger, and clasped to their bosoms the daughter of the Saxon?"

All thought of peace passed before the song of Cadwallon like dust before the whirlwind, and the unanimous shout of the assembly declared for instant war.

Raymond Berenger knew well that his rejection of Gwenwyn's suit meant war, and he made preparations accordingly. He sent messengers out to his dependents with warnings to be on the alert, and signals of alarm were echoed from every castle and tower on the border. His squire, Dennis Morolt, mustered the vassals and liegemen, and Wilkin Flammock, the Fleming, left his fulling-mills and came with his men and wains within the castle walls. The Garde Doloureuse was strong and could well hold out against any attack until the Constable of Chester could bring aid. But, to the surprise of all, and against the remonstrance of Dennis, Sir Raymond announced his intention to meet the Welsh in the open plain. When he had entertained Gwenwyn at Christmas, and the Welsh Prince had spoken of the advantages of fighting behind such walls, he proudly answered that if a prince of the Cymry should ever come again in hostile fashion against the Garde Doloureuse, let him pitch his standard in the plain, and Raymond Berenger would meet him willingly, be he many or be he few.

So, when Gwenwyn appeared with a great following Sir Raymond waited until the last Welshman had crossed the bridge, and then sallied out with his men-at-arms to meet them, leaving Wilkin Flammock in charge of the castle and of his daughter.

"I conjure thee, as an honest man and a true Christian, stand to the defense of the castle. Relief must speedily arrive. If you fulfil your trust to me and to my daughter, Hugo de Lacy will reward you richly; if you fail, he will punish you severely."

Wilkin Flammock needed no spur to do his duty in this responsible charge, for his own daughter Rose, a blue-eyed, plump Flemish maiden, had for some time kept company with the Lady Eveline, in a doubtful station betwixt that of a humble friend and that of a superior domestic.

Raymond Berenger rode gaily forth at the head of his men to meet the invaders and made a brave fight; but the enemy was too numerous, and neither he nor his good squire ever came back. The Welsh followed up their victory by a furious attack on the castle, but its defenders, though few, were encouraged by the presence of Eveline, who glided from post to post, addressing Normans, English, and Flemings in suitable words, and appealing to all to put their faith in God and Our Lady of the Garde Doloureuse. Her faith was soon rewarded; for that night, while watching on the battlements, she detected the sound of tramping horse and the clash of armor, and she knew that the chivalry of the Marches had come to her relief.

The British, usually alert at surprising their enemies, were themselves surprised by Hugo de Lacy; Gwenwyn and many of his chiefs were slain, and his followers, dispersed through the hills, were chased and slaughtered at will by the Norman cavalry, with cries of "Ha, Saint Edward! Ha, Saint Denis! Strike— no quarter to the Welsh wolves—think on Raymond Berenger!"

The Constable of Chester meanwhile planted his banner on the mound where Gwenwyn's had lately floated, and as soon as the slaughter ceased he sent a single knight toward the castle, which had displayed all its banners. The drawbridge was instantly lowered to admit him, and he rode in and alighted from his horse, whose sides were flecked with blood and foam. The rider was a young man of powerful frame, a countenance flushed with his recent exercise, an eagle eye, and a profusion of short chestnut curls. The women, who thronged into the court to see him, could not forbear mixing praises of his beauty with blessings on his valor.

"Peace, all of ye!" said Wilkin Flammock. "Stand back and let us hear what are the commands of the noble Lord of Lacy."

"These," replied the young man, "I can only deliver in the presence of the right noble demoiselle, Eveline Berenger, if I may be thought worthy of such honor."

The Fleming conducted the young squire across the court to the great hall of the castle, where Lady Eveline received him seated under a dais, attended by Rose and several Norman maidens.

"We greet with our thanks the messenger who brings us tidings of safety," said Eveline. "We speak—unless we err—to the noble Damian of Lacy?"

"To the humblest of your servants," answered Damian, "who approaches you in behalf of his noble uncle, Hugo de Lacy. He sends you these tokens that the comrade and friend of your noble father hath not left his lamentable death many hours unavenged."

So saying, he laid before Eveline the gold bracelets, the coronet, and the chain of linked gold which had distinguished the rank of the Welsh Prince.

"The slayer of my father is then no more. Heaven is just—may his sins be forgiven! One question more, noble sir. My father's remains—"

"An hour will place them at your disposal, most honored lady. As my kinsman is now God's soldier and bound by a vow not to come under a roof until he embark for the Holy Land, I will represent him, if such be your pleasure, at these honored obsequies."

The religious rites that followed the funeral of Raymond Berenger lasted six days. The Constable meanwhile busied himself in seeing that the castle was put into a good state of defense and in making a peace with the Welsh so as the better to secure its safety. When ready to return to Chester to resume his preparations for the Holy Land, he sent Damian to Eveline to ask for a personal interview, as he had certain matters of high import which could be entrusted to no third party. As his vow prevented his going to her, he begged her to grace him so far as to visit his pavilion, which he proposed to pitch at her castle gate.

The next day, in a magnificent pavilion of purple silk and gold, the Lady Eveline was received with feudal pomp by the Constable, who, after the ceremonies were over, requested a private audience with her. Eveline dismissed all her train except Rose Flammock.

"This maiden," she said, "is acquainted with my most inward thoughts. I beseech you to permit her presence at our conference."

"It were better otherwise," said De Lacy, "but your pleasure shall be obeyed."

He then explained briefly and bluntly the understanding with her father for a union of the two families. "My nephew Damian is hardly twenty years old, and hath a long career of adventure and peril to encounter before he can honorably propose to himself the duties of matrimonial engagements. Had ten years more passed over him with the honors of chivalry, I should have proposed him for the happiness to which I myself aspire."

"You—you, my lord? it is impossible!" said Eveline, endeavoring to suppress all cause of offense in her surprise.

"I do not wonder," replied the Constable calmly, "that you express surprise at this daring proposal; but, noble Eveline, the lady of Hugo de Lacy will be one of the foremost among the matronage of England. Your father had this union warmly at heart, as this scroll will show. The wife of De Lacy will have the rank of a princess; his widow the dowry of a queen. The short time left me ere departing on a perilous expedition must be an apology for my importunity."

"Hear, then, my present answer, my lord," said Eveline, rising from her seat. "To-morrow I go to the Benedictine nunnery at Gloucester, where my honored father's sister is Abbess. To her guidance I will commit myself in this matter."

When Lady Eveline had retired into her own chamber, Rose Flammock said: "Would I had influence to guide your path, lady."

"How mean you, maiden?" asked Eveline.

"I would have you recall the encouragement you have yielded to this proud Baron. He is too great to be loved himself, too haughty to love you as you deserve. If you wed him, you wed gilded misery, and, it may be, dishonor as well as discontent."

When Rose left the apartment Eveline said to herself: "Rose loves me truly; but she is jealous of every other person that approaches me. It is strange that I have not seen Damian de Lacy since my interview with the Constable."

The Lady Eveline remained nearly four months with her aunt the Abbess, during which time the Constable pressed his suit. As he grew more and more enamored, his engagements as a crusader became more burdensome, and he finally decided to make application to the Church for a delay and, if possible, a remission of his engagement. As he did not doubt that his request would be granted, the ceremony of betrothal, or *fiançailles*, was duly celebrated. But, though Sir Hugo made munificent offers, the Pope's legate in England looked with displeasure on the retreat of so important an associate, and flatly declined, and so it was agreed that the marriage should be postponed until the Constable's return from Palestine. This was displeasing to the Abbess, who insisted that the marriage should take place at once, or that the betrothal should be annulled; and, when this was declined by the parties most interested, she flatly refused to give shelter to her niece during the Constable's absence, asserting that her house was too mean for the residence of the vowed bride of a mighty Baron, over whom she could not exercise the authority she ought to possess over everyone under her roof. So it was decided that Eveline should return to the Garde Doloureuse and spend there the interval between her betrothal and her marriage.

In her conversations with Rose Eveline did not deny that she regarded this interval rather in the nature of a respite.

"It is my youth, Rose, that makes me fear the duties of De Lacy's wife. When I shall have attained the age of twenty

I shall be a full-grown woman, with all the soul of a Berenger strong within me, to overcome the doubts and tremors that agitate the girl of seventeen."

"Ah! my sweet mistress," answered Rose, "may God and Our Lady guide all for the best! But I would that this contract had not taken place, or that it could have been fulfilled by your immediate union."

When Eveline's return to the castle was settled Hugo de Lacy considered to whom he should entrust its guardianship, and by advice of his squire, Philip Guarine, sent for Wilkin Flammock and offered him the post of châtelain of the Garde Doloureuse, with the honor of knighthood. But the Fleming protested that knighthood would sit on him like a gilded helmet on a hog, and that a Flemish weaver was no fitting guardian for his plighted bride. He would listen to no compromise, and suggested that there was no one to whom the Constable could so honorably entrust such a charge as to his nearest kinsman.

"If you mean Randal de Lacy," said the Constable, "I care not if I tell you that I consider him as totally worthless, and undeserving of honorable confidence."

"Nay, I mean one nearer to you by blood, and if I mistake not, by affection. I mean your nephew, Damian de Lacy."

The Constable started, but presently replied with forced composure: "I can rely, it is true, on Damian; but he is young, Flammock—very young—and in that resembles too nearly the person who might be committed to his charge."

"Trust him, my lord. Your nephew is honest and true, and it is better trusting young lions than old wolves. He may err, but it will not be from premeditated treachery."

"Thou art right, Flammock," said the Constable, "but let what has passed be a secret betwixt us."

Thus it happened that Damian de Lacy, who had fully expected to go to the Holy Land, was entrusted with the care of the Lady Eveline, his uncle's betrothed, when the Constable set sail for Palestine. Immediately after his departure Eveline, after a cold parting with the Abbess, returned to the Garde Doloureuse under a proper escort. At morning and evening Amelot, Damian's page, came to Eveline for her orders, but Damian himself never appeared to her. When Rose's mistress

ventured to remark to her on the singularity of De Lacy's conduct, the bower-woman remarked:

"Damian de Lacy judges well, noble lady. He to whom
the safe-keeping of a royal treasure is entrusted should not indulge himself too often by gazing upon it."

Besides the garrison of the castle, under command of the
steward, a strong body of forces was disposed within a few
miles of the Garde Doloureuse, under the eye of Damian de
Lacy himself, and kept in constant readiness for action. While
the fortress was thus secure from hostile violence, the life of its
inmates was so monotonous that youth and beauty might be
excused for wishing for variety, even at the expense of some
danger. But when Eveline and Rose desired to extend their
airing beyond the castle gate, they could not move in safety even
so far as Wilkin Flammock's mills without an escort; and to
provide for this it was necessary to announce their purpose the
evening before, so that the country around might be scoured by
cavalry. Such formality allayed the pleasure of field sports, and
Eveline seldom resorted to amusements attended with so much
trouble.

Meanwhile, recollections of Damian de Lacy had not been
erased from Eveline's mind. While he never waited on her in
person, she knew that his whole attention was fixed upon her
convenience, interest, and safety; and though his messages were
conveyed to her through his page, a formality that appeared to
her unnecessary and even unkind, they served to fix her attention
upon the connection between them and to keep him ever present
in her memory. Thus the image of the handsome young cavalier was more frequently before the Lady Eveline's fancy than
perhaps his uncle, had he known it, would have approved.

One day a merchant came to the castle with some fine falcons
for sale. Raoul, the falconer, saw something reminiscent in his
face, and said:

"We have met before, friend, though I cannot remember
where."

"Like enough," replied the merchant; "I have been in this
country often."

"I will take the hawks, but I will see them strike a heron
first, if you will ride a mile or so by the waterside."

"Content, Sir Falconer. But is there no lord or lady in the castle who would take pleasure in the sport? I am not afraid to show them to a countess."

"My lady used to love the sport, but since her father's death she has moped and lived like a nun. Go ask her, Gilian, if she will come and see the sport."

The temptation to exercise was almost irresistible to Eveline, and, contrary to custom, she dispensed with her escort and rode out into the fields with Rose and Gilian, followed by only a single equerry. Finding no game along the river, the party crossed the bridge and rode to the Red Pool, where a heron was soon sighted. While all were watching the flight of the falcons, Lady Eveline, better mounted than her attendants, had ridden a little in advance, when she was suddenly surrounded by several wild-looking men, who, notwithstanding her screams, secured her to her saddle and hurried her off through the hills. Raoul and the others rode after her, but other men rose among the rocks and beat them back.

When Eveline recognized that she was a prisoner, she said: "If it be ransom you desire, name the sum, and I will send an order to treat for it."

"The Lady Eveline," answered a voice in the Anglo-Norman tongue, and in a tone inconsistent with the violence she had sustained, "will speedily find that our actions are more rough than our purposes."

"You cannot doubt that this atrocity will be avenged, if you know by whose banner my lands are protected."

"Under De Lacy's," answered the voice. "Be it so—falcons fear not falcons. But as you are the cause of strife and the reward of victory, your safety must be cared for. Please to alight, noble lady, or be not offended if I lift you from your saddle."

The next moment she was placed in front of a narrow opening, and ordered to creep forward on hands and knees. This she did for two or three yards, when the passage opened into a cave high enough for her to sit up. She heard her captors close the entrance with stones and soon afterward a confused sound reached her ears, in which she distinguished the tramp of horses, the clash of weapons, and the shouts and oaths of combatants. Influenced by desperation, she crept to the entrance and removed with her dagger some of the earth and sods. This gave her air, but a large stone prevented her egress. Her cries soon brought assistance, and she was extricated from her perilous position only to find that Damian de Lacy lay near by grievously wounded in body by an attempt to intercept the robbers, but more sorely tried in spirit that he had failed in his duty. Though faint from the effects of her confinement, and exhausted by her efforts to release herself, Eveline hastened to Damian's side and, with the eagerness of a sister, sought to stanch his blood and to recall him from his swoon. A litter was speedily constructed, and the wounded knight was conveyed to the castle, despite the protests of Rose, who insisted that he should be borne to his own camp.

"You should care for your honor—for your fame," whispered Rose in her mistress's ear.

"To the castle," said Eveline aloud, as if scorning secrecy. "Where I go, he shall go; nor will I be in safety a moment sooner than I know that he is so."

Thus it happened that Damian de Lacy became an inmate of the Garde Doloureuse, where he lay long with brain unsettled. Just before the event that led to his wounding the rabble in the west of England had taken up arms against the nobles, and pretended to be favored in their insurrection by both Randal and Damian de Lacy. Damian was prepared to march, by command of the King's lieutenant, to the relief of Wild Wenlock, who was besieged in a village ten miles distant, when he heard of Eveline's danger, and turned back to hasten to her rescue. This apparent disregard of orders led to the defeat and death of Wild Wenlock and to the breaking up and dispersion of the forces of Damian, some of whom said he was dead and others that he was the slave of the Lady Eveline, whom he loved *par amours*.

One day a flourish of trumpets at the gate, accompanied by a pursuivant and the royal banner, alarmed the castle. When the Lady Eveline hastened to the gate, she found there Guy Monthermer, the hereditary enemy of the house of Lacy, attended by fifty soldiers, under the guidon of England. When Monthermer demanded admission in the King's name, and Lady

Eveline declined to open her gates to him, the old warrior replied:

"Lady, I might proceed to proclaim you a traitor to the Crown, but the King remembers the services of your father. We are not ignorant that Damian de Lacy, accused of instigating this insurrection, of deserting his duty in the field, and abandoning a noble comrade to the sword of the brutal peasants, has found shelter under this roof, with little credit to your loyalty as a vassal or your conduct as a high-born maiden. Deliver him up to us, and I will dispense with the occupation of the castle."

"Guy de Monthermer," answered Eveline, "he that throws a stain on my name speaks falsely; as for Damian de Lacy, he knows how to defend his own fame. While he makes his abode in the castle of the betrothed of his kinsman, she delivers him to no one, least of all to his well-known enemy. Drop the portcullis, wardens."

"When I next approach the Garde Doloureuse," said Monthermer, "it will be not merely to intimate, but to execute, the mandate of my sovereign."

Three months later the Constable de Lacy, accompanied by his squire, Philip Guarine, both attired as pilgrims from the Holy Land, were passing about twelve miles from the Garde Doloureuse. When they reached a grassy mound marked on the top by a stone kistvaen or sepulchral monument, De Lacy said:

"This, then, is the place to abide tidings of our scout. May God send us good news of the Garde Doloureuse."

"Amen!" said the squire. "But if Renault Vidal brings it, it will be the first time he has proved a bird of good omen. Loath were I that your life or honor were at his mercy."

"Philip, thou art a jealous-pated fool. To recall no more ancient proofs of his fidelity, did he not aid our disguise when shipwrecked on the coast of Wales? If he had meant ill by us, why did he not betray us to the Welsh?"

"I may be silenced, my lord, but not satisfied. I have for him an instinctive aversion and suspicion. But here he comes to give such an account of our situation as shall please him."

"Welcome, my trusty Vidal," said the Constable as the

minstrel rode up with downcast eyes and embarrassed carriage. "Speak, man! In God's name, why art thou silent? Come, sir minstrel, I will spare you a pang—Eveline has forsaken and forgotten me?"

Vidal assented by a low inclination.

Hugo de Lacy paced a short turn to conquer his emotion. "I forgive her," he said at last. "Forgive, did I say? Alas! I have nothing to forgive. She used but the right I left in her hand. Our three years of engagement was ended; she had heard of my losses, my defeats, and took the first opportunity to break her engagement with one bankrupt in fortune and fame. She is married to Damian de Lacy, my nephew?"

"No, my lord, not *married*," answered Vidal.

"No—no—not married—but troth-plighted. Wherefore not? The date of her old affiance was out."

"The Lady Eveline and Sir Damian are not affianced, that I know of."

"Dost thou trifle with me! Speak the worst at once, or I will make thee minstrel to the household of Satan."

"The Lady Eveline and Sir Damian are neither married nor affianced, my lord. They have loved and lived together—*par amours*."

"Dog, and son of a dog," said De Lacy, "thou liest!"

"Were a lie to buy my own life," said the minstrel, "I would not tell one."

"Hear him, Philip Guarine, he tells me of my disgrace—of the dishonor of my house—of the depravity of those I have loved best—with a calm look and unfaltering tongue. Perhaps thou wilt make a ballad of it, ha!" he exclaimed, with a furious glance at the minstrel.

"Perhaps I might, my lord," replied Vidal, "but that I must record therein my own disgrace in serving a lord without either patience to bear insults and wrongs or spirit to revenge them on the authors of his shame."

"Thou art right, good fellow," said the Constable. "Vengeance alone is now left us."

Meanwhile events had moved rapidly at the Garde Douloureuse. King Henry had come against the castle and captured it, Damian de Lacy had been consigned to a dungeon, the Lady

Eveline confined in her own apartments, and Randal de Lacy, who had put himself at the head of the house and come to the King's aid with five hundred men, was high in the royal favor. It was currently reported that Lady Eveline was to be sent to a French nunnery; that her demesnes were to be declared forfeited to the Crown; and that the greater part of them would be bestowed on Randal de Lacy.

Renault Vidal, who had been ordered by his master to await him at the Battle-bridge, where Gwenwyn had been slain, took his station there with an abstracted air. He took some food from his wallet and tried to eat, but something at his heart affected his appetite, and after trying to swallow a morsel he threw it from him, and tried to drink from a flask. But this, too, seemed distasteful, and dropping it he drank of the cool water of the spring and bathed in it his hands and face.

While he was thus engaged, a procession moved from the Flemings' mills, to the music of pipe and tabor, toward the bridge. Vidal, on asking what it meant, was told that the Constable de Lacy was to grant solemn investiture to the Flemish weavers of the privileges the King had given them. Presently the shouts of "Long live the gallant Constable!" announced that he was close at hand. Vidal pushed his way through the crowd until he came within three yards of the Constable, and just as the rider was bending forward to deliver the royal charter to Wilkin Flammock, he sprang with singular agility on the croup of the horse, grasped with his left hand the collar of De Lacy's buff-coat, and struck him in the neck with a long, keen dagger. The blow was accurate, and the Constable fell to the ground, while the assassin, seated in his saddle, urged the horse to speed and might have escaped but for Flammock, who seized the bridle.

When King Henry, in the Garde Doloureuse, heard of the crime he ordered the prisoner to be brought immediately before him.

"Does anyone know this caitiff?" asked the King, looking around.

"So please you, my liege," said Philip Guarine, "he is a minstrel of my master's, by name Renault Vidal."

"Thou art deceived, Norman," replied the minstrel. "I

am Cadwallon the Briton, Cadwallon the bard of Gwenwyn of Powys Land, and his avenger!"

As he spoke, his eye encountered those of his late master, still in his palmer's dress, and his face became ghastly as he exclaimed: "Do the dead come before monarchs? Have I not slain the Constable?"

"Thou hast indeed slain the Constable," said King Henry, "but know, Welshman, it was Randal de Lacy on whom that charge was this morning conferred, by our belief that our faithful Hugo de Lacy had been lost by shipwreck. Thou hast cut short Randal's elevation but a few hours, for to-morrow's sun would have seen him again without land or lordship. Thine eyes will not cheat thee again, Welshman, for before the night is an hour older they shall close on all that is earthly."

Hugo de Lacy interceded for the minstrel's life, but in vain, and he was hurried to execution. He confessed that he had often made ready to take the Constable's life during the three years he had been with him, but had been deterred either by the vigilance of Guarine or by some noble trait in the conduct of De Lacy himself, which had influenced him to postpone his vengeance.

No one mourned for Randal de Lacy, who, it was discovered, had acted the part of a villain, and had even been the instigator of the attempted seizure of Eveline, which had ended so disastrously for Damian de Lacy. As soon as Hugo de Lacy found out the true condition of affairs between his nephew and his betrothed, that each had behaved during the time of his absence with a true regard for his interests, and that all the reports of their faithlessness were base calumnies, he secured his release from prison and withdrew in his favor all claims to the hand of Eveline. King Henry, to atone for his unmerited severity, attended the nuptials of the young couple; and shortly afterward created Wilkin Flammock a gentleman of coat armor, when Damian's page Amelot wedded his daughter Rose.

THE TALISMAN (1825)

This story, the second and last of the Tales of the Crusaders, *is a thrilling Eastern romance, equal to the best of Scott's efforts. The scene is laid in the Holy Land about the year 1193, during the truce with the Saracens which preceded the abandonment of the crusade led by Richard Cœur de Lion.*

 KNIGHT of the Red Cross, bearing on his shield a couchant leopard, was crossing the desert near the Dead Sea toward some palm-trees beside the well assigned for his midday station, when he saw a Saracen horseman approaching. "In the desert," says an Eastern proverb, "no man meets a friend"; so the crusader placed his lance in rest and prepared to meet the stranger. The Saracen came on at the speedy gallop of an Arab horseman, his green caftan floating in the wind, and wearing on one arm a rhinoceros buckler, while he brandished his long spear at arm's length above his head. He appeared to expect that the Christian would put his horse to the gallop to encounter him; but the knight, well acquainted with the customs of Eastern warriors, came to a dead halt, wheeling and facing his enemy while he made two complete circuits around him, seeking a vulnerable point of attack. When the Saracen made a third attempt to approach him, the knight hurled his mace with unerring aim at his adversary. The Saracen interposed his buckler, but the violence of the blow forced it down on his turban, and he was beaten from his horse. But ere the Christian could avail himself of this mishap, his nimble foeman called his horse and sprang again into his saddle without touching the stirrup. The knight had meanwhile recovered his mace, and the Eastern cavalier, remembering the dexterity with which the weapon had been thrown, strung his bow and again circling round his enemy discharged arrow after arrow with such skill

that nothing but the goodness of the Christian's harness saved him from many a wound.

At last a shot appeared to have found its way to a vital part, for the knight dropped heavily from his horse; but what was the surprise of the Saracen, when he dismounted to inspect the condition of his enemy, to find that it was but a ruse to bring him to close quarters. In the deadly struggle that followed, the Saracen was saved only by his agility and presence of mind. He unloosed his sword-belt, in which the knight had fixed his hold, and slipped from the grasp of his antagonist with the loss of his sword, his quiver of arrows, and his turban. These losses appeared to incline him to a cessation of hostilities, and advancing with his right hand raised, he said:

"There is truce betwixt our nations; let there be peace betwixt us."

"I am well contented," answered he of the couchant leopard, "but what security dost thou offer?"

"The word of a follower of the Prophet was never broken," answered the Saracen. "It is thou, brave Nazarene, from whom I should demand security, did I not know that treason seldom dwells with courage."

The crusader felt that the confidence of the Moslem made him ashamed of his own doubts, and the late foes, without an angry look, rode side by side to the palm-trees, where a fountain of sparkling water flowed from beneath a ruined arch. The Frank was a powerful man, with brown curly hair, bronzed features, and full blue eyes. He wore a moustache, but his chin was shaved, after the Norman fashion. Though he was tall, powerful, and athletic, his age could not have been more than thirty. The Saracen Emir formed a striking contrast, for though above the middle size he was at least three inches shorter than the European; but his frame, showing little more than bone, brawn, and sinew, was well fitted for exertion and fatigue. His features were small and delicate, though deeply embrowned by the Eastern sun, and his eyes were keen, deep-set, black, and glowing. He was in the very flower of his age, and might have been termed eminently beautiful but for the narrowness of his forehead.

When the Emir learned that his antagonist was on his way

to the cell of Theodoric of Engaddi, a holy man dwelling among the hills, he told him that the road was infested by robbers, and that to travel without a passport was but a wilful casting away of one's life.

"I have a pass," answered the knight, showing a parchment under the hand and seal of Saladin.

The Saracen bent his head to the dust as he recognized the seal of the Soldan of Egypt and Syria, and, kissing the paper with profound respect, returned it, saying: "Rash Frank, thou hast sinned against thine own blood and mine in not showing this when we met. Well for me was it that I failed to slay thee, with the safeguard of the King of kings on thy person. I myself will conduct you to the dwelling of Theodoric."

Before they set out the knight asked the name of the delicious fountain, which he said he should forever hold in grateful remembrance.

"It is called the Diamond of the Desert," said the Emir. "Now pardon me if I ask the name of the companion I have this day encountered."

"Among the soldiers of the Cross I am called Kenneth of the Couching Leopard; at home I have other titles. Let me ask, brave Saracen, which of the tribes of Arabia claims your descent?"

"I am no Arab, Sir Kenneth. I am Sheerkohf, the Lion of the Mountain. Kurdistan, whence I derive my descent, holds no family more noble than that of Seljook."

"I have heard," said the knight, "that your great Soldan's blood is from the same source?"

"Thanks to the Prophet that hath so honored our mountains as to send from their bosom him whose word is victory."

In time they reached their destination and were hospitably received by the anchorite, who showed the way into his cave with a lighted torch. He was of gigantic size, with long unshaven locks and beard, and deep-set wild eyes. He spoke no word, but mutely pointed them to seats, while he prepared food for them.

"He will not speak until we have eaten," said the Saracen; "such is his vow."

When their meal was ended, the hermit placed before the

Saracen a pitcher of sherbet, and before the Scot a flask of wine.

"Drink," he said, "my children, the gifts of God are to be enjoyed when the Giver is remembered."

With this he retired, and the knight took the occasion to inquire concerning him. His repute for sanctity, the Saracen said, had spread far and wide, and, as he was often wild and incoherent, he was respected by the Arabs as a *hamako* or insane person. But he had also a fame for wisdom, and as he had an observatory for viewing the heavenly bodies Saladin had issued orders for his protection, and he was often visited by Moslem lords of rank, he himself having frequently been to consult him.

"I noted," said the knight, "that he called thee by another name than Sheerkohf."

"My name, in the tent of my father, was Ilderim. But hush, the *hamako* comes."

The anchorite entered, and, folding his arms, said with a solemn voice: "Blessed be His name, who hath appointed calm sleep to refresh the wearied limbs." With this he indicated couches for them, and making a reverence to each again left them.

Kenneth was awakened in the night by a pressure on his chest, and on opening his eyes saw the anchorite beside his bed with a small silver lamp in his hand.

"Arise," he said in French, "put on thy mantle and follow me."

When they reached the outer apartment, the hermit said: "You bring me a greeting from Richard of England?"

"I come from the council of Christian princes," replied the knight.

"Your token?" demanded the recluse.

"My password," said Sir Kenneth, "is this: 'Kings begged of a beggar.'"

"It is right," replied the hermit. "Come."

The anchorite passed behind the altar, and pressing a spring opened a small iron door, disclosing a narrow staircase.

"Bind mine eyes," said the hermit, handing him a veil, "for I may not look on the treasure thou art to behold."

When blindfolded he gave the lamp to the Scot and went up the stairs until a second door was reached.

"Put off thy shoes," he said, "and banish profane and carnal thoughts."

When Sir Kenneth had complied with this command the hermit told him to knock three times, and when the door opened spontaneously and he bade him enter, he stepped into a small chapel, brilliantly lighted with silver lamps that emitted sweet perfumes. In this chapel, hewn out of the solid rock, the knight saw various mysteries, including the opening of a casket and the display of a piece of Vera Crux, the true cross, and kept his vigil until daybreak, when he heard the lauds, or earliest office of the Church, sung by a choir of female voices. While he knelt in devotion, a procession, preceded by beautiful boys who swung censers and scattered flowers, entered. Behind them came six nuns of the order of Mount Carmel, with black scapularies and veils over their white garments and carrying rosaries, with others in white veils bearing chaplets of red and white roses. They moved around the chapel, paying no heed to Sir Kenneth, though their garments nearly touched him as he kneeled. But when they passed a second time, one of the white-stoled maidens dropped a rosebud beside him. The knight started, but suppressed his emotion, thinking it might have been an accident; but when on the next round a beautiful hand stole through the folds of the gauze and dropped another rosebud before him, he knew it was not fortuitous. He recognized, too, on a finger the matchless ruby ring worn by Edith Plantagenet, the lady of his love, whom he worshiped in secret and to whom he had vowed his knightly devoir, but to whom he had never spoken. She moved in a circle that his knightly privilege might permit him to approach, but never to enter.

The procession passed like a dream, but Sir Kenneth rose from his knees buoyed by the thought that he was in the neighborhood of the Lady Edith and had received tokens of her grace. At the entrance he found his guide still groveling in the dust where he had left him.

"Take the light," said the hermit, "and lead me down, for I may not uncover my eyes until I am far from this hallowed spot."

When Sir Kenneth again sought his couch, his Moslem friend was still sleeping. In the morning he held a conference with the hermit on matters of importance which had brought him thither, the result being that he was detained two days longer at the grotto, but he was not again admitted to the chapel.

King Richard of England lay ill in his tent in the camp of the crusaders between Jean d'Acre and Ascalon. Afflicted with one of those slow wasting fevers peculiar to Asia, he grew at first unfit to mount on horseback, and then unable to attend the councils of war. He chafed under this restraint and was greatly incensed when he heard that the council had made a truce with Saladin for thirty days. The only one that dared to come between him and his wrath was Sir Thomas de Multon, the Lord of Gilsland, in Cumberland, called by the Normans the Lord de Vaux, who nursed the intractable patient with anxious care. Richard was still more angry when he learned that Queen Berengaria and the ladies of the court had gone on a pilgrimage to the Convent of Engaddi to intercede for his deliverance from the fever.

One day Sir Thomas brought him news that the Scottish knight, Sir Kenneth, had returned from a mission to the hermit of Engaddi, and that he had brought back with him a learned physician sent by Saladin to effect his cure.

" 'Sdeath and hell!" said Richard, starting up. "Who dared send anyone thither when our Queen was in the convent on her pilgrimage for our recovery?"

"The Council of the Crusade sent him, my lord, but for what purpose I know not."

"It shall be looked into," said Richard. "So this Scottish man met with the physician at Engaddi?"

"No, my liege, he met with a Saracen Emir who, hearing of your Majesty's illness, undertook that Saladin should send his own physician to you; and he came attended like a prince, with these letters of credence from Saladin."

When Richard had read the letters he sent for Sir Kenneth and questioned him about his mission, as to who had sent him, and the object of his journey; but the knight could only answer that he had delivered a sealed packet to the hermit and that while

he knew the object was to negotiate a peace, he knew nothing of
the terms.

"Sir Knight," said the King in a sterner voice, "I must know
more.   Were you not in the chapel of the Carmelite nuns at Engaddi, and did you not see there the Queen of England and the
ladies of her court?"

"My lord," said Sir Kenneth, "I was in a chapel and beheld
a choir of ladies, but I saw not their faces, nor heard their voices
save in the hymns they sang."

"And was none of these ladies known to you?"

"My lord," said Kenneth, after some hesitation, "I might
guess."

"And so may I," said Richard, frowning.   "Leopard as you
are, Sir Knight, beware tempting the lion's paw.   Enough—begone—speed to De Vaux and send him hither with the Arabian
physician."

When the physician, a bearded man in a long robe and a
turban, entered, he made a solemn obeisance to all, and then,
taking Richard's hand, felt his pulse long and attentively.   He
next filled a cup with water, and dipped into it a talisman resem-
bling a small red purse.   When the draught was sufficiently medi-
cated, he was about to offer it to the patient, when Richard said:

"Hold!   Let me feel thy pulse.   I, too, know something of
thine art."

The Arabian yielded his hand without hesitation.

"His blood beats calm as an infant's," said the King.   "De
Vaux, whether we live or die, dismiss this *hakim* with honor and
safety."

He then drained the cup and sank back on the cushions as if
exhausted, and the physician, by an expressive sign, requested
all to withdraw.

King Richard had enemies in the persons of Conrade, Marquis of Montserrat, and the Grand Master of the Knights Tem-
plars, both of whom, jealous of his fame and resentful at his
assumption of superiority, would have rejoiced at a fatal termina-
tion of his illness.   With Philip of France, who desired to return
home, and Leopold, Grand Duke of Austria, who hated Richard, they did all they could to resist what they considered the
usurping power of the King of England.   One day, when the

Marquis of Montserrat was dining with Leopold, he craftily suggested to him that the island sovereign was presumptuous in displaying his banner alone on the great mound in the midst of the camp. "But," he continued, "I doubt not you, my lord, have deep reasons for submitting to English domination."

"I submit," cried Leopold, who was full of wine, "I submit to this king of half an island—this grandson of a Norman bastard! All the camp shall see that I know how to right myself. Up, my lieges and merry men—up and follow me!"

With that he seized his own banner, displayed before his pavilion, and marched, followed by his shouting guests and attendants, toward the mound where England's banner floated.

King Richard had just awakened from the effects of the *hakim's* draft, and finding that the fever had left him, sat up; but the physician begged him to compose himself a while longer, as injury might ensue from too early exertion. But when Richard heard shouts and revelry without and learned, by close questioning, that the Grand Duke of Austria was disputing his right to the mound, he hastily threw on his clothes and, seizing his great sword, ran out of the pavilion. Sir Thomas, calling to an equerry to summon Lord Salisbury and his men to come instantly to St. George's Mount, followed.

Richard burst his way through a disorderly crowd surrounding the mount to the summit, where he found Leopold of Austria and others contemplating with satisfaction the Austrian banner, which he had planted beside that of England.

"Who has dared," cried Richard, laying his hands on the Austrian standard, "to place this paltry rag beside the banner of England?"

"It was I, Leopold of Austria," said the Grand Duke, who was not wanting in courage.

"Then shall Leopold of Austria see how his pretensions are rated by Richard of England."

So saying, he splintered the spear to pieces, threw the banner on the ground, and placed his foot upon it.

There was an immediate tumult, and the Earl Wallenrode struck at the King a blow that might have been fatal had not Sir Kenneth caught it on his shield.

"I have sworn, Wallenrode," said King Richard, "never to

strike one whose shoulder bears the cross.   Therefore live, but live to remember Richard of England.''

As he spoke he grasped the tall Hungarian round the waist and hurled him down the mount to the base, where he lay like one dead.   Philip of France came between the contestants at this juncture, and after a long talk succeeded in bringing about peace between them.

Richard looked after the Grand Duke as he retired, and said: ''I must not leave this banner unguarded in darkness.   Valiant Scot, I owe thee a boon, and I will repay it richly.   There stands the banner of England; watch it as a novice contemplates his armor on the night before he is dubbed.   Dost thou undertake the charge?''

''Willingly,'' said Kenneth, ''and will discharge it upon penalty of my head.''

At midnight Kenneth stood watch on St. George's Mount, beside the banner of England, his sole companion a large stag-hound, on whose vigilance he trusted for early warning of a hostile footstep.   While meditating on the event that had caused Richard to entrust the guardianship of his banner to one but lately an adventurer of slight note, he was aroused by the bark-ing of his dog.

''Who goes there?'' he called, seeing someone advancing on the shadowy side of the mount.

''Tie up your four-footed demon,'' answered a hoarse voice, ''or I come not near you.''

A moment later into the moonlight came a misshapen dwarf, whom he recognized as one he had seen in the train of Queen Berengaria.

''I come to ask you to attend me,'' said the dwarf, ''to the presence of those who have sent me to summon you.''

''My orders,'' said Sir Kenneth, ''are to abide by this banner till daybreak; so till then I must be excused.''

''Sir Knight, look thou here,'' continued the dwarf, ''and, as thou knowest or disownest this token, so obey or refuse her commands who hath deigned to impose them on thee.''

So saying, to Sir Kenneth's great surprise the dwarf placed in his hand a ruby ring, which he at once recognized as that belonging to Lady Edith.

"In the name of all that is sacred, from whom didst thou receive this?"

"We list not to parley further than to command thee, in the name and by the power of that ring, to follow me to her who is the owner of the ring. Every minute thou tarriest is a crime against thy allegiance."

Sir Kenneth debated seriously what he ought to do; but when he learned from the dwarf that he was wanted at a neighboring pavilion in sight of the mound, he followed the dwarf thither, leaving his post in charge of his dog. When admitted into the pavilion he overheard a conversation that told him he had been made the victim of a heartless jest, and in shame he hastened back to the mound. But he was too late; the banner was gone and his faithful hound lay, apparently dying, beside the broken staff.

Overcome with grief and shame, he was found by the Arab physician, who tried to console him, offering to cure the hound and to give him high rank under Saladin, if he would fly to him. But Sir Kenneth declined his offers, and at sunrise presented himself at the King's pavilion. When Richard heard the unfortunate knight's story his anger knew no bounds, and he threatened to brain him with his battle-ax; but De Vaux interposed, saying: "My liege, this must not be—here—nor by your own hand."

"You are right, De Vaux," said Richard. "Remove him and put him in fetters. Let his head be severed from the trunk by the executioner, without mutilation of body or shame to his arms."

Queen Berengaria, attended by the Lady Edith, waited on Richard and explained the circumstances, but the King would not listen. After them a Carmelite monk, who had been sent to shrive the prisoner, interceded for him, telling the King that Sir Kenneth had confided to him, under the seal of the confessional, a secret which, if the King knew, would utterly turn him from his bloody purpose. But Richard was inexorable and bade ladies and priests to withdraw if they would not hear orders to displease them.

Finally Adoubec el Hakim, the physician who had cured him of the fever, came and added his request that the King would spare the life of the prisoner. Richard was long obdurate, but the entreaties of Adoubec at last prevailed, and the King signed a warrant and handed it to him, saying: "I would rather thou hadst asked my crown jewels. Take this Scot to thy keeping; use him as thy bond-slave, only let him beware how he comes before the eye of Richard."

Sir Kenneth, thus become the property of the Arab physician, was taken by him to the tents that contained his goods and retinue. The next day, at break of morning, the camp was broken up and laden upon camels, and Adoubec and the knight, mounted upon horses, set out into the desert. At night, when Sir Kenneth, overcome by his mental troubles and by lassitude, showed signs of fever, the physician gave him a sleeping-draught; and when next the knight awoke he found himself in a soft couch under a splendid silken pavilion, and surrounded by luxuries such as he never before had known. Beside his bed was a Saracen costume of rich materials, with saber and poniard, and all befitting an emir of distinction. To his still greater astonishment, when the physician entered to greet him, though the voice was still that of Adoubec, the form, dress, and features were those of Ilderim or Sheerkohf, his former foeman.

When Ilderim, or Adoubec, had enjoyed for a time Sir Kenneth's surprise at his transformation, he suggested a method of detecting the thief who had stolen the banner of England by means of the hound, which had recovered from his wounds. His proposition was to disguise both knight and dog and to send them to the camp of Richard, the only condition being that he should safely deliver to the Lady Edith a letter from the Soldan. Now the physician had previously talked with Sir Kenneth of the plan of the Crusade leaders to end the Crusade by bringing about an alliance between Saladin and the Lady Edith, but Sir Kenneth had always scouted the idea as one unworthy of consideration; yet, when Ilderim asked him to bear the letter, he agreed to deliver it safely, with the understanding that his mediation should go no further.

One day a Nubian slave, named Zohauk, came to King Richard with a letter from Saladin, King of kings, to Melech Ric, the Lion of England, asking the King to accept him in part requital of bounties from him. Richard, who loved to look on a well-formed man, was pleased with his appearance and, finding that he was a mute, accepted him, saying: "Thou shalt wait in my chamber, and on my person. Begin thy office presently, for I see a speck of rust on that shield."

The Nubian prostrated himself and, retiring to the back of the tent, began his duties. While engaged in polishing the shield, he saw reflected in it a dervish, who, after dancing for the soldiers without, had fallen apparently exhausted. He saw that this man raised his head occasionally and moved suspiciously toward the entrance of the King's pavilion. When about ten yards distant the fellow bounded to his feet and rushed toward Richard with a brandished dagger in his hand. But the Nubian was too quick for him: he caught his uplifted arm and dashed him to the ground, receiving himself a wound from the dagger on his arm. King Richard cried "Ha, dog!" and dashed out the dervish's brains with a stool; then applied his lips to the Nubian's wound to suck out what he thought might be poison. When officers entered the Nubian hastily covered his arm with a scarf, and Richard said:

"Neville, take this Nubian to thy quarters. I have changed my mind concerning him. But hark—in thine ear—see that he escapes thee not; there is more in him than seems."

The Nubian now indicated by signs that he wanted writing materials, and when they were brought he wrote in French that he had been sent to discover for Richard the thief of the banner, and that he could do so if he could have paraded before him the leaders of the Christian host.

"Now, by Saint George!" cried the King, "thou hast spoken most opportunely. To-morrow the princes have agreed to pass before our new standard on the Mount and to salute it. Prepare to perform the feat thou hast promised, and, by the word of a king, thou shalt choose thine own recompense."

The next day King Richard sat on his horse, about half way up the Mount, with a morion on his head, surmounted by a crown, and by his side stood the Nubian, holding a noble hound in leash. Rank after rank passed by unnoticed by the hound, but when Conrade of Montserrat rode past the dog uttered a furious yell, and leaping upon his charger seized the Marquis by the throat and dragged him from the saddle.

"He hath pulled down the right quarry, I warrant," said Richard. "Pluck the dog off, lest he throttle him."

Though Conrade denied the theft of the banner, the decision of the Council was that, as Richard still accused him, he should meet in combat a champion selected by the King of England and thus decide the question. King Richard despatched the Nubian with a letter to Saladin, asking him to prepare a neutral place where the combat could take place, and inviting him to witness it. "We think, too, thou mightst find in that camp some cavalier who, for the love of truth and his own augmentation of honor, will battle with this same traitor of Montserrat?"

The Nubian fixed his eyes on the King with eager ardor and then raised them to heaven, as the water glistened in them.

"And now to another point," said the King, speaking rapidly; "have you yet seen Edith Plantagenet?"

The mute looked up suddenly, as if about to speak.

"Why, lo you there!" said the King. "That name hath almost power to make the dumb speak. Thou shalt see this beauty of our court and do the errand of the Soldan. But hearken, if thy powers of utterance should be miraculously restored speak no word in her presence, or thy tongue shall be extracted by the roots."

But when Edith saw him she said: "Is it you? Is it indeed you, brave Knight of the Leopard, thus servilely disguised— thus surrounded by an hundred dangers?"

When he answered her not and presented the Soldan's letter, she became angry, and exclaimed: "Tell thy master that I scorn his suit as much as I despise the prostration of a worthless renegade to religion and chivalry—to God and to his lady!"

So saying, she burst from him and left the tent.

When Saladin had been asked by King Richard to provide a place for the combat, he chose a site near the fountain called the Diamond in the Desert. Then he received both parties to the quarrel right royally, but paid special honors to King Richard, whom he entertained in a magnificent pavilion. When Richard asked to see the learned leech whom Saladin had sent to him, the Soldan, to the King's astonishment, exchanged his turban for a Tartar cap, and addressed him in a grave and altered voice.

"A miracle!" exclaimed Richard. "And it was through thy intercession that the Knight of the Leopard was saved from death? And by thy artifice that he revisited my camp in disguise?"

On the morrow Kenneth of Scotland met Conrade of Montserrat in the lists and overcame him, the Marquis being borne from his horse at the first encounter, with Sir Kenneth's lance in his breast.

While drum, clarion, trumpet, and cymbal rang forth in honor of England's champion, and English cheers mingled with shrill Arab yells, King Richard said:

"Brave Knight of the Leopard, thou hast shown that the Ethiopian *may* change his skin and the leopard his spots, though clerks quote Scripture for the impossibility. Come, we will to the pavilion, where Queen Berengaria awaits us."

Supported by his sponsors, Richard and William Longsword, Sir Kenneth knelt before the Queen.

"Unarm him, my mistress," said the King. "Undo his spurs, Berengaria. Unlace his helmet, Edith—thou shalt, wert thou the proudest Plantagenet of the line, and he the poorest knight on earth!"

Both ladies obeyed, Edith blushing and growing pale alternately.

"What expect you from beneath this iron shell?" said Richard, as Sir Kenneth's noble countenance came into view. "Is he an Ethiopian slave, or a nameless adventurer? No, by my good sword! The Knight Kenneth arises David, Earl of Huntingdon, Prince Royal of Scotland!"

WOODSTOCK: OR, THE CAVALIER (1826)

This romance, ostensibly founded on the manuscripts of a certain apocryphal Dr. Rochecliffe, chaplain of Sir Henry Lee's regiment in the Civil War, was written at the time of the calamitous wreck of the author's fortunes, amid declining health, and was hastily finished, but is not unworthy of his fame. The scenes are laid chiefly in and around the Manor of Woodstock, Oxfordshire, famous as the site of the labyrinth built by King Henry II for Fair Rosamond; and the time is 1651, immediately after the battle of Worcester, in which Charles II was defeated by Cromwell. Woodstock Manor is now Blenheim Park, the residence of the Duke of Marlborough.

AFTER the decisive battle of Worcester, which Cromwell called a "crowning glory," commissioners were sent, by order of Parliament, to Woodstock to dismantle the royal manor and to erase, if possible, all traces of its ancient fame. This order was especially displeasing to the inhabitants, many of whom had long enjoyed certain privileges in the park, such as right of pasturage and of cutting firewood in the royal chase. The ranger or keeper of Woodstock Park was Sir Henry Lee, an old Cavalier who had led a regiment in the time of the first Charles, and who was prevented from taking part in the battle of Worcester only through the earnest solicitation of his son Albert, who had himself followed the fortunes of the King. Besides his son, Sir Henry's family consisted solely of a daughter, Alice, a beautiful girl in love with her cousin, Markham Everard, who, on account of political differences, was out of favor with Sir Henry.

Colonel Everard, who was not only an officer in the Parliamentary army but a friend of Cromwell's, endeavored to prevent the destruction of the park and lodge, largely on account of Sir Henry and his family, and obtained an order from Cromwell permitting the old Cavalier to retain his place as ranger. When Everard went to Woodstock with this order, he found the lodge occupied by the commissioners—Desborough, Harrison, and Bletson—Sir Henry and Alice having gone to the hut of a dependent, a forester named Joceline Joliffe.

The commissioners, who saw a prospect of large personal gains from the dismantling of Woodstock, were surprised when Colonel Everard appeared at the Lodge, of which they had taken possession, and were at first indisposed to acknowledge Cromwell's order; but that night their sleep was broken by apparently supernatural noises and incidents, which even Colonel Everard was unable to explain; and when they learned that they were to be employed in a more profitable business, they gladly resigned their rights and departed from Woodstock.

If Colonel Everard had known the object of Cromwell in thus using his power to throw out the commissioners of Parliament and to restore Woodstock to so malignant a Cavalier as Sir Henry Lee, he would hardly have written a letter thanking him in the most grateful terms and promising his own exertions in the public service by every mode within his power.

The wily Cromwell, who had been searching for Charles Stuart ever since the day of Worcester, calculated that nothing would be more probable than that Albert Lee should bring the wanderer to the Lodge at Woodstock, which was famous for its secret hiding-places. While he would not openly propose to so honorable a man as Everard the making of Woodstock a trap, with Alice Lee as a bait, to catch the royal fugitive, he was thus willing to use his friend as a catspaw; and Everard, who knew nothing of the movements of Charles, thus aided his scheme without being conscious of it.

As Colonel Everard had had a stormy interview with his uncle at their last meeting, Sir Henry's uncompromising loyalty refusing to recognize either honor or honesty in his nephew's sentiment, he did not dare to go to the old knight personally with Cromwell's order for his reinstatement, but sent his secretary, Roger Wildrake, who, by pressing the chaplain, Dr. Rochecliffe, into his service, succeeded in inducing Sir Henry to return to the Lodge.

Sir Henry found the Lodge well provisioned by the commissioners, who, anticipating a long stay, had laid in a large stock of meats, barrels of confectioner's ware, pipes of sack, muscadine, ale, etc.; but he declined to feed on the fragments of "such scum of the earth," as he called the representatives of the Parliament, and ordered Joliffe to give all to the poor. But when a steward of the commissioners, one Tomkins, commonly known as Trusty Tomkins or Honest Joe, left behind to pack up some of their belongings, assured him that the provisions were paid for out of his own rents at Ditchley, he declared that he would make use of his own.

"But, hark ye," he said, "I will taste no water from the cistern out of which these slaves have served themselves. Fetch me a pitcher from Rosamond's Spring."

As everybody was employed in setting the rooms to rights, Alice took a pitcher and walked to the spring for the water. When she approached the fountain she saw a woman seated beside it, but as it was broad daylight she had no fear and gave but a glance at her. The stranger was evidently of the lower rank, her red cloak, russet kirtle, and coarse steeple hat indicating her to be perhaps the wife of a small farmer. But Alice's quick eye noted that her clothes were indifferently worn, and that her features were harsh and swarthy. She wished she had sent Joceline for the water, but it was too late, so she proceeded to fill her pitcher.

"Perhaps, my pretty maiden," said the woman, "if you would accept my help your work would be sooner done."

"I thank you," replied Alice, "but had I needed assistance, I could have brought with me those to render it."

"Are the good dames of Woodstock so careless of their pretty daughters as to let the flower of them all wander about without a protector?"

"I have help near, if I need it."

Alice spoke not without warrant, for at the moment a noble hound broke through the bushes, fixing his eyes that glanced fire on the woman, whom he evidently regarded with suspicion, and uttering a low, determined growl. But the stranger, seemingly undaunted, drew a pistol and cocked it.

"My pretty maiden, let not your four-footed protector loose on me; I should be sorry to do him an injury."

"Hold, woman—hold!" cried Alice; "the dog will do you no harm. Down, Bevis—down! He is the favorite hound of

Sir Henry Lee, who would severely revenge any injury to him."

"And you, pretty one, are the old knight's housekeeper, doubtless?"

"I am his daughter, good woman."

"His daughter! I was blind. But I trust I have given my young mistress no offense, and that she will allow me, in token of reconciliation, to carry her pitcher for her."

"As you will, good mother. I will send someone to relieve you of the pitcher."

She turned and walked rapidly toward the lodge, but in a moment the woman was by her side.

"Pardon a stranger, lovely Mistress Alice, who was not capable of distinguishing between a lady of your high quality and a peasant wench, and who I fear has spoken with a freedom that has given offense."

"No offense whatever," replied Alice. "But I am near home and can excuse your further company. You are unknown to me."

"But it follows not that *your* fortunes may not be known to *me*. Let me look upon your pretty hand, and you shall hear what will please you."

"I hear what does *not* please me," said Alice, with dignity.

"Yet you would fain hear of a certain colonel, I warrant you, whom unhappy circumstances have separated from his family."

"I know nothing of what you speak, good woman. If you want alms, there is a piece of silver. Take it—give me my pitcher. Yonder comes one of my father's servants. Joceline —Joceline!"

The fortune-teller hastily dropped something into the pitcher, and disappeared in the wood. When Joceline took the pitcher from her, he exclaimed: "How now! what jingles at the bottom?"

"The woman dropped something into the pitcher," said Alice. "Pour out the water and refill it."

He emptied the pitcher on the grass, and found in it a ruby ring of some value.

"Hasten to the well," said Alice, "and tell the woman that Alice Lee desires none of her gifts."

That evening after supper, Sir Henry had fallen asleep in his chair, and Alice was seated near him, when she became sensible that someone was looking into the room through the great oriel window. She screamed to her father to awake, and at the same time took a pistol from the wall and presented it at the intruder, in whom she imagined she recognized the features of the woman she had seen at the well. Sir Henry sprang up and seized his sword, and the person at the window, alarmed at these demonstrations, missed his footing and fell to the ground. A terrific bark and the sound of a struggle below indicated that Bevis had come upon the scene. This was followed by a loud voice: "Here, Lee—Forester—take the dog off, else I must shoot him!"

"If thou dost," cried Sir Henry from the window, "I blow thy brains out on the spot. Thieves, Joceline—thieves! Bevis, hold on!"

"Back, Bevis—down, sir," cried Joceline. "I am coming —I am coming, Sir Henry."

The scuffle seemed to end by Joceline's interference, and there was close whispering for a moment, which led Sir Henry and Alice to doubt Joceline's faithfulness.

"All is quiet now," said a voice. "I will up and prepare the way for you."

Almost immediately a form appeared at the window and sprang into the room. Before he had gained a sure footing, the old knight, who stood ready with his rapier drawn, made a desperate pass at the intruder which bore him to the ground. Joceline, who climbed up next with a dark lantern, cried out:

"Lord in heaven, he has slain his own son!"

"No—no—I am not hurt," exclaimed Albert Lee. "No noise, on your lives; get lights instantly."

He arose from the floor as quickly as he could, with his cloak and doublet skewered together by the rapier, and saw that his father had fallen, on hearing the fatal words, and lay in his chair without color or sign of life.

"Oh, brother," said Alice, "how could you come in this manner?"

"Ask no questions. Good God! for what am I reserved?" cried Albert, as he gazed on his father.

When the old knight recovered consciousness and had embraced his son, his first question was of the King, of whom he had heard only flying rumors since the defeat at Worcester.

"The King, Albert—the King—in my ear—close!"

"Our last news was that he had escaped from Bristol."

"Thank God for that—thank God for that!" exclaimed Sir Henry. "Joceline!—what ho, Joceline! My son is half starving."

"And there is a lad, too, below, a page, he says, of Colonel Albert's, who I think could eat a horse. He has devoured a whole loaf of bread, as fast as Phœbe could cut it. He is impatient, like all gentleman pages, and saucy among the women."

"What page hast thou got, Albert, that bears himself so ill?" asked Sir Henry.

"The son of a dear friend, a noble lord of Scotland, who followed Montrose's banner and was with us at Worcester."

"He hath ordered a bath," said Joceline, "and supper, he said, might be got ready meantime. He commands all as if he were in his own father's castle."

"Indeed?" said Sir Henry. "A forward chick to crow so early. What is his name?"

"Kerneguy—Louis Kerneguy," said Albert. "His father was Lord Killstewers, of Kincardineshire."

"Truly," said the knight, "these Northern men's names and titles smack of their origin."

The conversation was interrupted by the appearance of Master Kerneguy, a tall, raw-boned lad with a shock of red hair, whose face was swarthy from exposure. His costume was even more dilapidated than his features, and his limping gait and ungainly manner would have excited ridicule had not compassion predominated. At supper he displayed an enormous appetite, eating in silence as if he expected never to have another meal, looking neither to right nor to left.

"God ha'e mercy, Albert," whispered Sir Henry to his son, "if this be the son of a Scots peer, I would not be the English plowman who would change manners with him. But soh! he wipes his mouth and dips his fingers in the ewer, and dries them, I profess, with the napkin! There is some grace in him, after all."

When Albert embraced and saluted his sister before parting

for the night, Master Kerneguy appeared desirous to follow his example, but was repelled by Alice, who replied to his offered salute with a curtsey.

"I am glad to see, young man," said Sir Henry, in response to an awkward bow and good night, "that you have at least learned the reverence due to age. More will I speak with you at leisure on your duties as a page, which office in former days used to be the very school of chivalry."

Albert interposed, saying that the poor lad was almost asleep on his legs.

"Louis, take the candles and light us; here comes Joceline to show us the way."

As soon as Joliffe was dismissed, Master Kerneguy changed from a cubbish lout to one familiar with the best company. He handed the light he held to Albert, with the easy indifference of a superior, while young Lee lighted him across the chamber without turning his back upon him. As Albert proceeded to disrobe him with the reverence of a first lord of the bedchamber, Charles exclaimed:

"What a devil means all this formality? Thou complimentest poor Louis Kerneguy's rags as if he were the King of Great Britain."

"And if your Majesty's commands and circumstances have made me for a moment seem to forget that you are my sovereign, surely I may be permitted to render my homage as such while you are at Woodstock."

Charles threw himself indolently into a chair, and, while receiving Albert's kind offices in undressing, spoke of Sir Henry and his services, finally leading the conversation to Alice, with whom, he declared, he had already made a sort of acquaintance when disguised in a woman's dress.

"I found out, too, that there are other colonels in the wind besides you, Colonel Albert Lee. Who can this colonel be that more than rivals you in your sister's affection? Will you give me leave to take her to task about it?"

"May it please your Majesty," said Albert, who well knew the King's mode of thinking where the fair sex was concerned, "I did not expect—"

"And what is it that Master Lee does not expect?" asked

Charles with marked gravity. "I hope that Colonel Lee does not see in a silly jest anything offensive to the honor of his family. But I ask your pardon, Albert, sincerely, if I have really hurt you."

So saying, he extended his hand, which Albert kissed with reverence.

Charles Stuart's position in the family of Sir Henry Lee, and his obligations to his son, did not prevent him from making love to Alice with a pertinacity that aroused the suspicions of Phœbe Mayflower, who resolved to inform Colonel Everard that a wasp was buzzing about his honeycomb. It happened that when Master Louis Kerneguy desired to change his shabby clothes, Joceline had furnished him with a suit that Colonel Everard had left at Woodstock. One day, when walking in the park in this borrowed suit, he was accosted by a young man, tall and muscular, and well armed with rapier, poniard, and pistols, who touched him on the shoulder with his cane. "Joceline Joliffe, is it not?" asked the stranger.

"I am not Joceline Joliffe, as you may see," said Charles, dropping the cloak with which he had muffled his face.

"Indeed!" exclaimed the stranger, in surprise. "I certainly recognize that costume for my own, and I concluded you must be Joceline, in whose custody I left it at the lodge."

"If I had been Joceline, sir," replied Charles with perfect composure, "methinks you should not have struck so hard."

With this he bowed gravely and turned away, but to his embarrassment he could not rid himself of the stranger. Between anxiety, vexation, and anger, Charles suddenly faced his pursuer, and said:

"Sir, you have already been guilty of one piece of impertinence. If your purpose is merely curiosity, know that I will not suffer myself to be dogged in my private walks by anyone."

"When I see my own cloak on another man's shoulders," replied the stranger dryly, "methinks I have a natural right to see what becomes of it. I must ask how you came by that cloak and where you are going with it."

"Sir, you seem to be a gentleman. I have no objection to tell you that I also am."

"Or somewhat higher, perhaps? Do you deny being the Lord Wilmot?" asked Colonel Everard, for it was he.

"Neither lord nor earl am I," said Charles.

"Can you look at that ring and deny that you are Lord Wilmot?" asked Everard, showing the ring that had been dropped into Alice's water-pitcher. He pressed a spring in the setting, on which the stone flew back and showed within the cipher of Lord Wilmot. "What say you now, sir?"

"That probabilities are no proofs," replied Charles. "Though I have had that ring in my possession, I never knew the trick of the gem you have shown me."

"Young gentleman," said Everard, "though you may not be Lord Wilmot, I have little doubt that you are a proficient in the school of debauchery of which he and Villiers are professors. Your conduct at Woodstock has proved you an apt scholar. I intended only to warn you; it will be your own fault if I add chastisement to admonition."

"Warn me, sir," said the Prince indignantly, "and chastisement! Draw, sir."

The passions of both were now fully up, and they engaged in combat with apparently equal skill and courage. But while they were hotly engaged, Sir Henry Lee came up and rode in between them, commanding them on their lives to hold.

"Let me tell both of you," he said, "that while old Henry Lee is at Woodstock, the immunities of the park shall be maintained as much as if the King were still on the throne."

Sir Henry, after bringing about a cessation of hostilities, invited both to the lodge to join him in a cup of sack. Everard, glad of a reconciliation with his uncle, and anxious to see Alice again, accepted, but was unfortunate enough to quote some verses which the old knight praised highly when ignorant of the authorship. When he was informed by Master Kerneguy that the writer was John Milton, "the creature and parasite of that grand impostor, Oliver Cromwell," he flew into a violent rage, exclaiming: "Markham Everard, I will never forgive thee—never—never. Speak not to me, sir, but begone."

In vain Everard tried to explain, to apologize; the old knight would not listen, and Everard was obliged to leave without his promised sack, and smarting under the triumphant smiles of Master Kerneguy as he led Alice from the apartment.

The result was that Everard sent Wildrake with a challenge to Kerneguy, which was promptly accepted. The two met in a retired glade, but were interrupted by Dr. Rochecliffe and Alice, both of whom knew the identity of the King. Everard, still believing that Lord Wilmot was the lover of Alice, and that she regarded him with favor, bade her an eternal farewell and was about to leave when Charles tapped him on the shoulder, saying with an air of command:

"One word with you, sir. Colonel Everard, I am Charles Stuart."

Everard recoiled in surprise, and exclaimed: "Impossible! The King of Scots has escaped from Bristol. My Lord Wilmot, this will not pass upon me."

"The King of Scots, Master Everard," replied Charles, "since you are pleased so to limit his sovereignty, is before you. Dr. Rochecliffe shall be my voucher. Peace, Dr. Rochecliffe," said he, as Rochecliffe put on a look of anxiety. "We are in the hands of a man of honor. At any rate, the avowal is made; and it is for Colonel Everard to consider how he is to conduct himself."

"Sire," said Everard, as if awaking from a dream, and bowing with profound deference, "for your safety being endangered by me, let not such an imagination for an instant cross your mind."

"Come, doctor," said Charles, "as there will be no more tilting, we may as well return to the lodge and leave these two for mutual explanations."

"No—no!" exclaimed Alice. "My cousin Everard and I have nothing to explain. My father has my promise, we must not correspond or converse for the present. To the town, Cousin Markham; and if danger should approach, give us warning. Farewell, till God send better days."

Meanwhile Trusty Tomkins, who remained at Woodstock, visited the lodge occasionally and had long conversations with Dr. Rochecliffe. He was also well received below stairs, where Joceline welcomed him with cordial frankness and the flagon went merrily round, for Trusty had an attachment to strong liquors. He had also an attachment for pretty Phœbe May-flower, whose loyalty to Joceline would not permit her to listen to his advances. But one day Tomkins found Phœbe at Rosamond's fountain about sunset, when he had been drinking freely, and began to expound to her the doctrines of the sect called Ranters or the Family of Love. When Phœbe, frightened at his advances, ran from him, he pursued, calling loudly on her to stop, and brandishing a pistol to frighten her. Phœbe stumbled over the root of a tree, and Tomkins was about to seize her when Joceline, hearing her cries, came running. Tomkins, roused to fury, discharged the pistol at Joliffe, the ball grazing his face; and Joceline, in return, struck him over the head with his quarter-staff a blow that proved almost instantly mortal.

"Oh, what have you done, Joceline?" exclaimed Phœbe. "You have killed him."

"Better than he should have killed me," said Joceline. "Let me drag him out of the path. He must not lie here in all men's sight. Go to thy chamber, Phœbe, and compose thyself. I must seek Dr. Rochecliffe."

That night Colonel Everard was at supper with Roger Wild-rake, having as his guest the Rev. Nehemiah Holdenough, when the door of the apartment opened and a stout man, enveloped in a cloak, entered.

"Markham Everard, I greet thee in God's name."

Everard, surprised at recognizing General Cromwell, endeavored in vain to find words to express his astonishment.

Cromwell cast his keen eye around the apartment. "How is this?" he asked sharply and anxiously. "One hath left the room since I entered."

Wildrake, who had been absent but a minute or two, stepped forward and said: "Not so, sir; I stood but in the background out of respect." But in that brief interval he had succeeded in despatching a trusty boy to the lodge with a feather, with instructions to give it to Mistress Alice Lee, if possible, if not, to Joceline Joliffe.

Cromwell had come on information received from Trusty Tomkins, who had promised to meet him at a certain hour and conduct him to Charles's hiding-place; but after waiting until considerably after midnight, he said: "Ah! Everard, thou mightest put this gear to rights if thou wilt! Thou knowest all the passages about Jezebel's palace down yonder. Let me know how they may be guarded against the escape of any from within."

"I cannot aid you in this matter, sir. I know not all the posterns about Woodstock, and if I did, I am not free in conscience to communicate with you on this occasion."

"We shall do without you, sir," replied Cromwell haughtily. "I will make bold to take you to the lodge to inquire into affairs in which the state is concerned. Give your sword to Captain Pearson and consider yourself under arrest."

Albert Lee had returned that night from the coast with news that a vessel was ready to receive the royal fugitive. When Wildrake's messenger arrived with the feather and told of soldiers in Woodstock, the King was hastily guided to Joceline's hut, where horses were provided for his escape, while Albert, dressed in the clothes that Charles had worn, remained at the lodge to deceive Cromwell, if possible, by impersonating his royal master.

Cromwell, angry and mortified at Tomkins's failure to meet him at the village, moved at last against the lodge and surrounded it. As his party approached the buildings two men were caught in a thicket digging a grave by the light of a lantern. They proved to be Dr. Rochecliffe and Joceline Joliffe, and the body awaiting burial was that of Trusty Tomkins.

"Tomkins, and murdered!" cried Cromwell. "Dogs, confess the truth. You, whom I believe to be Dr. Albany Rochecliffe—to you I give the choice of being hanged at daybreak to-morrow, or of telling what you know of the secrets of yonder house."

"Truly, sir," replied Rochecliffe, "you found me but in my duty as a clergyman interring the dead."

"Remove him," said Cromwell, "and let him not speak with his yoke-fellow yonder. Move on to the lodge."

When the lodge was summoned and Sir Henry Lee refused to open, the door was shattered by a petard and Cromwell and his men entered to find only the old knight and two frightened women.

"Disarm the malignant rebel," said Oliver. "Art thou not

ashamed, sir, to detain me before the door of a house thou hadst no force to defend? Knowest thou not that, that by martial law, deserves hanging?"

"It is better to be hanged like honest men than to give up our trust like cowards and traitors," said Sir Henry.

"Ha! say'st thou?" said Cromwell. "But I will speak with thee by and by. Pearson, take this scroll; search every place laid down therein, and arrest, or slay, on resistance, whomsoever you find."

Guided by the plan furnished by Trusty Tomkins, the soldiers went through every room and secret passage, and finally blew up Rosamond's Tower, in which Albert Lee had taken refuge. Albert escaped by leaping a broad chasm just before the explosion, but was captured and taken before Cromwell, who, thinking that Charles Stuart was at last in his power, exclaimed: "Ha, youth! I have hunted thee from Stirling to Worcester, and from Worcester to Woodstock, and we have met at last. But is this— Ah! whom have we here? A cheat—a cheat! Pluck the disguise from him!"

Cromwell went up to him with his teeth set and hands clenched, and said: "Thy name, young man?"

"Albert Lee, a faithful subject of King Charles."

"I might have guessed it," said Cromwell. "Ay, and to King Charles shalt thou go. Pearson, let him be carried to the others; and let them be executed at twelve exactly."

"All, sir?" asked Pearson, surprised.

"*All*," repeated Cromwell. "Let a court-martial sit on them presently. Place guards till we repose ourselves for an hour or two. Wake me if the court-martial should require instruction."

But it was not to be. Pearson was a young soldier, and he was persuaded by some older ones that if he followed Cromwell's orders given in anger the General would not be pleased. When Cromwell awoke and asked for Pearson's report and the captain informed him that he had not yet executed the Malignants, he exclaimed:

"What execution? what Malignants?"

"But one of them," said Pearson, "called Joliffe, certainly deserves death, since he owns that he killed honest Joseph Tomkins."

"He rather deserves a reward for saving us a labor," said Cromwell. "He was a most double-hearted villain. I have found evidence among papers here that, if we had lost the fight at Worcester, we should have had reason to regret that we had ever trusted Tomkins. Write us down debtor, not creditor to Master Joliffe."

THE FAIR MAID OF PERTH: OR, ST. VALENTINE'S DAY (1828)

This story is the second in the *Chronicles of the Canongate*, assumed to have been written by Mrs. Martha Bethune Baliol, who lived at Baliol Lodging in the Canongate, Edinburgh. The scene is laid in Perth in the reign of Robert III (1390–1406).

SIMON GLOVER, who derived his surname from his trade, was a substantial citizen of Perth, with a house in Couvrefeu or Curfew Street, where he lived with his only child, Catherine. The glover's daughter was universally acknowledged to be the most beautiful young woman of Perth or its vicinity, and such was her renown as the Fair Maid of Perth that even the gallants of the court were more attentive to exhibit feats of horsemanship as they passed old Simon's door than to distinguish themselves before the eyes of the noblest dames of Scotland. But the glover's lovely daughter showed no inclination to listen to the gallantries of those above her station, and fully acceded to the sentiments of her parent, who declared:

"I will have no son-in-law that thinks himself better than me; and for these lords and knights, I trust thou wilt always remember thou art too low to be their lawful love, and too high to be their unlawful loon."

Simon Glover had in his service an apprentice named Conachar, a young Highlander who usually attended his master when he went forth, though he bore no weapon but a stout staff. He was a handsome youth with brown, curling tresses surmounted by a small scarlet bonnet, and wearing a yeoman's habit that displayed his fine limbs to advantage. But, though his service was due to his master, it was easy to discern that his eyes were for the daughter and that it was to her that he was most anxious to dedicate his good offices.

130

On St. Valentine's Eve the glover and his daughter were returning home from church, followed by Conachar, when the latter said:

"Master, walk faster—we are dogg'd."

"By whom, and how many?"

"By one man in a cloak, who follows us like a shadow."

"You are not afraid of one man, Conachar?"

"Afraid!" answered Conachar indignantly. "You shall soon know whether I am afraid."

"Thy temper has no middle course, foolish boy. There is no occasion to make a brawl. Walk thou before with Catherine, and I will take thy place."

While Conachar and Catherine went on, Simon turned back and called out: "Come, step forward, my friend, and show us thy shapes."

"Why, so I can, Master Glover," said a deep voice, "I can show my shapes well enough, only I wish they could bear the light something better."

"Body of me!" exclaimed Simon, "is it thou, Harry Gow? Come in. Kate will be right glad to see thee."

Simon Glover shook his hand again and again, and Catherine freely offered her hand, which the stranger held as if he designed to carry it to his lips. Her father, seeing his guest's hesitation, called out:

"Her lips, man—her lips! and that's a proffer I would not make to everyone who crosses my threshold. But I am so glad to see thee again that it would be hard to tell the thing I could refuse thee."

The newcomer was below the middle stature, but his broad shoulders and brawny arms argued unusual strength. His dress was of buff hide; and he wore in his belt a heavy broadsword and a dirk, as if to defend his purse, which also hung from it. Aside from the bashful expression of his face, as he modestly saluted the Fair Maid, there was daring and resolution in his dark eye, and his forehead was high and noble.

"Let me hope," said Catherine, as she yielded the courtesy with a smile, "that I welcome back to Perth a repentant and amended man."

Henry Gow, or Smith, as he was indifferently called, was a master armorer, who had just returned from a trip southward.

"I trust thou hast made a saving voyage of it, son Henry?" asked the glover, who always used that affectionate style of speech, though he was in no way akin to the young artisan.

"A thriving one, father. I sold the steel habergeon for four hundred marks to the English Warden of the East Marches. The beggarly Highland thief who bespoke it boggled at half the sum, though it had cost me a year's labor."

"What dost thou start at, Conachar?" said Simon to his apprentice. "What is it to thee that an Englishman thinks that cheap which a Scottishman may hold dear? Bestir thee, and thou shalt have a cup of the nut-brown for thyself, my boy."

Conachar poured the liquor for his master and for Catherine, and sat down.

"How now, sirrah! Fill to my guest."

"Master Smith may fill for himself," said Conachar. "The son of my father has demeaned himself enough for one evening."

"Now, by the best glove I ever made," said Simon, "thou shalt help him from that cup and flagon, if thee and I are to abide under one roof."

Conachar arose sullenly and, approaching the smith, contrived to stumble and spill the ale over his person and dress. Henry's patience gave way under the provocation, and seizing the youth by the throat, as he arose from his pretended stumble, cast him from him, saying:

"Had this been in another place, young gallows-bird, I had stowed the lugs out of thy head."

Conachar sprang to his feet with the activity of a tiger, drew a knife from his bosom, and, leaping on Henry, struck at him over the collar-bone what must have been a mortal blow had not the smith been quick to defend himself. When Conachar felt himself in his powerful grasp, he became deadly pale, and stood mute with shame and fear, as Smith quietly said:

"Thou art but a boy, and I, a grown man, ought not to have provoked thee. But let this be a warning."

Conachar left the room without replying, and Catherine swooned at sight of the trickling blood.

"Let me depart, Father Simon," said Henry Smith mournfully. "I spread strife and bloodshed where I would wish most to bring peace and happiness."

"It was the fault of yon Highland cateran; but he shall go back to his glens to-morrow. This breaks all bonds between us. But let me see thy wound."

"Nay, it is nothing. Look to Catherine."

But Catherine was soon herself again, and the armorer proceeded to beg forgiveness for having offended her in the first hour of his return.

"Your father blames me not, Catherine, and cannot you forgive me?"

"I have no power to forgive," said Catherine, "what I have no title to resent. If my father chooses to have his house made the scene of night-brawls, I must witness them—I cannot help myself."

"And is this the manner you receive my friend—nay, my son—after his long absence?" said her father. "Do you treat him as if he had done wrong in dashing from him the snake that was about to sting him!"

"Our friend will not deny," replied Catherine, "that he lives in an atmosphere of strife, blood, and quarrels. He hears of no swordsman but he envies his reputation, and sees no brawl but he must strike in the midst of it. His days are days of battle, and, doubtless, he acts them over again in his dreams."

"Daughter," said Simon, "your tongue wags too freely. Quarrels and fights are men's business, not women's, and it is not maidenly to think or speak of them."

But Catherine would not be appeased, and she declaimed against war and tournaments with a vigor and feeling which surprised her listeners, and caused Henry much pain.

"You speak in vain, Catherine," said the smith. "I may, indeed, turn monk and retire from the world, but while I live in it I must practise my trade; and while I form armor and weapons for others, I cannot myself withstand the temptation of using them."

"Then throw from you, my dear Henry," said the enthusiastic girl, "the art that is a snare to you. Resign the manufacture of arms, and deserve the forgiveness of Heaven by renouncing all that can lead to the sin which most easily besets you."

"Preach peace as much as thou wilt," said her father; "but as for bidding the first armorer in Scotland forego the forging of swords and harness, it is enough to drive patience itself mad. Out from my sight! and next morning remember, if you see Henry Smith, that you see a man who has not his match in Scotland at the use of broadsword and battle-ax."

Henry remained with the glover until after midnight, when he went to his home in the Mill Wynd at the western end of Perth; but he promised to return at the peep of dawn and whistle at the lattice window in the eastern gable.

"I will contrive," said Simon, "that Catherine shall look out at the window, and thus thou wilt have all the privileges of being a gallant Valentine through the rest of the year."

"Amen, father," said the armorer, "you shall hear the smith's call by cock-crowing."

Accordingly, he dressed himself in his best and set out just before dawn for his rendezvous; but as he came near Simon Glover's, two men started up as if to intercept his passage. Alarmed, he tripped one and struck down the other with his sword, and ran toward the house, where he observed a party beneath the windows. One came toward him, saying:

"What noise was that, Kenneth? Why gave you not the signal?"

"Villain," said Henry, "you are discovered and shall die the death."

He dealt the stranger a blow that would have made his words good, had not the man raised his arm and received on his hand the blow intended for his head. As he fell with a groan, Henry sprang forward upon a party of men who were placing a ladder against the lattice window. Crying the alarm-word of the town, he rushed on them, threw down the ladder, and placed his foot on the body of a man who had been about to mount it. His companions struck at Henry, but his mail-coat stood him in good stead, and he repaid their blows with interest, until his cries brought help, when his assailants sought safety in flight, bearing off their wounded. While the citizens gave chase, the armorer secured the captive under his foot, who entreated for his freedom.

"As thou art a gentleman, let me go," he said, "and what is past shall be forgiven."

"I am no gentleman," said Henry. "I am Hal of the Wynd, a burgess of Perth; and I have done nothing to need forgiveness."

"Villain, thou hast done thou knowest not what! But let me go, and I will fill thy bonnet with gold pieces."

"I shall fill thy bonnet with a cloven head presently," said the armorer, "unless thou stand still as a true prisoner."

"Hear me, Simon Glover," appealed the prisoner, as the glover appeared; "let me speak but one word with you in private and I will show that no harm was intended to thee or thine."

"I should know that voice," said Simon. "Son Smith, let him speak with me. I will be answerable for him."

So saying, Simon pulled in the prisoner and shut the door, leaving Henry without in surprise. Meanwhile the citizens who had chased the party returned and reported that they had been unsuccessful, as all had sought asylum in the Dominican convent. They had hardly gone when Simon Glover opened his door and invited Henry in.

"Where is the prisoner?" demanded the armorer.

"He is gone—escaped—fled," said the glover. "He got out at the back door and through the garden. Think not of him, but come and see the Valentine whose honor and life you have saved."

But Catherine was on her knees giving thanks for her deliverance, and Henry Smith, declining to go to bed again, sat down in a chair by the chimney-side to await the dawn. Meanwhile, Catherine, who began to think she had treated her deliverer too coolly and perhaps unjustly, arose and dressed, saying to herself: "I will not be ungrateful, though I cannot yield to his suit. I will seek him and choose him for my Valentine myself."

She went down-stairs and peeping in saw the armorer fast asleep. "He looks very stern," she thought; "and if he should awake—but I will not suppose that Henry can misconstrue what I do in sisterly love and honor, and I will not let a childish bashfulness put my gratitude to sleep."

She tripped quietly up and kissed the sleeper's lips; but the touch, slight as it was, waked Henry, and before she could escape he caught her in his arms and returned her salute in ecstasy.

Just then Simon Glover entered and, seeing the situation, said:

"Cheer up, thou silly girl, and be not ashamed that thou hast made the two happiest men in Perth, since thy old father is one of them. What! weeping, love? nay—nay, this is more than need. Henry, help me to comfort this little fool."

But Catherine escaped from the room, whereupon Henry looked so grave that the father chided him.

"Alas, father!" he replied, "there is that written on her brow which says she loves me well enough to be my Valentine, but not well enough to be my wife."

When Conachar appeared at breakfast he announced his immediate departure, as there was to be a great meeting at which his presence was necessary. When Simon asked him about his return, he said:

"I cannot exactly answer; perhaps never, if such be my father's pleasure."

But for Catherine the Highlander and Henry would have come to blows again, and when Conachar bade farewell to Simon and his daughter he cast a look of scorn on the smith, which the latter answered only with a laugh.

Though Henry treated Conachar thus scornfully, Simon Glover shook his head as he said:

"His father is a powerful man—hath long hands—reaches as far as he can, and hears farther than it is necessary to talk of him."

It turned out that the party that had made the attack on Simon Glover's house was under the lead of David, Duke of Rothesay, son of the King Robert III and heir to the throne; and the person whose hand was cut off by the smith was Sir John Ramorny, his equerry. The hand, with a valuable ring on one of the fingers, was picked up by Oliver Proudfute, a bonnet-maker, who aspired to a reputation for bravery, and taken to Sir Patrick Charteris, the Provost of Perth, who had it displayed in a public place in hope of finding its owner.

Meanwhile Sir John Ramorny was in bed with his wound,

The lists were prepared in the Skinners' Yards hard by, and the combatants, clad in steel caps and buff-jackets, and armed with axes, met amid a throng of witnesses—nobles, priests, and commons. When the signal was given, Bonthron aimed a mighty blow at his antagonist, but Henry avoided it by stepping aside, and before he could recover his guard dealt Bonthron a sideling blow that felled him.

"Confess, or die," said the victor, with his foot on the body of the vanquished.

Bonthron confessed his guilt, but averred that he mistook his victim for the man who had now vanquished him, who had wronged the man he served. When asked whether he meant Sir John Ramorny, he answered: "No, it was a greater than he." And he pointed to the Prince.

"Wretch!" said the astonished Duke of Rothesay, "do you dare to hint that I was your instigator?"

"You yourself, my lord," answered the unblushing ruffian.

"Die in thy falsehood, accursed slave!" said the Prince, and he would have run him through but for the Lord High Constable, who said he must be dealt with by the executioner.

Bonthron was hurried away to the gallows, and the Prince turned from the lists, disdaining to notice the gloomy and threatening looks of the crowd as he passed. He determined to seek an interview with his father at once, but he was too late. His uncle and enemy, the Duke of Albany, had already reached the King's ear with Bonthron's story, and the Prince was met by the Earl of Errol with the information that he was to be restricted for the present to the seclusion of his (the High Constable's) lodgings.

A Carthusian monk, one Father Clement, had been teaching the doctrines of Wickliffe in Perth. When Father Francis, Catherine's Dominican confessor, learned by secret and leading questions that she had become infected with his teachings, he threatened her with temporal punishment and eternal condemnation, and told her that her only safety was to renounce wedlock and take the veil.

"Remain in the world," he said, "and thy father and thou shall be brought to trial as heretics; assume the veil, and the errors of both shall be forgiven and canceled."

When Simon heard this he was greatly troubled, and he became still more so when Sir Patrick Charteris rode up to his door and informed him that warrants had been issued for the arrest of himself and his daughter, under a charge of heresy, and that his only hope lay in flying and in lying concealed a few days or weeks until the return of the Earl of Douglas, whose presence would control the Duke of Albany and the priests. Simon told him that he had just title to the protection of the Highland chief, Gilchrist MacIan, of the Clan Quhele, but that he could not take his daughter thither on account of his son Conachar, who had lived so long in his family. It was finally settled that while the glover sought refuge in the Highlands with the Clan Quhele, Catherine should be placed with Marjory, Duchess of Rothesay, the neglected wife of the Prince of Scotland, who was then at Falkland, a castle lent to her by the Duke of Albany.

Father and daughter were soon in the saddle and on the way to Kinfauns, the seat of Sir Patrick Charteris, where Simon left his daughter and rode into the Highlands. On reaching Tay he was alarmed to hear that Gilchrist MacIan was dead, and that his son Eachin MacIan, whom he had known as Conachar, was now captain of Clan Quhele. He also learned that preparations were making for a battle to be fought at Perth, on the coming Palm Sunday, between the Clan Quhele and the Clan Chattan, thirty champions on a side, to decide their long-standing quarrels.

Meanwhile, Sir John Ramorny, hearing that Catherine Glover was to be sent to Falkland, used the fact as a bait to draw thither the Prince of Scotland, against whom he had conceived a deadly hatred for flippant remarks about the loss of his hand. The Prince was induced to leave the residence of the Earl of Errol and to journey in a boat down the Tay. On the way they passed another boat with the glee-woman on board, and the Prince, against the wishes of Ramorny, insisted that she should accompany them, promising her a place in the service of the Duchess. When the party arrived at Newburgh a cold rain had set in, but the Prince, though insufficiently clad, insisted on mounting and riding to Falkland with reckless haste. The glee-woman, inured to hardship, bore the journey well; but the Prince arose the next morning with pain and signs of fever, though he refused the services of Dwining the leech.

An hour before noon Catherine Glover, escorted by a groom of Sir Patrick's, arrived at Falkland, where she was received by Dwining, disguised as an old woman. Shortly afterward the same fictitious old woman ushered her into a carefully darkened apartment, where the supposed Duchess of Rothesay lay on a couch.

"Let the maiden approach, Griselda, and kiss our hand," said a carefully modulated voice.

Catherine knelt beside the couch and kissed the gloved hand extended to her; but the arm instantly encircled her neck and drew her downward with such strength that she screamed aloud.

"Peace, fool! it is I—David of Rothesay."

With this the Duke tore off his veil. Catherine looked around her; the nurse was gone.

"Now be present with me, Heaven!" she said, repressing her disposition to scream. "The jest hath been played," she continued, with as much firmness as she could assume. "May I entreat that your Highness will now unhand me?"

The Duke of Rothesay, whose virtuous feelings were as easily excited as they were evanescent, said, when he found her proof against all his sophistries: "Forgive me if I have alarmed you, maiden; thou art too noble-minded to be the toy of passing pleasure. What, ho! who waits without?

"Ramorny," he continued, as the knight entered, "let the glee-woman wait upon this young person till she can be sent where she desires to go. It is noon, I believe; command them to serve up dinner."

At the close of the repast the Prince, under the influence of drugs administered by Dwining in his wine, fell into a lethargic sleep. Sir John and the physician bore him to his room, and the next morning the report was spread that the Prince was dangerously ill of an infectious disorder.

Several days later the Earl of Douglas arrived at Falkland with a body of horse, but he was too late. The emaciated body of the Prince, who had been starved to death, was found, and the perpetrators of the crime, convicted through the testimony of Catherine and the glee-woman, were hanged from the battlements. Catherine and the glee-woman were sent to the care of the widowed Duchess of Rothesay, to whom the Earl gave directions to meet him at Perth. Douglas, who suspected that the head of the Duke of Albany was behind the hand of Ramorny, but knew that to break with Albany meant civil war, gave strict orders that silence should be kept concerning what had happened until after the battle of Palm Sunday, when he himself would lay the facts before the King.

On Palm Sunday the lists were prepared on the North Inch of Perth for the battle between the clans. The Clan Quhele was entertained hospitably at the Abbey of Scone, while their rivals of the Clan Chattan were cared for by Sir Patrick Charteris at his Castle of Kinfauns. The two attended mass at different places, the one at the Dominican Convent, the other at that of the Carthusians. When Henry Smith of the Wynd saw the chief of Clan Quhele he could hardly recognize in the splendidly armed man of military bearing the passionate boy whom he had brushed off as he might a wasp that had stung him; but when he caught his eye and saw the glance of fiery hatred in it he felt that his own embrowned features colored up like the heated iron on which he wrought.

The battle was to take place within a palisade, at one extremity of which was a range of galleries for the King and his courtiers. On two other sides were galleries for spectators, and on the fourth side was the river. A strong body of men-at-arms guarded the entrances, where the Earl Marshal and Lord High Constable examined each combatant, to see whether he had the appropriate equipment—steel cap, mail-shirt, two-handed sword, and dagger. When all seemed ready, the Earl of Errol declared that the Clan Chattan lacked one of the required number, and that the combat could not proceed until the inequality should be removed. Proclamation was made at once for a substitute for the missing man, and as soon as Henry Smith heard of it he leaped the barriers and offered his services. When this was noised through the town, the widow of Oliver Proudfute, at whose house had been left Henry's weapons, worn by the bonnet-maker the night he was slain, came running with them. Henry joyfully put them on, and seizing his great two-handed sword, hastened to take his place in the ranks of Clan Chattan.

The battle raged fiercely more than an hour, man after man falling on one side or the other, until at last the fight appeared to depend on Henry Smith for Clan Chattan and Torquil of the Oak for Clan Quhele. Eachin, the young chieftain, who was still unharmed, ran to Torquil's aid; but before he reached him the latter fell under Henry's sword, and Eachin, fearful of meeting his redoubtable enemy, plunged into the Tay.

Henry, who had sunk to the ground with faintness, was congratulated by the Duke of Albany and by the Black Douglas, who offered him knighthood on the spot and lands to sustain it.

"I thank you humbly, my lord, but I have shed blood enough already."

"A churl will savor of churl's kind," said the haughty Douglas, turning aside.

"Henry, my beloved son Henry," said Simon Glover, "what tempted you to this fatal fray? Dying—speechless?"

"No—not speechless," said Henry. "Catherine—"

"Catherine is well, I trust, and shall be thine—that is, if—"

"If she be safe, thou wouldst say," said the Douglas. "She is safe, and shall be rich."

"For her safety, my lord, accept the heartfelt thanks and blessings of a father. For wealth, we are rich enough."

"A marvel!" said the Earl: "a churl refuses nobility, a citizen despises gold!"

ANNE OF GEIERSTEIN: OR, THE MAIDEN OF THE MIST (1829)

This is a story of Switzerland and the Swiss in the latter half of the fifteenth century, when the hardy mountaineers and shepherds, who had overthrown the chivalry of Germany at Laupen, at Sempach, and on other less noted fields, fought successfully with the mercenaries of the Duke of Burgundy, slew him, and achieved their independence. Duke Charles is the same autocratic and truculent ruler described in *Quentin Durward*, who, a vassal of Louis XI of France, aspires to wear the crown of a sovereign and to extend his dominions, by the absorption of Provence, to the Mediterranean.

WO Englishmen, father and son, apparently merchants, were traveling from Lucerne, on the Lake of the Four Cantons, toward Unterwalden, when they lost their way in the intricate paths across the Alps. They reached at last a point where they could look down into the valley of a stream, where their guide pointed out, amid pine forests on the opposite bank, the tower of Geierstein, the deserted castle of an ancient family, near which, he said, dwelt Arnold Biederman, Landamman of the Canton of Unterwalden, who would receive them hospitably.

"I have heard of him," said the elder of the travelers, whom the guide addressed as Seignor Philipson, "a good and hospitable man, but how to reach the vulture's castle unless we have the lammergeier's wings is a question hard to answer."

As they could see no way to lead them down into the valley, which the mists had now obscured, Arthur, the younger of the travelers, proposed to go in search of the path, and after some objections from his father, he left them and began the descent, the path being narrow and difficult. He encountered many dangers on the way and became so agitated at his perilous situation that his senses reeled, when he was recalled to consciousness by hearing a female voice, in a high-pitched but musical accent, as if calling to him. On looking in the direction of the sounds

144

he saw, on the summit of a pyramidal rock, a figure nearly obscured by the mist. Arthur's first thought was that the Virgin had appeared in answer to his prayers, but when her voice again reached him with a shrill halloo, he recognized her as a maiden of the mountains, probably familiar with their dangerous paths. Presently she stood before him, regarding him with a mixture of pity and wonder.

"Stranger, who are you and whence come you?"

"I left Lucerne this morning, with my father and a guide, who are not three furlongs hence. May it please you, gentle maiden, to tell them of my safety?"

"Willingly," said she; "but I think my uncle, or some of my kinsmen, must have found them already. Can I not aid you? Are you hurt?"

"No, saving some bruises of little import; but my head turns, and my heart grows sick, when I see you so near the edge of the cliff."

"Be not downcast. Raise yourself on the trunk of the tree, and advance closer to the rock. By one bold step you can then reach the rock on which I stand."

To prove her words, she sprang lightly from the rock to the trunk of the tree, and then back again to the cliff; then, extended her hand and invited him to accept her aid. But shame now overcame Arthur's fears so much that he took heart and, leaping the chasm, stood on the cliff beside her. To seize her hand and raise it to his lips, in token of gratitude and respect, was his first action; his next was to look for his father and the guide. Just then a horn sounded, and the maiden, saying it was to announce that help had reached them, invited him to follow her to Geierstein.

A circuitous path led them down to a ruinous bridge giving access to the old castle, a square pile on the verge of a precipice, down which the waters of the river poured in a cascade a hundred feet in height. Arthur followed the maiden across the bridge and through the donjon of the dismantled castle, beyond which lay a plantation of about a hundred cultivated acres. The principal object in this little domain was a huge house of logs, amid groves of walnut and chestnut, orchards, and a vineyard, and beyond it pasture-lands with cattle. Arthur viewed this pleasing landscape but one or two hurried minutes, and then hastened to greet his father, whom he saw on the lawn in front of the farmhouse, surrounded by several other persons. Anne of Geierstein, his conductress, had but time to say: "Yonder old man, Arnold Biederman, the Landamman, is my uncle, and the young men are my kinsmen," when his father advanced and said in a tone of censure rather than of affection:

"Arthur, may the saints forgive the pain thou hast this day given me."

"Amen," said the youth, "but I acted for the best. That I did not meet with the worst is due to this maiden."

"To the maiden my thanks shall be rendered," said his father, "but is it well or comely that you should receive from her the succor which it is your duty as a man to extend to the weaker sex?"

Arthur blushed at this reproof, and Arnold Biederman, sympathizing with his feelings, hastened to say:

"Never be abashed, my young guest, to be indebted for counsel or assistance from a maid of Unterwalden. The freedom of their country owes no less to their wisdom than to that of their sons."

Meanwhile Arthur felt that he was the subject of merriment among the young men, who had evidently been questioning Anne concerning him. "She, too, must despise me," he thought, "though civility, unknown to these ill-taught boors, has enabled her to conceal contempt under the guise of pity."

Shortly afterward, when they were seated at a meal in the great hall of the house, the walls of which were hung with trophies of the chase and with armor and weapons, another guest appeared—Rudolph of Donnerhugel, a cousin of the young men. He was tall, well proportioned, and active, with brown, curling locks and darker moustachios, and his clothes were finer and more ornamental than those of his cousins. He handed a sealed despatch to the Landamman, and seated himself beside Anne in a place yielded by the courtesy of one of the others.

The young Englishman soon saw, by the glances in his direction and the disconcerted looks and blushes of the maiden, that he was the subject of their merriment. "If I had either of these sons of the mountain on six feet of level greensward," he thought, "I were more likely to spoil their mirth than to furnish food for it. It is marvelous to see such conceited boors under the same roof with so courteous and amiable a damsel; but I need not concern myself with either her beauty or their breeding, since morning will separate me from them forever."

But it was not to be, for the English merchant, who was on his way to the court of Charles of Burgundy, was induced by his Swiss host to await the departure of an embassy to the same court, of which he himself was to be a member. While the two were discussing this question, all the younger ones having gone to the lawn for athletic exercise, Anne came in with a bashful air and whispered to her uncle.

"The bow of Buttisholz, my dear?" he said in surprise. "Have they grown stronger than last year, when none could bend it?"

"It is this gentleman's son, sir," replied the maiden, "who, unable to contend with my cousins in running, leaping, or pitching the stone, has challenged them to ride or to shoot with the English long-bow."

"To ride were difficult, where there are no horses, but an English bow he shall have. Take it, with the three arrows, and say for me that he who bends it will do more than William Tell could have done."

While the Landamman was explaining how the bow came into his possession through his grandfather, who took part in the battle of Buttisholz, they were drawn without by shouts of astonishment.

"Has the young stranger bent the bow?" asked the Landamman.

"He has, father," said Rudiger, "and three such shots were never made. He removed the pole a hundred yards beyond our mark and shot the three arrows with incredible rapidity. The first cleft the pole, the second cut the string, and the third killed the bird as it rose."

"It was chance—pure chance," said Rudolph of Donnerhugel. "No human skill could have done it. If not chance, it was illusion or witchery."

"What say'st thou, Arthur," said his father—"was thy success by chance or by skill?"

"I have done but an ordinary feat for an English archer," said Arthur. "If the fair maiden will open the note that I put into her hand before shooting, she will find evidence that I had chosen my three marks before I drew the bow."

Anne handed the scroll to the Landamman, who opened it and read:

> "'If I hit mast, and line, and bird,
> An English archer keeps his word.
> Ah! maiden, didst thou aim at me,
> A single glance were worth the three.'

Fine words to make foolish maidens vain," said the Landamman, shaking his head. "But you must allow, Rudolph, that the stranger has fairly attained the three marks he proposed."

"He has attained them, but that he has done so fairly may be doubted."

"Shame—shame, Rudolph," replied the Landamman; "can spleen and envy have weight with so brave a man as you!"

The Bernese colored under this rebuke, to which he ventured no reply; but before they parted he made arrangements with Arthur to meet him in the court of the old castle at sunrise.

Meanwhile the Landamman, who had strolled with his guest into the old castle, gave him an account of the family of Geierstein, surprising him with the remark that he had but to put on the old helmet in his hall, or stick a falcon's feather in his cap, and call himself Arnold, Count of Geierstein.

"I see you are confounded," he said, "at my degeneracy; but this land holds many such gentle peasants, sir merchant. My father, Count Williewald, who, like his father before him, had adopted the cause of the Confederacy, became a citizen, and distinguished himself so much that he was chosen Landamman of the republic. He had two sons, myself and a younger brother, Albert. When about to die, he offered me, as the eldest, the estates of Geierstein, reserving enough to make my brother one of the wealthiest citizens of Unterwalden. But Albert was dissatisfied and threatened to appeal to the Emperor. My

father was incensed and would have dismissed him with male-
dictions, when I offered to become a citizen of the republic, and
to let Albert wear the coronet and bear the honors of Geierstein.
My father at last adopted my proposal, and my brother became
Count Albert of Geierstein, and I Arnold Biederman. My
father died soon afterward. My brother had other possessions
in Swabia and Westphalia, and seldom visited his paternal castle,
which he left in charge of a seneschal, Ital Schreckenwald, a
cruel man, who doubtless considered me a poor-spirited clown
who had disgraced my noble blood. In the mean time my
Bertha, now in heaven, had given me six stately sons, five of
whom you have seen. Albert also married, but had only one
daughter, Anne of Geierstein. When the wars broke out between Zurich and the Forest Cantons, Albert embraced the
alliance of Austria, and admitted an Austrian garrison into Geierstein, with the aid of which Schreckenwald laid waste the country. My house was burned, my flocks destroyed, and my youngest son slain. With the peasants of Unterwalden, I stormed
and dismantled it as you see it. When the war ended and Austria was obliged to make peace with us, sentence of banishment
for life was passed on Albert; but that he retained some affection
for his country and his brother was shown by his sending his
daughter to me when she was ten years old, with a request that
she be cared for and nurtured in my family. Since then she has
been to me as a daughter; and while I have inured her to all our
mountain exercises, she has grown up not devoid of the higher
breeding that belongs to her rank. If she should make a worthy
choice of a husband, the state would doubtless assign her a large
dowry out of her father's possessions. Rudolph of Donnerhugel,
who would gladly marry her, is brave and highly esteemed, but
is violent of temper and more ambitious than I would desire for
my niece's companion through life. But I am fortunately released from care on that score, for my brother has lately written
asking me to send her to him at the court of the Duke of Burgundy."

At sunrise the next morning Arthur Philipson met Rudolph
of Donnerhugel in the court of the old castle and, though the
Swiss was armed with an immense two-handed sword, and the
Englishman with only his ordinary weapon, they fought on ap-

parently equal terms until the combat was interrupted by the coming of the Landamman and his guest.

"On your lives, forbear!" cried the Landamman. "Rudolph of Donnerhugel, give thy sword to me. Shame it is that it should be drawn on a helpless stranger. And you, young sir," he continued, addressing Arthur, whose father said: "Yield up your sword to the Landamman."

The result was that the two quarrelsome youths joined hands and promised to forget their feud. About ten days later the deputation commissioned to go to the court of Burgundy assembled at Geierstein. It consisted of five members, including the Landamman and Rudolph of Donnerhugel, who represented Berne, and was attended by a retinue of selected youths from various cantons, including Arnold's three eldest sons. All traveled on foot, their baggage being carried on sumpter-mules, led by boys. Two asses were provided for Anne of Geierstein and her Swiss attendant, who traveled in the rear. The young Englishman would fain have offered courtesies to the maiden, but he did not dare to bestow attentions that the customs of the country did not seem to permit. So he pursued the amusements that interested the others, and was obliged to content himself with an occasional view of Anne in the distance.

Meantime the elder Philipson, who seemed a man of much acquaintance with the world, in which he had evidently acted a part hardly in keeping with that he now sustained, had many serious talks with his companions, who freely discussed with him the policy of the cantons. The city cantons, aggrieved by taxes imposed on their commerce by the Duke of Burgundy, and privately instigated to take up arms by the largesses of Louis XI, were eager for war, but were restrained by news that Edward the Fourth of England had entered into an alliance, offensive and defensive, with the Duke. Edward, renowned for his victories over the rival House of Lancaster, had now turned his eyes to regaining the rich possessions in France that were lost under Henry VI, and was on the point of crossing with his army to Calais. The wisest policy of Charles of Burgundy would have been to avoid all cause of quarrel with the Helvetian Confederacy; but he was haughty, proud, and uncompromising, and despising what he termed the paltry associations of herdsmen and shepherds, omitted no opportunity of showing his contempt for them.   In the little castle and town of Ferette, near Bâle, which served as a thoroughfare to the traffic of Berne and Soleure, he posted a seneschal, Archibald von Hagenbach, one of the most lawless of the robber knights known to the frontiers. Though both the commercial towns of Germany and the Swiss League had complained of his arbitrary exactions and insolent treatment of merchants, the Duke treated all with contempt.

When the deputation approached La Ferette Arthur informed his father what he had learned in regard to the exactions of Von Hagenbach, and that he would unquestionably seize upon his baggage and merchandise, under pretext of levying dues for the Duke.   He also informed him that the Swiss youth, regarding him as under their protection, were determined to resist this exaction.

The elder Philipson, seeing that this would give the Duke a pretext for the war that Arnold Biederman was so anxious to avoid, at once determined to separate from the deputies and go on alone.   Notwithstanding the protestations of the Landamman, who complained that to leave them because danger approached was a poor compliment to their courage or constancy, the Englishman set out early the next morning for La Ferette.

Archibald von Hagenbach, when the two Philipsons were brought before him, engaged them in a long train of captious interrogatories concerning their business in Switzerland, their connection with the Landamman, and the cause of their traveling into Burgundy.   To all his questions the elder gave direct and plain answers, excepting to the last, declaring that his business with the Duke was of a private nature, and could be communicated to him alone.

Von Hagenbach foamed with rage when Philipson declined to tell him the contents of a packet addressed to the Duke of Burgundy, and ordered the two confined in separate dungeons. When they were removed he broke the seal of the packet and took out a small case of sandalwood containing a necklace of large diamonds, apparently of great value.   With it was a note commending the bearer to the Duke, and desiring him to give full credence to all the bearer should say in behalf of the one who sent it.

Arthur Philipson had resigned himself to death in his dungeon when he was aroused by the coming of a party with a torch, one of whom was clad in black like a monk and the other bore the form of Anne of Geierstein. The two raised him, and the woman, making him a sign to be silent, beckoned him to follow. At the top of the stair his conductress disappeared, and the monk led him into a room and bade him put on the gown and hood of a novice.

"Draw the cowl over thy face, and return no answer to any man who questions thee. I will say thou art under a vow."

The monk passed the sentinels and led him into a turret, with a stair leading to a sally-port, and dismissed him, saying:

"Hasten to meet the Swiss, who are advancing. Say to Rudolph of Donnerhugel that the priest of St. Paul's waits to bestow on him his blessing at the northern sally-port."

When the Landamman of Unterwalden and his little company appeared before the walls of La Ferette, they were admitted within the gate, but found their further progress opposed by a barricade across the street. Von Hagenbach had arranged this and had surrounded it by his soldiers, who had orders to attack whenever he shouted "Burgundy to the rescue." But when, after a stormy interview, in which he treated the Swiss envoys with the utmost insolence, he gave the signal, a loud shout arose in the rear and the youth of Bâle, admitted to the town by the citizens of La Ferette, burst over the barriers and attacked the soldiery in the rear. Taken by surprise, some threw themselves from the walls, and some fled where they could, pursued by the townsmen. Arnold Biederman, commanding his men to stand firm and to take no part in the fray, went with Arthur to release his father. They found his dungeon, but were some time in getting it open, and when they returned to the street they were just in time to see the head of Archibald von Hagenbach struck off by the executioner.

The two Philipsons, having recovered the diamond necklace, now procured horses and a guide and pursued their journey along the Rhine in search of the Duke of Burgundy, who was said to be in Lorraine, near Strasburg. Their guide, Brother Bartholomew, was a palmer said to be under a vow to travel for four years from one shrine to another. When they approached Hans's Ferry the guide persisted that it was their duty to stop at the chapel of Our Lady of the Ferry; and the elder Philipson, astonished at his pertinacity, was about to answer angrily when they were overtaken by three strangers on horseback. The foremost, a young woman elegantly attired and wearing a black vizard, rode close to Arthur in passing, and said in the accents of Anne of Geierstein:

"Do not start, but hear me. You are beset by dangers. On this road your lives are laid in wait for. Cross the river at the Ferry of the Chapel, to Kirchhoff. At the Golden Fleece you will find a guide to Strasburg."

But the elder Philipson decided that Arthur should take the diamond necklace and cross to Kirchhoff alone, while he himself should continue his journey on the other side of the Rhine. After taking leave of Arthur Philipson went to the chapel, when the door suddenly opened and the black priest of St. Paul's, whom he had seen that morning at La Ferette, came out. As soon as the guide saw him he folded his arms on his breast and stood with bowed head as if awaiting sentence of condemnation.

"Villain," said the priest, "dost thou lead a stranger into the house of the holy saints that thou mayst slay him and possess his spoils? Tell thy brother miscreants that the stranger is under *my* protection, which those who presume to violate will meet with the reward of Archibald von Hagenbach!"

Bartholomew stood motionless until the priest stopped, and then retreated at a hasty pace without replying. The priest explained that Bartholomew's avarice, awakened by the sight of the jewels, had induced him to act as guide, with the intention of detaining him until his party came up to rob him. The black priest then offered to conduct him to an inn where he might lodge in safety. There was something mysterious and gloomy about the priest which made the Englishman hesitate to accept his offer; but when he reflected how much he already owed him he courteously thanked him. As they rode along, side by side, Philipson noted that his companion's horse was more like a warrior's charger than the ambling palfrey of a priest, and that his manner of managing him was devoid of either awkwardness or timidity.

"We travel," said the priest, as they approached the village, "like two powerful enchanters, each conscious of his own high and secret purpose, and neither imparting to his companion the direction or purpose of his journey. But here is the inn. I have to visit a penitent in the village. Adieu for the present."

Philipson was very uncomfortable at the inn, and was denied any accommodation save that afforded by the general room; but when the black priest came in the evening and assumed the seat of honor at the board, the landlord became more courteous and, apologizing for his previous behavior, led him to a private apartment where he had a bed to himself. Wearied after a day of fatigue, Philipson went at once to bed, but before sleep had seized upon him he felt his bed descending, and a minute later he became conscious that he was in a large subterranean apartment. Before he could rise, his arms were pinioned, and he was presently surrounded by many persons in black robes with cowls drawn over their heads, each bearing a torch. At once it occurred to him that he was in presence of the Initiated or Judges of the Secret Tribunal of the Vehmegericht, and this thought gave him a clue to the character of the black priest of St. Paul's.

He was soon placed before an altar on which lay a cord and a dagger and was solemnly tried on a charge of entering the sacred territory under an assumed name and disguised profession, and of speaking at various times in terms of contempt of the Holy Tribunal. Philipson defended himself bravely against the accusations and was finally acquitted by vote, and after being warned against mentioning what he had seen and heard, on penalty of death, was restored to his room. He left the dangerous neighborhood the next morning and arrived at Strasburg without further accident.

At Strasburg Philipson met his son, and the two were recognized in the cathedral by Margaret of Anjou, the unfortunate Queen of Henry VI of England, as the Earl of Oxford and his son, Sir Arthur de Vere. Margaret, then living at Aix with her father, René of Provence, informed the Earl that Edward of York had crossed into France with a large army, but that the Duke of Burgundy had not yet decided to join him, being then engaged in overrunning Lorraine. Ferrand de Vaudemont, a youth who claimed Lorraine in right of his mother, Yolande of

Anjou, sister of Queen Margaret, had fled into Germany or Helvetia, being unable to withstand Charles.

"Let Burgundy beware of him," said the Earl, "for if he obtain allies among the hardy Swiss the Duke will find him a formidable enemy. We are strong only in Burgundy's strength, for my friends in England will not stir without men and money from the Duke. With a thousand Hainault lances I can soon be in the North; the Scotch and the West will rise—the Red Rose will raise its head once more—and so, God save King Henry!"

"Promise Burgundy everything to induce him to stir in our cause," said the Queen. "I know his inmost soul: he is set on extending his dominions. Tell him that my father René shall disown the opposition to the Duke's seizure of Lorraine, and that he will declare him his heir and cede Provence to him the moment his Hainaulters depart for England. René's wants are few. Mine are fewer. Revenge upon York, and a speedy grave. For the gold we need thou hast jewels to pledge. Let us part here, you for the Duke at Dijon, I to Aix. Farewell! we may meet in a better hour."

When the Earl of Oxford reached the camp of the Duke of Burgundy he found him meditating an alliance with Edward of England, his brother-in-law; but Oxford suggested the danger to himself of building up in France a power greater even than that of the French king, and proposed instead the plan of Margaret of Anjou, which would enable Burgundy to extend his dominions to the Mediterranean. The Duke acceded to this as the better for his interests, and promised to go in person with the Earl to the coast of Flanders to see to the embarkation of troops for England as soon as he could dispose of a gang of Swiss robbers, who had availed themselves of a mutiny of the burghers of La Ferette to seize on Archibald von Hagenbach, the commander, and put him to death in the market-place.

In vain did the Earl of Oxford explain the peaceable character of these men, with whom he had traveled, and declare that they were in no wise responsible for the execution of Von Hagenbach. The Duke would not listen, and informed Oxford that he had already given orders for their execution by hanging; and it was not until he had reminded Charles of their former companionship, and that he owed his life to him, who had been fortunate enough to rescue the Duke in the fight at Mont L'Héry, that he was induced to relinquish his purpose.

"Let them live, then," exclaimed the Duke. "We will hear to-morrow how they justify their proceedings toward us. But, my Lord of Oxford, we are now clear of obligation; you have obtained life for life. Pshaw! I am half choked. Soho! Bring me to drink!"

At their next interview the Duke showed the Earl of Oxford a scroll of parchment which he had found stuck to his toilet by a knife. It announced that judgment had been done on Von Hagenbach for tyranny, violence, and oppression, by order of the Holy Vehme, and that it was executed by their officials, who were responsible to their tribunal alone.

"A band of secret assassins!" exclaimed the Duke, "whom I will not permit to meet in my dominions. Could I but catch them they should know what the life of a nobleman is worth."

"For the sake of every saint in heaven," said the Earl, "forbear, my lord, to speak of these tremendous societies, whose creatures are above, beneath, and around us. Thou art surrounded by mercenaries—Germans, Italians, and other strangers. I—the friend of thy house—must needs tell thee that the Swiss hang like an avalanche over thy head, and the secret associations work beneath thee like the first throes of the coming earthquake. Provoke not the contest; a single word of defiance or a flash of indignant scorn may call their terrors into instant action."

It would have been well for the Duke of Burgundy if he had taken the advice of his English guest; but, firm in his own conceit, he rejected the proposals of the Swiss delegation and made war upon them. The result was what Oxford had foreseen: Charles was defeated with heavy loss at Granson and again more severely at Morat, where at least half his army was driven into the lake. The Duke retreated with his shattered forces into Upper Burgundy and gave himself up to despair. Gloomy and dispirited, he sulked in his tent, while his soldiery became an undisciplined mob, more dangerous to their friends than to their enemies.

When the Earl of Oxford heard of the plight of his old

friend he felt it to be his duty to go to his aid. Understanding his condition and temperament, he taunted him with acting like a laggard who lies rolling on the sands of the lists after being overcome. The Duke was furiously angry at first, but finally saw the justice of his remarks, took his advice and came out of his retirement. From this time all was activity in his court and army: money was collected, soldiers were levied and preparations made for a new campaign.

News having come that Ferrand, the young Duke of Lorraine, in command of the forces of the confederates, was advancing, the Duke of Burgundy moved forward to meet him. As the Earl of Oxford felt it incumbent upon himself and his son to bear arms in behalf of the Duke, he sent a letter to the Landamman, who was with the opposing forces, acquainting him of his decision and regretting its necessity. The pursuivant brought back a courteous letter from Arnold Biederman and a challenge for Arthur from Rudolph of Donnerhugel, who, desirous of settling their quarrel begun in the castle court at Geierstein, would send him word when a fair and equal meeting could be had on neutral ground.

A few days later, when Arthur, in command of a company of Stradiots, was doing scouting duty, he saw a body of cavalry advancing. Observing that the knight who appeared to be the leader bore on his shield the Bear of Berne, he felt that Rudolph of Donnerhugel was before him. He was sure of it when the cavalier halted his troop and advanced toward him alone with his lance in rest. Arthur accepted his challenge and rode to meet him, and the next moment the giant Swiss was hurled to the ground with Arthur's lance through his body.

Ferrand of Lorraine, who was present in person, ordered the successful knight to be made a prisoner, but said, when Arthur was brought before him:

"You are free, Sir Arthur of Oxford. Your father and you were faithful to my royal aunt Margaret, and I do justice to your fidelity. You, Sir Count, will, I think, see our captive placed in safety."

Arthur bowed and turned to go, accompanied by the person addressed.

"We have been fellow-travelers before, young man."

Arthur observed the vulture crest of Geierstein on his helmet, but when the knight opened his visor he showed the dark features of the priest of St. Paul's.

"Count Albert of Geierstein!" exclaimed Arthur.

"The same," replied the Count, "though thou hast seen him in other garb."

"My lord Count," said Arthur eagerly, "I cannot too soon entreat you to return. You are in peril. The Duke has placed a price on your head."

"I laugh at him. Hear me, young man. Thy lance has this day done an evil deed to Switzerland, to Berne, and Duke Ferrand, in slaying their bravest champion. But to me the death of Rudolph of Donnerhugel is welcome. Now mark me, Arthur de Vere! My daughter has told me of the passages betwixt you and her. Your sentiments and conduct are worthy of your house, which I well know ranks with the noblest in Europe. If your noble father gives his consent my daughter knows that she has my willing consent and my blessing. We are about to part. The time is short, the place dangerous—"

"And you, my lord, who have been the author of all this happiness, will you not be the witness and partaker of it?"

"Forbear such folly. My last scene is approaching. The Duke of Burgundy is sentenced to die, and the Secret and Invisible Judges have given the cord and the dagger to my hand."

When Arthur expostulated with him, he said: "Peace, foolish boy. The oath by which I am sworn is higher than that clouded sky. No, Arthur de Vere, I seek Charles with the resolved mind of one who, to take the life of an adversary, exposes himself to certain death. Say to Charles of Burgundy that he has wronged Albert of Geierstein and must die. Farewell!"

After the battle on the following day, in which the Swiss were again victorious, the bodies of the Duke of Burgundy and of Count Albert of Geierstein were found side by side.

COUNT ROBERT OF PARIS (1831)

This and the succeeding story, *Castle Dangerous*, constitute the fourth series of *Tales of My Landlord*, purporting to be told by the landlord of the Wallace Inn. They were written after Scott's health had broken under repeated shocks of paralysis and apoplexy, and are little more than shadows of his finer work. The scene is in Constantinople in the reign of the Emperor Alexius Comnenus (1081–1118), in the time of the First Crusade.

WHEN, in the First Crusade, the soldiers of the Cross, under Godfrey of Bouillon, reached Constantinople, they met with varied treatment from the Greek Emperor, Alexius Comnenus. While the more powerful chiefs were feasted by the wily Emperor with every delicacy, their followers at a distance were supplied with adulterated flour, tainted provisions, and bad water, so that they died in great numbers. Frequently, too, bodies of the invading hosts approaching the Greek capital by circuitous routes were cut to pieces by troops that passed, with the ignorant men of the West, as Turks, Scythians, or other infidels, and were sometimes actually such, but were in the service of the Grecian monarch. These aggressions did not pass without complaint, and on more than one occasion the two parties were on the eve of open war.

But Godfrey, Raymond of Tholouse, and other leaders, considered that their expedition would be stained with scandal if their first exploit should be a war on the Greek Empire, which might justly be called the barrier of Christendom, and which it was their duty and interest to protect. Besides, they had exaggerated ideas of the wealth of the Empire and needed the help of Alexius in crossing the Bosporus. These and other considerations induced the chiefs to consent, before crossing into Asia, to acknowledge the Greek Emperor, originally lord paramount of all these regions, as their liege lord and suzerain. Alexius

159

seized with eagerness on the admission of Godfrey and his com-
peers that the Emperor was entitled to the allegiance of all who
should war on Palestine, and resolved to make the ceremony
public and to invest it with such a display of imperial pomp and
magnificence as to make it forever memorable.

On an extensive terrace, overlooking the Propontis, was
placed an elevated throne for the use of the Emperor only, the
Greeks thus endeavoring to secure a point of ceremony dear to
their vanity, that none but he should be seated. Around the
throne of Alexius were ranged in order, but standing, the dig-
nitaries of his splendid court, from the Cæsar to the Patriarch,
in magnificent costumes and robes, and behind them, sheathed
in mail and plate, in concentric lines, the Varangians or Imperial Guard, formed of exiled Anglo-Saxons in the imperial
service. Beyond them, in still greater numbers, were bands of
Greeks or Romans, another branch of the guards, in lofty crests
and splendid apparel, called Immortals, a title borrowed from
the Persians.

In front of this exalted throne passed the Crusaders, or the
Counts, as they were called by the Greeks—that being the most
common title among them—each bending the knee to Alexius
and placing the hands in his, according to the ceremony of
feudal fealty. By some this homage was rendered with every
appearance of gravity, but by others in mockery. Among these
latter were the nobles of Frankish origin, remarkable for their
contempt of every other nation engaged in the Crusade, who
regarded with scorn the assumption of authority by the Greek
Emperor. The Emperor struggled with feelings of offended
pride, tempered by a prudent degree of apprehension, as these
haughty counts filed past; but when Bohemond of Antioch
approached, desirous to show special honor to this wily person,
who had once been his enemy, Alexius arose and advanced several paces to greet him.

This deference to Bohemond exposed Alexius to a cutting
affront, which nearly led to trouble. Following Bohemond
came Count Robert of Paris, who rode up attended by a half
score of horsemen. Without waiting for the Emperor, Count
Robert sprang from his horse and, seating himself on the vacant
throne, began indolently to caress a large wolf-hound that had

followed him, which stretched its form with as much ease as its master on the carpets of silk and damask that tapestried the imperial footstool.

The Varangians would have avenged the insult on the instant if they had not been restrained by their commander, Achilles Tatius, who was uncertain what the Emperor would do. Meanwhile Count Robert spoke aloud in French:

"What churl is this," he asked, "who has remained sitting when so many noble knights stand uncovered around among the thrice-conquered Varangians?"

"If the Normans desire battle of the Varangians," replied a clear, deep voice, "they will meet them in the lists man to man, without the poor boast of insulting the Emperor of Greece."

Bohemond, fearing trouble, ran quickly and, catching the crusader by the arm, obliged him to leave the Emperor's seat.

"How is it, noble Count of Paris?" said Bohemond. "Is there one who can see with patience your name quoted in an idle brawl with hirelings? For shame! Do not, for the discredit of Norman chivalry, let it be so!"

"I am not nice," said the crusader, rising reluctantly, "in choosing the degree of my adversary, when he bears himself like one willing and forward in battle. Turk or Tartar, or wandering Anglo-Saxon, who escapes the chain of the Norman only to become the slave of the Greek, is equally welcome to whet his blade against my armor."

The Emperor, who with fear and indignation had heard all, instantly resolved to let the insult pass as one of the rough pleasantries of the Franks.

"What is the name of that singular and assuming man?" asked the Emperor.

"It is Robert Count of Paris," answered Baldwin, "one of the bravest peers around the throne of France."

Alexius Comnenus, fearing some new cause of quarrel, ordered the ceremonial of the day discontinued and invited the leaders to return to the various palaces where they had been hospitably entertained.

Count Robert, laughing at the threatened displeasure of the Emperor, and seeming to think there would be a peculiar pleasure in braving Alexius at his own board, set out for Constantinople with Brenhilda, his Countess. The Countess of Paris was one of those stalwart dames whom the writers of romance delighted to paint, who despised the pursuits of her sex and donned arms and armor in the lists. While most of the gallants who met her in the games of chivalry flinched from doing so handsome a woman an injury, and had permitted her to win many a victory, Count Robert of Paris adopted different tactics and unhorsed and unhelmed her. This led to mutual esteem, and soon afterward the two were wedded and set out on the Crusade.

Count Robert had sent his horses aboard ship to cross the Bosporus, therefore he and his Countess, attended only by a squire and a maid, were on their way to the city on foot. Oppressed by the heat and the dust of the main road, they turned into a bypath that led amid trees and fountains, where they met with an old man of venerable aspect, who kindly asked them whether they had missed their way. He proved to be the cynic philosopher Agelastes, who invited them to accept the hospitality of his house, not far distant. Though a pathway partly hidden by vegetation the old man led them up a few broad, marble steps to a velvety lawn in front of a kiosk or temple, the back part of which overhung a cataract. At a signal from Agelastes the door was opened by an African slave, Diogenes, and the party entered into an outer hall, whose chairs and couches were covered simply with Eastern woven mats. But on the touching of a spring an interior apartment was displayed, with furniture and hangings of straw-colored silk from the looms of Persia. Preparations were made here for an entertainment in the manner of the ancient Romans, couches being laid beside a table ready decked, on which the male guests at least were expected to recline, while seats, placed among the couches, showed that women were expected, who would observe the Greek custom of eating while seated.

Strains of music and the peal of a trumpet having drawn Agelastes to the door, the Count and the Countess followed and were in time to see their host prostrate himself before a huge beast which was unknown to them. The elephant, on whose back was a splendid palanquin bearing the Empress Irene and her daughter Anna Comnena, was attended by a gallant body of light horse in splendid armor, commanded by the Cæsar, Nicephorus Briennius, the husband of Anna Comnena.

Agelastes, sensible of the necessity of introducing his guests, spoke of them to his imperial visitors as of the great host from the west who had come to enjoy the countenance of Alexius Comnenus and to aid him in expelling the paynims from the bounds of the sacred empire, and garrison those regions as vassals of his Imperial Majesty.

"Madam," said Count Robert, displeased at the words of Agelastes, "we neither owe Alexius fealty nor had we the purpose of paying him any when we took the vow that brought us to Asia. The wisest and most prudent among us have judged it necessary to acknowledge the Emperor's authority, since there was no such safe way to the discharge of our vow as that of acknowledging fealty to him. We, though independent of any earthly king, do not pretend to be greater men than they, and therefore have condescended to pay the same homage."

The Empress colored several times with indignation in the course of this speech, but, as she had received instructions from her imperial spouse to beware how she gave or took offense, made a graceful reverence, as if she hardly understood what the Count had explained so bluntly. While Count Robert and his lady were objects of curiosity to the Empress and her daughter, who thought they never had seen finer specimens of human strength and beauty, the Cæsar, Nicephorus, kept his eyes steadily on the Frankish Countess when he could do so without attracting the attention of his wife and mother-in-law. When the Empress Irene seated herself at the head of the table, her daughter took the arm of Count Robert and led him to a seat beside herself, explaining that her husband would attend the Countess.

The feast, so far as the western guests were concerned, was finished with a celerity which surprised the host as well as his imperial visitors. Count Robert and his spouse soon rose from the table, and Agelastes and his imperial guests were under the necessity of either permitting them to depart alone or of accompanying them to the city. They concluded to waive the etiquette of rank and to take their departure on the motion of their wilful guests, though the officers and their troops were thus moved from their repast at least two hours earlier than usual.

On the journey to the city Nicephorus took his place on the elephant beside the Queen; but Anna Comnena preferred to ride with the strangers, who were provided with horses. Desirous of complimenting the Count, she took the opportunity to praise the Normans so extravagantly that Count Robert felt it incumbent on himself to explain that, though sometimes so named, he and his followers were not Normans, but Franks.

The Princess, whose vanity was touched by being detected in an error, explained that she had had her information from a false slave, who probably knew not what he was saying.

"Call Hereward hither," she said to an officer—"yonder tall man with the battle-ax on his shoulder."

Hereward made his military obeisance with a look of sternness as his glance rested on the proud Frank beside Anna Comnena.

"Did I not understand thee, fellow," said Anna Comnena, "to inform me that the Normans and the Franks were the same people and enemies to thy race?"

"The Normans are our mortal enemies, lady," answered Hereward. "The Franks are subjects of the same lord-paramount, and therefore neither love the Varangians nor are beloved by them."

"Good fellow," said the Count, "you do the Franks wrong and ascribe to the Varangians, who have ceased to exist as a nation, an undue degree of importance."

"I am no stranger," replied Hereward, "to the pride of your heart, or the precedence you assume over those less fortunate in war than yourselves. But there is no prospect to which the Varangians would look forward with more pleasure than that a hundred of their number should meet in a fair field either the oppressive Normans or the vain Frenchmen, and let God be the judge which is most worthy of the victory."

"You take an insolent advantage of your chance," said the Count, "to brave a nobleman."

"It is my sorrow and shame," replied the Varangian, "that there is a chain around me which forbids me to say: 'Slay me, or I'll kill thee, before we part from this spot.'"

"Thou foolish and hot-brained churl," said the Count, "thou

art mad, or hast drained the ale-cup so deeply thou knowest not what thou sayest."

"Thou liest," said the Varangian.

The Frenchman made a motion toward his sword, but paused and said with dignity: "Thou canst not offend me."

"But thou hast offended me in a matter that can be atoned only by thy manhood. Thou hast this day put a mortal affront on a great prince whom thy master calls his ally, and by whom thou hast been received with every rite of hospitality; and this dishonor thou hast done to him in the face of his own chiefs and princes and the nobles from every court in Europe. I therefore tell thee, Sir Knight, or Count, there is mortal quarrel between thee and the Varangian Guard until thou hast fought it out in fair and manly battle, body to body."

As all this passed in the French language, the Princess, suspecting its import, said: "I trust you feel that poor man too far beneath you to admit of your meeting him in what is termed knightly battle?"

"The Varangian," replied the Count, "is a brave man and a strong one. It is contrary to my vow to shun his challenge. Perhaps I shall derogate from my rank by accepting it; but he is yet to be born who has seen Robert of Paris shun the face of mortal man."

When the Blacquernal Palace was reached, Count Robert would have bidden adieu to the Princess, to seek his quarters of the night before; but Anna Comnena would not listen to it, and insisted that he and his Countess should become her guests. When Alexius Comnenus heard of this, he summoned Agelastes and consulted with him as to the possibility of holding the Count and his wife as hostages, or of winning them as allies. The philosopher told the Emperor that they were not to be won by gold, which they esteemed but as yellow dross, but were avid of fame to be won by the overcoming of difficulties and dangers.

"Trust me with the matter," said Agelastes, "but entrust me with the signet, which will give me the command of thy dens of wild beasts."

"You make me wonder," said the Emperor, handing him the signet, "by what charm you will subdue these untamed savages."

"By the power of falsehood," replied Agelastes, with deep reverence.

"I believe you are adept in that," said Alexius, as the philosopher left the presence. "The ungrateful Cæsar, the boastful coward Achilles Tatius, and the bosom serpent Agelastes shall know whether Alexius Comnenus has been born their dupe. When Greek meets Greek, comes the strife of subtlety, as well as the tug of war."

When Count Robert awoke the next morning at a time when it seemed to him that daylight should stream into his window, the darkness was almost palpable. As he gazed eagerly around, he discerned nothing but two balls of red light, which shone with a self-emitted brilliance, like the glaring eyes of a wild animal. The Count started up with the intention of putting on his armor, but the instant he stirred, a deep growl rang through the room, mingled with the clash of chains and the springing toward his bedside of a great monster, prevented by some fastening from reaching its bound. The roars now came thick and fast, and must have resounded through the palace. The Count heard the breathing of the beast, and even thought he could feel the heat of its respiration. While he was a brave man, he was not altogether unappalled by a sense of danger so unexpected; "but come death when it will," he thought, "it shall never be said that Count Robert was heard to receive it with prayers for compassion or with cries of pain or terror."

Just then he bethought him of a flint and match that he usually carried, and with as little noise as possible he lighted a torch by the bedside, at the same moment springing out of bed. The tiger, terrified by the flame, leaped backward, and Count Robert, seizing a massive wooden stool, hurled it at the blazing eyes with such force as to fracture the skull of the beast, whose dying agonies he hastened with his dagger.

By the light of his flambeau he saw that he was in a bare dungeon-like cell, very different from the room in which he had gone to bed overnight, and he came to the conclusion that the wine he had drunk at the banquet the evening before had been drugged. But the thought that troubled him most was concerning the fate of Brenhilda. His confidence in her fidelity and his trust in her uncommon strength and activity were his greatest comforts. "Heaven will not abandon its own," he thought.

While he was thus meditating, a strong light streamed down from a trap door that had been opened above, and he heard these words in Anglo-Saxon: "Leap, sirrah; come, no delay; leap, my good Sylvan."

Something of great size, in the form of a human being, jumped down from the trap. It was more than seven feet high, but it alighted with perfect safety, rebounding from the floor so as almost to touch the roof. The orang-utan, for such it was, bore a torch in its left hand, with the light of which it explored every corner until it came to the dead body of the tiger, and then, as if conscious that someone must have slain it, began searching for the slayer. When it encountered Count Robert it sprang backward with an instinctive cry of terror, and then advanced on tiptoe, holding the torch forward to examine its adversary.

Count Robert seized a fragment of the bedstead and struck the animal a blow that felled it, and drawing his dagger, as he kneeled upon its body, was about to kill it. But the huge animal seized the dagger, cutting its paws so severely that it covered its eyes with its unwounded hand, and set up a melancholy cry so human that the knight took compassion on it. The creature appeared sensible of the clemency, and moaned and wept, and when Count Robert applied some balsam to its wound and bound it up, it stooped and embraced his knees as if to swear eternal gratitude and fidelity.

In about an hour the same voice called from above through the trap: "Sylvan—Sylvan, where loiterest thou? Come instantly, or thou shalt aby thy sloth. Come, thou lazy rascal, thou shalt have the ladder to ascend by. Come, and for once I will spare the whip."

Count Robert, by showing his dagger, obliged the animal to keep quiet, and the warder at last descended the ladder to find out the reason of its silence. But he had no sooner reached the floor than he was seized by Count Robert from behind. The fellow cried: "Treason—treason! Help! Ho there—Varangian—Hereward!"

Before he could say more Count Robert plunged his dagger

into his throat, and both fell heavily, the jailer undermost. While they were struggling Hereward ran down the ladder and seized the Count with the same advantage that the latter had over his opponent. He was about to stab him when his arm was held with a vigor that turned him around, giving the French knight an opportunity to spring to his feet, while the orang-utan fled up the ladder.

As the two strong and courageous men stood facing each other, each armed with a dagger, the Varangian said:

"Are you not the bold Frank who was yesternight imprisoned here with a tiger?"

"I am," answered the Count.

"Where is the tiger?" asked Hereward.

"He lies yonder," said the Count, pointing to the body.

"And thou hast slain my comrade? With your patience, I will examine his wound."

After examining the man by means of his dark lantern, Hereward said to the Count:

"This is no place to fight as becomes the champions of two nations. Let us postpone our dispute until we effect your deliverance from these dungeons. If a poor Varangian should be of service to you in this matter, would you refuse to meet him in fair fight?"

"If," said Count Robert, "thou wilt extend thy assistance to my wife, who is also imprisoned somewhere in this inhospitable palace, be assured that, whatever be thy rank, country, or condition, Robert of Paris will, at thy choice, proffer thee his right hand in friendship, or raise it against thee in fair and manly battle; and this I vow by the soul of Charlemagne, my ancestor."

Chance having thus brought about a temporary alliance between these two men, who resembled each other in disposition more closely than either would like to admit, Hereward conducted Count Robert through the intricacies of the subterranean apartments and to the gardens of Agelastes, where, by order of the Cæsar, the Countess had been sent. The two hid in the shrubbery surrounding a pavilion and overheard a conversation between Briennius and the Countess. The Cæsar informed her that, though he did not know the fate of Count Robert, he had probably been made to expiate his affront to the Emperor;

and that she had better consider him as no more, but choose a better protector. When she exclaimed that no better knight existed in all the world, the Cæsar assumed a martial attitude and said: "This hand should decide that question, were the man thou thinkest of still on the earth and at liberty."

"Observe what I am about to say," replied Brenhilda, the fire of indignation flashing from every feature: "Robert of Paris is gone, or captive, I know not where. He cannot fight the match thou desirest, but here stands Brenhilda of Aspramonte, wedded wife of the good Count of Paris. She never was matched in the lists save by the Count, and since thou art so grieved that thou canst not meet him in battle, thou canst not object if she is willing to meet thee in his stead?"

"Do you propose, madam, to hold the lists against me?" said the Cæsar in surprise.

"Against you and all the Grecian Empire, if they shall affirm that Robert of Paris is lawfully confined."

"And the vanquished shall then be at the pleasure of the conqueror, for good or evil?"

"I do not refuse the hazard," said the Countess; "only that, if the other champion shall bite the dust, Count Robert shall be set at liberty, and allowed to depart with all suitable honors."

"This I refuse not," said the Cæsar, "if it be in my power."

Hereward now took Count Robert to his quarters and concealed him in the room of his squire; and, to avoid suspicion, sought Achilles Tatius to inform him of the escape of the prisoner. He found his commander in the gardens of Agelastes and received orders from him to search for the Count and secure him in the strong rooms in the barracks, until he could make him friendly to his schemes by restoring his wife to him.

As Hereward was leaving he heard screams, and hastening toward the sounds received in his arms a woman terrified at the sight of Sylvan, who, escaped from confinement, was enjoying his freedom in the wood. It proved to be Agatha, the maid of the Countess of Paris, but, to his astonishment and delight, Hereward recognized in her comely features Bertha, the Saxon maiden to whom he had plighted his troth years before in Devonshire.

Hereward learned from Bertha that she was on her way to

find some of the chiefs of the Crusade, to inform them of the peril of the Countess and to ask their aid. But he told her to return to the Countess and tell her to appear boldly in the lists on the appointed day; that when the trumpet should sound thrice her own noble lord should appear to do battle in her stead, and if he should fail Hereward himself would do battle in his place, to requite the Countess's kindness to his betrothed.

"Will you, indeed?" said the damsel. "That was spoken like the son of Waltheoff. I will home and comfort my mistress; but you hint that the Count is here—she will inquire about that."

"She must be satisfied to know," said Hereward, "that he is under the guidance of a friend who will endeavor to protect him from his own extravagances and follies."

The Emperor Alexius was an astute prince and had kept himself well informed in regard to the actions of the conspirators against his authority, well knowing that his own son-in-law, the Cæsar, the philosopher Agelastes, and the commander of the Varangians were deeply implicated. While keeping a wary eye on these, he took into his confidence Hereward the Varangian, in whom he imposed full trust, telling him that he should succeed Tatius and hinting that even a higher dignity might be in store for him. But Hereward declined all preferment and declared that his sole ambition was to be able to return to his island home when he had served the Emperor as far as he was able.

In the mean while Agelastes, who had entered into the conspiracy against the Emperor ostensibly in aid of the pretensions of Briennius, but really in hope of securing the throne for himself, with Anna Comnena for his Empress, was suddenly removed from the scene of his activities by the orang-utan Sylvan, which throttled him in his own house, in the presence of the Countess of Paris. Achilles Tatius, who did not know of the death of his confederate, looked in vain for Agelastes when the day of the combat between the Cæsar and the Count of Paris arrived, the name of Count Robert having been substituted for that of the Countess in the proclamations. Nor did he know that Briennius had been arrested and condemned to death, but pardoned by Alexius on the very way to execution.

When he arrived at the lists he saw much, too, to disquiet him; for the Imperial Guards were in greater force than usual, and those about the person of the Emperor were other than those he had selected.

As the combat was an international affair, the Crusaders had been asked to send representatives to see that fair play was accorded to their champion, and Tancred, the Prince of Otranto, had accordingly come attended by a body of knights. The Emperor, who thought he had securely provided against the appearance in the lists of either of the parties, and had actually prepared an exhibition of another sort, in which wild animals were to contend with each other, was astonished and confused when, at the last note of the trumpet, Count Robert of Paris stood forth, armed *cap-à-pie*, with his mailed charger led behind him, ready to mount. Alarm and shame were visible on every face around the imperial presence when no Cæsar appeared to meet him; but hardly had the name and title of Count Robert been announced when one of the Varangian Guards sprang into the lists and announced that he was ready to do battle in the name and place of the Cæsar Nicephorus Briennius, and for the honor of the Empire.

Prince Tancred at once interposed, saying that the lists were open only to knights and nobles.

"Let Count Robert of Paris look upon my countenance," said the Varangian, "and say whether he has not agreed to waive all objection to our contest founded on inequality of condition."

Count Robert acknowledged that he held himself bound by his solemn word to give Hereward a meeting in the open field, though he regretted, in consideration of his eminent virtues and the high services he had received at his hands, that they should now stand upon terms of such bloody arbitration. He admitted, too, that the combat should take place on foot and with battle-axes.

"Let us then lose no more time," said Hereward.

"I am ready," said Count Robert, taking a weapon from the hand of a Varangian and putting himself on the alert.

The first blows were given and parried with great caution, the strength and agility of the two being about equally matched, but when they became heated and strokes came thick and fast accident seemed to favor Count Robert, and the Varangian reeled. The Count was about to follow up his success, when a woman's voice reached his ear:

"Count Robert of Paris, forget not that thou owest a life to Heaven and to me!"

"I acknowledge my debt," said the Count, "alike to Bertha of Britain and to the Almighty. You have seen the fight," he continued, turning to Tancred and his chivalry, "and can testify that it was maintained fairly on both sides."

The Emperor gladly embraced the opportunity and threw down his warder in signal that the duel was ended. Strongly affected by the gratitude he felt was due to Hereward for thus upholding the imperial honor, he said:

"Speak to me, my soldier, and tell me in what manner I can best reward thee for so manfully defending the honor of the country."

"My lord," answered Hereward, "your Imperial Highness values my poor services overhighly, and ought to attribute them to the noble Count of Paris, first for his condescending to accept of an antagonist so mean in quality as I; and next in generously relinquishing victory when he might have achieved it by another blow. But the boon I have to ask is not from your Imperial Highness, but from my noble antagonist."

"And has reference to Bertha?" asked the Count.

"Even so," said Hereward. "I ask for my discharge from the Varangian Guard, and permission to share in your lordship's pious vow for the recovery of Palestine, with liberty to fight under your honorable banner and permission to recommend my love-suit to Bertha, the attendant of the Countess of Paris, and that I may finally hope to be restored to my own country, which I never have ceased to love over the rest of the world."

"Thy service, noble soldier," replied the Count, "shall be as acceptable to me as that of a born earl; I will gladly prefer thee to what honor I can, and will strain what interest I have with the King of England to settle thee in thine own native country."

"Bear witness, heaven and earth," said the Emperor, "that we would rather have lost the brightest jewel from our imperial crown than the services of this true and faithful Anglo-Saxon. But since we must, it shall be our study to distinguish him by such marks of beneficence as to make it known that the Emperor Alexius acknowledges a debt to him larger than his Empire can discharge."

CASTLE DANGEROUS (1831)

This story constituted, with *Count Robert of Paris*, the fourth and last series of *Tales of My Landlord*. The scene is in Lanarkshire, Scotland, in and around Castle Douglas, near the town of Douglas, and the time is the beginning of the fourteenth century, when Robert Bruce was battling against the power of Edward I of England. The Sir James Douglas of the narrative is the knight who bore the heart of Bruce to the Holy Land, and who fell in 1330 (on his return from Jerusalem) in Spain while assisting the King of Arragon in an expedition against the Moors. The remains of his once splendid monument, mutilated, it is said, by Cromwell's troops, are still to be seen in the kirk of St. Bride, Douglas.

WO travelers were riding near sunset through the moorlands of Lanark on their way to Douglas Castle. The elder, who was well and even showily dressed, was evidently a minstrel, for he bore on his back a case containing a harp or viol. His doublet was blue, his hose violet with slashes showing a lining of the same color; and his bonnet was parti-colored, of different stripes of blue and violet, with a plume also of the same colors. As it was war time he would have been justified in riding well armed, but his only visible weapon was a small crooked sword.

The younger traveler appeared to be a gentle boy in early youth, whose Sclavonic gown, the appropriate dress of a pilgrim, was worn more closely drawn about him than the coolness of the weather seemed to require.

"Bertram, my friend," said the younger of the two, "how far are we still from Douglas Castle? We have already come more than the twenty miles from Cammock—or how didst thou call the hostelry we left at daybreak?"

"Cumnock, my dearest lady—I beg ten thousand excuses— my gracious young lord." His air was deferential, as one of inferior rank would address a superior, yet showed, in tone and gesture, something of interest and affection.

"Call me Augustine," replied his comrade, "if you mean to speak as is fittest for the time."

"If your ladyship can condescend to lay aside your quality, and is pleased to command me to treat you as my own son, shame it were to me if I were not to show you the affection of a father, especially since I have served your house of Berkely as minstrel for twenty years."

"How far is it yet to Castle Douglas?" asked the lady.

"It is still three good miles away."

"What are we then to do? Will not the castle gates be locked before we can get there?"

"For that I will pledge my word," answered Bertram. "The gates of Douglas, under the keeping of Sir John de Walton, do not open easily. If your ladyship will take my advice you will turn southward again, where men's wants are provided for, and the secret of this journey shall never be known to living mortal but ourselves."

"I thank thee for thy advice, honest Bertram, but I cannot profit by it. I have come thus far to see Douglas Castle and I mean to accomplish it. If thou knowest any decent house, rich or poor, I would willingly take quarters there for the night."

"We are not far from the house of Tom Dickson of Hazelside, an honest fellow who may be trusted as any knight or gentleman of the land. What is your pleasure?"

The lady of Berkely, who was thoroughly wearied, announced her desire of accepting Dickson's hospitality, but when the farm was reached, it was found to be in the possession of men-at-arms who were holding it as an outpost of Castle Douglas. Dickson excused the coolness of his welcome on account of the presence of these unwelcome guests, but agreed to give Bertram's son Augustine, whom the minstrel described as just recovering from an attack of the disease called the black death, then prevalent in England, a quiet bed for the night in an airy room.

When Augustine had been thus disposed of, an archer, who seemed to be in charge, in the absence of the commander of the post, questioned Dickson closely in regard to his guests, and when he learned that the youth was recovering from the English disorder he at once declared that one so lately attacked by a

contagious disease could not be permitted to pass into a garrison
of a thousand men.   Soon after this the commander of the post,
Sir Aymer de Valence, arrived.   He also questioned the minstrel
in regard to his business at the castle, and agreed that it would
be dangerous to permit Bertram's son to go thither.   But he
consented that Bertram himself should go with him in the morning, and suggested that the youth should remain in the convent
hard by until Sir John de Walton should express his pleasure
on the subject.   Bertram, overjoyed that Sir Aymer did not demand to see Augustine, acceded willingly to this, and Augustine,
who saw that it would be useless to object, removed the next
morning to the Abbey of St. Bride.

The Castle of Douglas, situated not far from the borders of
England and Scotland, had long been the subject of contention
between the two nations.   It had been entrusted by King Edward I to different officers after the coronation of Robert Bruce
in 1306, but had twice been wrested from him through the
efforts of Sir James Douglas, who claimed it as his patrimony.
At the time of this story it was held by Sir John de Walton, a
valiant knight, under the assurance that if he should keep it
safe from the Scottish power for a year and a day he should
obtain the barony of Douglas, with its extensive appendages,
in free property as his reward; while, if he should suffer the
fortress to be taken within this space, either by guile or by open
force, he should become liable to dishonor as a knight and to
attainder as a subject.   Sir John de Walton also bound himself
voluntarily to surrender all hope of obtaining his mistress's
favor if he failed to hold for the time named the Castle Douglas,
which had won, from the mischances of its previous commanders, the name of Castle Dangerous or Perilous.

Bertram, the minstrel, who rode to the castle with Sir Aymer
de Valence on the following morning, discussed with the knight
various stories he had heard concerning the fortress and its
former inmates, and, declaring that he looked upon it in some
degree as a fated place, said he longed to see what changes time
had made in it during the twenty years that had passed since
his last visit.   But, above all, his present visit was induced by
his desire to secure, if possible, a volume written by the famous
rhymer Thomas of Ercildoun, containing a fund of forgotten

minstrelsy and of prophecies concerning the fate of the British kingdom.

Sir Aymer, who was second to Sir John de Walton in command, listened with pleasure to Bertram's discourse, and said: "I think, sir minstrel, that I have power enough in this garrison to bid you welcome, and Sir John de Walton, I hope, will not refuse access to hall, castle, or knight's bower to a person of your profession, by whose conversation we shall profit somewhat. I cannot, however, lead you to expect such indulgence for your son, considering the state of his health; but he can remain unmolested at the convent of Saint Bride until you are disposed to set forward on your journey."

But when they reached the castle, old Gilbert Greenleaf, the archer, one of the sentinels, looked hard at the minstrel and reminded Sir Aymer of the strict orders of watch, and declared he durst not admit Solomon King of Israel if he came as a strolling minstrel, without the authority of Sir John de Walton. He hoped Sir Aymer would not take offense if he should detain his guest in the guard-room until Sir John should return from a ride to the outposts.

Sir Aymer replied that it was saucy in him to suppose that his commands could have anything contradictory to those of Sir John de Walton, but told him to report to the commander on his arrival that the minstrel was admitted by his invitation.

After the knight had left Bertram in the guard-room, he began to think that possibly he had done wrong in bringing a stranger thus into the castle, and that his action might not have the approbation of Sir John de Walton. He was a young knight, who had only lately won his spurs, and had been placed by his uncle, the Earl of Pembroke, in Sir John's charge to learn the duties of military service. Somewhat troubled in mind, he returned to the guard-room and informed Bertram that the permission he had given him to enter the castle must be sanctioned by Sir John de Walton.

When Sir John returned and heard Gilbert Greenleaf's report, he was troubled in mind. Common report had exaggerated the military skill and the variety of enterprise ascribed to James, the young Lord of Douglas. In the opinion of the soldiers of the garrison he had the faculties of a fiend rather than those of a mortal, and his appearance was looked for at almost any time and in any guise. The variety of his devices and the frequency of their recurrence kept Sir John de Walton's anxiety so perpetually on the stretch that at no time did he think himself out of the Black Douglas's reach any more than a good Christian supposes himself out of reach of the wiles of the devil. Sir John therefore suspected in the coming of Bertram another device of the Douglas, and in his conversation with the archer made some remarks not altogether complimentary to Fabian, the squire of Sir Aymer, whom he considered too young to be the assistant of one so inexperienced.

The conversation was overheard by Fabian, who carried it with additions to Sir Aymer, and thus began a misunderstanding between the two knights, which developed into a coolness, and finally into a disagreement which threatened to end their friendship. After considerable friction between them, Sir Aymer thought himself under the necessity of writing to his uncle, the Earl of Pembroke, stating that his superior, Sir John de Walton, had unfortunately taken some degree of prejudice against him, and asked that his place of service should be changed. But Pembroke, a rigid old warrior, who entertained the most partial opinion of Sir John de Walton, was indignant to find that his nephew, whom he considered as a mere boy elated by winning knighthood at an age unusually early, reminded him that the study of chivalry consisted in the faithful and patient discharge of military service and denied his request. This did not mend matters between Sir John and his lieutenant, and their intercourse was soon limited to a cold and stiff degree of official formality.

When Bertram had been an inmate of the castle several days, Sir John asked Sir Aymer if he did not think a week long enough to express the hospitality due to a minstrel.

Sir Aymer declared that he had no interest in the minstrel's movements. "But," he added, "if you hold the presence of a wandering old man and the neighborhood of a sick boy dangerous to the castle under your charge, you will, no doubt, do well to dismiss them."

"Pardon me," said De Walton; "the minstrel came here as one of your retinue, and I could not, in courtesy, send him away without your leave."

"I am sorry, then," answered Sir Aymer, "you did not mention your purpose sooner. I would not ask to have the residence in this castle of any servant or dependent of mine prolonged a moment beyond your pleasure."

"Then I will go straight to my point, and use the ordinary precautions I should employ in Normandy or Gascoigne. What ho! page! Send hither Greenleaf the archer."

Sir John questioned the old archer concerning what he knew or had heard about the minstrel, but Greenleaf knew very little, though he expressed the opinion, as an old soldier, that it was not safe to permit a stroller, whether of English or of Scottish birth, to lounge about the castle and communicate everything passing within to a son who lay at St. Bride's under pretense of illness.

"How do you say?" exclaimed the governor. "Is he not then really indisposed?"

"He may be sick to the death for aught I know," said the archer; "but if so would it not be more natural that the father should attend the son's sick-bed than range about this castle?"

"Thou hast convinced me, Gilbert Greenleaf, and I will look into this man's business. Get two or three of thy comrades and follow me. Keep out of sight, but within hearing. It may be necessary to arrest this man."

Sir John de Walton found Bertram in a small room called the study, where he was seated at a table copying from an old manuscript volume. After some preliminary conversation, he propounded three questions: whether Bertram was his real name, whether he had any other profession than that of a minstrel, and whether he had any connection with any Englishman or Scottishman beyond the walls of Douglas Castle?

"To these questions," replied the minstrel, "I have already answered the worshipful knight, Sir Aymer de Valence, and having satisfied him, it is not, I conceive, necessary that I should undergo a second examination."

"Will you answer the inquiries which it is my duty to make, or am I to enforce obedience?"

He clapped his hands and two or three archers appeared, attired only in their shirts and hose. But Bertram only protested that he would not be held liable for any words he might utter under torture.

"Hark you, sir," said De Walton; "I will for the present consign you to a place of confinement suitable to one suspected of being a spy. In the mean time I will myself ride to the Abbey of Saint Bride, and satisfy myself whether the young person you would pass as your son is possessed of the same determination which you yourself seem to assert."

With this he gave orders to Greenleaf concerning his prisoner and turned to go, when the voice of the old man was heard calling on him to return a moment.

"What hast thou to say, sir?" asked De Walton.

"I advise thee," said the minstrel, "for thine own sake, to beware how thou dost insist on thy present purpose, by which thou thyself alone, of all men living, will most severely suffer. If thou harmest a hair of that young man's head—nay, if thou permittest him to undergo any privation which it is in thy power to prevent—thou wilt prepare for thine own suffering a degree of agony more acute than anything else in this mortal world could cause thee. It is my interest, as well as thine, to secure thee in the safe possession of this castle; but there are some things I know respecting it I am not at liberty to tell without the consent of that youth. Bring me but a note under his hand, consenting to my taking thee into our mystery, and, believe me, thou wilt soon see the clouds charmed away."

He spoke with so much earnestness that Sir John de Walton was at a loss to know which way his duty lay; but he finally said:

"I will give thee leave to address thy son by a line under thy hand, and I will await his answer before proceeding further in this matter, which seems very mysterious. My duty requires, however, that in the mean time thou be kept in strict confinement."

Sir John de Walton rode at once to the abbey, and, on interrogating the Abbot concerning the youth in his charge, was informed that he had not been so well and that his indisposition appeared to be of that contagious kind which had been prevalent on the English border. Upon this the knight gave the Abbot a letter which Bertram had written and bade him deliver it to Augustine and to get an answer. The old man returned with a message so bold that he was afraid to deliver it as it was given. Its purport was that he could not and would not receive Sir John then, but that if he would come on the morrow after mass he might learn something of what he wanted.

"This is not an answer," said the knight, "to be sent by a boy to a person in my charge; and methinks, Father Abbot, you consult your own safety but slenderly in delivering such an insolent message."

The Abbot trembled at Sir John's anger, but pledged his sacred word that the inconsiderate character of the boy's message was owing to the waywardness arising from indisposition. De Walton, although not satisfied, was unwilling to antagonize the Church, and finally said:

"At your request, Father Abbot, I will indulge this youth with the grace he asks before taking him into custody, with the understanding that you will be responsible for him. To this end I will give you power to command our garrison at Hazelside, to which I will send a reënforcement on my return to the castle."

Sir John despatched Sir Aymer de Valence that night to Hazelside to take charge of the small garrison there, with orders to keep a strict watch. Sir Aymer noticed various suspicious signs of the presence of an enemy in and around the village, and, determined to investigate, rode at once to the abbey and summoned the Abbot to his presence. The good father complained bitterly of being called out of his bed at midnight in such raw weather, but the knight explained the necessities of the case and demanded to see at once the youth called Augustine. The Abbot protested that there was nothing in the conduct of the youth to excite suspicion, that he had had no intercourse with any persons without the convent, and that he had shown for those within a marked preference for the company of the sisters rather than for that of the brethren.

"Scandal," said the knight, "might find a reason for that preference."

"Not in the case of the sisters of Saint Bride," said the Abbot with a grim smile, "most of whom have been either sorely misused by time or their comeliness destroyed by some mishap."

The English knight, to whom the sisterhood was well known, felt also inclined to smile, but said that he must insist on seeing the youth. "I will await your return," he continued, "and either carry the boy to the castle or leave him here, as circumstances may seem to require."

The Abbot bowed and hobbled out, promising his utmost exertions to induce the boy to appear. He remained so long absent that Sir Aymer began to think the delay suspicious, but the old man finally appeared accompanied by Augustine, who was fully dressed and closely muffled in pilgrim's costume. As soon as she found herself in the same apartment with Sir Aymer, the young woman assumed a bolder and more determined air than she had displayed before.

"Your worship," she said, addressing him before he spoke, "is a knight of England. I am an unfortunate lad obliged, for reasons which I am under the necessity of keeping secret, to travel in a dangerous country, where I am suspected, without just cause, of being accessory to plots and conspiracies contrary to my own interests and which I abhor. Nevertheless, you will not believe my solemn protestations and are about to proceed against me as a guilty person. In so doing, Sir Knight, I must warn you that you will commit a great and cruel injustice."

"I shall endeavor to avoid that," said Sir Aymer, "by referring the duty to Sir John de Walton. I must take you to Douglas Castle."

"Must I then accompany you thither?"

"If you delay me longer, young man, I must carry you thither by force."

"But Abbot Jerome will assure you that I cannot travel without danger of my life."

"Do you hold, reverend father," asked Sir Aymer, "that there is real danger in carrying this youth to the castle to-night?"

The Abbot replied that there was danger of a relapse, to say nothing of the possibility of introducing the malady into the garrison. So Sir Aymer decided to place a sentinel at Augustine's door and to wait until morning to pursue his investigation. Sir Aymer himself saw the door of Augustine's apartment safely locked and, satisfied that there was no other means of entrance and exit, stationed an archer to guard it and betook himself to rest.

At the first peep of day, when the bells of the convent summoned to morning prayers, Sir Aymer, after attending to his devotions, demanded his prisoner. The Abbot tapped on Augustine's door, but received no response.

"What means this?" exclaimed the Abbot. "My patient must have fallen into a syncope or a swoon."

"We shall speedily see," said the knight, ordering crowbars and levers to be brought.

As the shattered door fell crashing within De Valence sprang into the apartment, followed by Father Jerome. To the fulfilment of the knight's worst suspicions, it was empty. From certain garments left behind Father Jerome concluded that Augustine had been accompanied in his flight by Sister Ursula, who in the world had been Lady Margaret de Hautlieu, a novice who had not yet taken full vows. But what interested the knight most was a scroll left by Augustine, in which Bertram was not only empowered but commanded to reveal the purpose of the writer in coming to the Castle of Douglas, a purpose which the writer could not unfold without shame. In conclusion, she freely and willingly forgave Sir Aymer de Valence for having been involved in a mistake, and hoped to meet him in future as an acquaintance; but requested Sir John de Walton to consider whether his conduct had been such as he himself ought to forget or the writer to forgive. It ended by saying that all former connections must henceforth be at an end between him and the supposed Augustine.

"This is midsummer madness," said the Abbot, "not unfrequently an accompaniment of this disease."

"Hush! my reverend father," said De Valence, "a light begins to break in upon me. John de Walton, if my suspicion be true, would sooner have his flesh hewn from his bones than have this Augustine's finger stung by a gnat. I must send out at once in quest of the fugitives, and must hasten back to inform Sir John de Walton what turn affairs have taken."

Sir John de Walton was thunderstruck when he recognized the full purport of the letter which De Valence had brought him, and would have lost all heart if the younger knight had not cheered him and begged him to chase desponding gloom from his brow as ill becoming a man and a belted knight.

"See you not," replied Sir John, "that her offending lover

is expressly excluded from the amnesty granted to you? Explain how the concluding words of her note can have any but a plain sense of condemnation and forfeiture of contract, implying destruction of my hopes."

De Valence did his best to persuade him that Lady Augusta de Berkely, who had made De Walton her choice, though known to her only as a flower of English chivalry, would hardly seize the opportunity to show unwonted and unusual vigor toward him when the victim of a pardonable mistake, in order to balance her extension toward him of a somewhat unusual degree of encouragement. Sir John listened to his arguments and finally said in a solemn and animated tone: "Aymer de Valence, Douglas Castle shall be defended; and come of me what list during my life, I will die the faithful lover of Augusta de Berkely, even although I no longer live as her chosen knight. But meanwhile we must endeavor, if possible, to discover the lady's too hasty retreat, by which she has done me great wrong—for she could not have supposed that her commands would not have been fully obeyed had she honored with them the governor of Douglas Castle."

Sister Ursula, who had been taken into the confidence of Lady Augusta de Berkely, had had, as Margaret de Hautlieu, a romance of her own. Her father, Maurice de Hautlieu, was a noble Norman baron who, settled in Scotland, held the shrievalty of Lanark. When the wars began between Bruce and Baliol he espoused the cause of the latter, who was aided by the English king. Meanwhile Margaret, his daughter and heiress, had loved and been loved by Malcolm Fleming of the house of Biggar, who was a follower of Bruce. Her father opposed the match and, when Margaret would not give up her lover, immured her in the abbey of St. Bride, announcing that he would force her to take the veil unless she agreed to marry his nephew, a youth bred at the English court. Malcolm Fleming attempted to carry off his affianced from the convent, but the Abbess, who had got wind of the proposed abduction, informed the father of it and the plan was unsuccessful. Fleming escaped, but the ladder on which Margaret was descending was thrown to the ground and she fell on the stones below, suffering such injuries that she was disfigured for life.

When Sister Ursula aided Lady Augusta de Berkely to escape from the abbey through a secret passage the two fled into the wood, where horses were provided by friends of Lady Margaret. They were soon beyond pursuit from the castle, but fell into the hands of the adherents of Sir James Douglas. Sir James treated Lady Augusta with every indulgence, but held her a prisoner subject to certain conditions, agreeing to deliver her in all honor and safety to Sir John de Walton, provided that the latter would deliver up to him the Castle of Douglas, with its outposts and garrisons, and with all the provisions and artillery within its walls.

Sir John de Walton, who had met by chance in the wood Sir James Douglas's ambassador, bringing the lady and this message, was made so angry by it that he struck down the man with his sword.

"Alas! De Walton, what have you done?" said Lady Augusta. "This man was only an ambassador, and should have passed free from injury. The Scots are in arms near here, and may exact vengeance."

"Fear not, empress of De Walton's thoughts," answered the knight. "If you can but pardon what I shall never be able to forgive myself, I will defy in thy name all these ruffians to instant combat."

As Sir John spoke a tall knight in black armor stepped out of the thicket. "I am James of Douglas," he said, "and your challenge is accepted."

"So be it, in God's name," said the English knight, and making a sign to Lady Augusta to retire behind him, he advanced and attacked the black knight. The two fought long and fiercely and apparently with equal skill and endurance, until at last the lady appealed to them, in a momentary pause, to stop the combat, calling their attention to the abbey bells ringing for the service of the day, which was Palm Sunday.

"For Heaven's sake," she said, "for your own sakes, and for that of lady's love and the duties of chivalry, hold your hands only for an hour, and take chance that means will be found of converting the truce into a solid peace."

Under her earnest intercession, the two agreed to postpone their feud until after the services, each entertaining a well-grounded hope of finding at the church a sufficient number of adherents to decide the contest in his own favor. In this hope both were gratified, for the church was well filled by the partisans of each party, Sir Aymer de Valence being on hand with many followers, and the knight of Fleming, the lover of Lady Margaret, appearing with others in support of the Douglas.

At the conclusion of the services the parties separated at the sound of bugles and the bloody contest began. Sir Aymer de Valence, overcome by Fleming, was obliged to yield, rescue or no rescue, but the two leaders, Douglas and De Walton, passed three quarters of an hour in hard contest with little apparent gain on either side, save that the English knight showed signs of weariness. Douglas, noting this, generously signaled to his antagonist to pause an instant.

"Brave De Walton," he said, "there is no mortal quarrel between us. But my father's house and the graves of my ancestors call upon me to prosecute the strife to win them back, while you are as welcome to the noble lady, in all honor and safety, as if you had received her from the hands of King Edward himself. I give you my word that the utmost honors which can attend a prisoner, and a careful absence of injury or insult, shall attend De Walton when he yields the castle and his sword to James of Douglas."

"It is the fate to which I am perhaps doomed," replied Sir John; "but never will I voluntarily embrace it, save in the last extremity. Pembroke is on the march to rescue the garrison of Douglas. I hear the tramp of his horses' feet even now; and I will maintain my ground while I am in reach of support. Come on, then, and treat me as one, whether I stand or fall, who fears not to encounter the utmost force of my knightly antagonist."

As he spoke a Welsh knight rode up to the door.

"Is Pembroke near?" asked De Walton.

"No nearer than London Hill; but I bring his commands to John de Walton. The Earl, completely defeated by Bruce, sends his instructions to Sir John de Walton to make the best terms he can for the surrender of the Castle of Douglas and trust nothing to his support."

"Noble knight," said De Walton to Douglas, "it is at your

pleasure to dictate the terms for the surrender of your paternal castle. I submit to my fate."

"God forbid," said James of Douglas, "that I should take advantage of so brave a knight. I will take example from the knight of Fleming, who has gallantly bestowed his captive upon a noble damsel here present; and in like manner I transfer my claim upon the person of the redoubted knight of Walton to the high and noble Lady Augusta de Berkely, who, I hope, will not scorn to accept from the Douglas a gift which the chance of war has thrown into his hands."

MOLLY ELLIOT SEAWELL

(United States, 1860)

PAPA BOUCHARD (1901)

Gallic gaiety and volatility are eminently characteristic of all Miss Seawell's stories of French life; and this, the author's favorite of all her romances of European society, became highly popular on both sides of the Atlantic immediately on its publication. We present here the author's own shortened version of her story.

NE morning in June, 1901, a cataclysm occurred in the apartment of Mademoiselle Céleste Bouchard, in the quietest street in Paris. This was the simultaneous departure of everything masculine in the establishment. The masculine element consisted of Monsieur Paul Bouchard, a correct and elderly bachelor, who had been in leading-strings all his life to his sister, Mademoiselle Céleste, ten years his senior. Then there was Pierre, husband of Elise, Mademoiselle Céleste's elderly maid. Pierre had been under Elise's thumb ever since she had promised, thirty years before, to love, honor, and obey him.

The third and last masculine member of the household was Pierrot, the parrot, heretofore an exemplary bird, as Pierre was an exemplary husband, and M. Paul Bouchard the most exemplary man in Paris. But in every masculine bosom there is a germ of lawlessness which no discipline can kill. And this germ suddenly developed at the same time in M. Paul, in Pierre, and in Pierrot.

It was the parrot that made the first break for liberty. After seventeen years of irreproachable conduct, he suddenly, on this June morning, jumped off the balcony, where he had been sedately walking, and scuttled off in the direction of the gayest quarter of Paris.

With subtle sympathy M. Paul watched Pierrot as he gaily sidled around the corner.

"Poor devil!" thought M. Paul, "he is sick of the deadly propriety—weary of the moral maxims—tired of the whole business of being so mortally good."

Inspired by Pierrot's example, M. Paul went out and engaged a bachelor apartment for himself in the most modern and dissipated quarter of the city. Then he had to break the news of his impending departure to Mademoiselle Céleste. The good lady, seeing determination in M. Paul's eye, knew it was impossible to hold him, but insisted that he should take with him to his new quarters Pierre, upon whom she thought she could depend to keep an eye on her brother.

M. Paul very much objected to having a detective on his track, as he knew Pierre would be, but was finally bullied into consent. But Pierre was delighted to get away from the strict rule of his wife, Elise, and in his first interview with M. Paul in his new quarters he astonished his master by saying:

"Monsieur Bouchard, my wife, I have reason to know, expects Monsieur to watch me and report to her, and Mademoiselle Céleste expects me to watch Monsieur and report to *her*. Now, what prevents us from each giving a good account of the other and meanwhile doing as we please?"

After the first shock of surprise M. Bouchard saw the advantage of this arrangement. As a beginning he ordered Pierre to bring him a very luxurious dinner, with champagne. Just as Pierre left the room, the door opened and in walked Captain de Meneval, husband of Léontine de Meneval, the ward of M. Bouchard. Léontine's fortune was under control of M. Bouchard, who would allow her and her husband only a portion of her income. Léontine and De Meneval were young, gay, and extravagant, but devotedly fond of each other. De Meneval was a captain of artillery, whose regiment was then stationed at Melun.

M. Bouchard suspected that De Meneval was in want of money, and De Meneval finally confessed to owing a bill of nineteen hundred francs nineteen centimes at the Pigeon House, a music-hall at Melun, where he was stationed, and that he had not the money to pay it.

M. Bouchard indignantly refused to pay this bill. Then De Meneval coolly produced a diamond necklace, which was his wedding-gift to Léontine, and said that in that case he should be compelled to pawn it. When he bought it he was advised by the jeweler to buy a paste imitation of it to use in emergencies. Léontine knew nothing of this supernumerary necklace, so De Meneval had put the paste one in the case and taken the real diamonds, prepared to pawn them if M. Bouchard would not advance him the money he needed.

M. Bouchard, realizing the danger of pawning Léontine's diamonds, was finally forced to advance the money, taking the necklace himself as security.

De Meneval immediately recovered his spirits, and prepared to depart with a check for nineteen hundred francs and nineteen centimes. Just as he was leaving the room Léontine herself entered. In order to escape detection, De Meneval snatched up and hastily donned M. Bouchard's mackintosh and hat and rushed past Léontine without being recognized.

Léontine then confessed to "Papa" Bouchard, as she called him, that she had very large bills at a dressmaker's, and demanded the money to pay them. This Papa Bouchard sternly refused to give her. Then Léontine, taking out the paste necklace, which she supposed to be the real one, informed Papa Bouchard that she was prepared to pawn her diamonds in order to raise the money to pay her bills.

At that moment her eyes fell upon the real diamonds, which she at once mistook for an imitation, and she demanded that Papa Bouchard should tell her how he came by it. Papa Bouchard was unprepared with an explanation, and Léontine boldly accused him of having bought the necklace himself as a present for a lady. This she followed up by asking him about a certain pretty little widow whom she knew he had met several times on the train.

Papa Bouchard was staggered by this, and by Léontine's threat to tell Mademoiselle Céleste the story of the mysterious necklace and of her suspicions about the fascinating widow; so he decided to buy Léontine's silence by giving her a check for six thousand francs, and took the paste necklace from her without telling her it was an imitation. At the same time he returned to her the genuine diamond necklace, telling her it was only paste, thereby making sure that she would not attempt to raise money on it. He himself retained the paste necklace, as he pretended, for security.

When Léontine had succeeded in getting the check from Papa Bouchard, and was leaving the room, De Meneval, supposing she had gone, returned, in order to bring back the mackintosh and hat.

Papa Bouchard, getting them together, and knowing that each was anxious to keep from the other the story of debts and bills and the efforts of each to raise money on Léontine's diamonds, proceeded to lecture them and demanded that they leave Paris and take a cottage near Melun. Both were aghast at the idea of leaving Paris, but under the fear of exposure they agreed to do it, and forthwith departed dolefully.

By the time they were out of sight the door opened again, and in walked Madame Vernet, the interesting little widow Papa Bouchard had accidentally met three times during the preceding week. Madame Vernet, at sight of Papa Bouchard, showed the utmost alarm and explained that, having taken an apartment in the same building, she had mistaken M. Bouchard's quarters for her own.

M. Bouchard, much infatuated, entered into conversation, but was extremely disconcerted when Madame Vernet, seeing the paste necklace lying on the table, picked it up and clasped it around her neck. M. Bouchard, alarmed and embarrassed, assured her that it was merely paste. But Madame Vernet, seeing that it was very pretty, laughingly protested that as it was of so little value, and at the same time was so charming, she would accept it as a gift from M. Bouchard. In spite of M. Bouchard's efforts to get it back the little widow managed to carry off the necklace, when she left the bewildered bachelor overwhelmed with her charms but terrified at the thought of the duplicate of Léontine's necklace being in her possession.

Poor M. Paul, recognizing the predicament in which he was placed by the disappearance of the supposed diamond necklace, was forced to confide the matter to Pierre, and together they at once began negotiations.

Acting under Pierre's advice, M. Bouchard wrote to Madame

Vernet, and offered money for the return of the necklace. Ma,
dame at first professed indignation, but in the course of a week's
correspondence agreed to accept two thousand francs for it
(which was much more than it was worth) if M. Bouchard would
meet her at the Pigeon House at Melun.

Now, it was extremely awkward for the correct M. Bouchard
to appear at the Pigeon House, which was a very gay music-hall
and garden, but there was no help for it, he must go.

On the same evening Léontine had persuaded De Meneval
to take her to Melun, where she wished to have supper in the garden of the Pigeon House. Bouchard arrived there first, and
was met in the garden by Madame Vernet, who wore around
her neck the paste necklace. Annoyed and perplexed as he was
by her possession of the necklace, Bouchard could not help suc-
cumbing to her charm of manner.

He wished to remain unknown, but as soon as he appeared a
parrot, which was no other than his sister's runaway Pierrot,
which had been caught in the garden and caged, began to scream
from his cage in a small summer-house: "Bad boy, Bouchard!
Aren't you tired of being so devilish good?"

To complete Bouchard's discomfiture, Léontine and De
Meneval entered the garden and caught him in the little widow's
gay company. However, both Léontine and De Meneval were
equally discomfited, for they saw Madame Vernet wearing what
they supposed to be Léontine's diamond necklace, and each was
afraid to let the other know that money had been screwed out of
Bouchard on the strength of that necklace.

At last, meeting Papa Bouchard face to face, Léontine took
him off in a corner of the garden to insist that he should tell her
how Madame Vernet came by the necklace, which Bouchard had
represented to her as being the real diamonds.

De Meneval, left alone with Madame Vernet, promptly
charged her with having on his wife's diamonds, and demanded
that she return them. When Madame Vernet refused, De Meneval left the garden in order to call the police. At that moment
Dr. Delcasse, a celebrated alienist, entered the garden. Madame Vernet introduced herself to him and said that the excited
young man who had just left her was her brother, whose mind
was affected. His latest delusion was that he was not her

brother, but a captain of artillery, and a married man, and that she, his sister, was wearing a diamond necklace which belonged to his imaginary wife. He had suddenly grown violent, and the best thing to do was to have him carried off to Dr. Delcasse's sanatorium. Dr. Delcasse at once telephoned for attendants, and when a few minutes later De Meneval reappeared with two policemen, Delcasse explained to the officers that the young man had become suddenly insane and was to be taken to his sanatorium. In spite of De Meneval's resistance he was carried off and shut up as a violent lunatic.

Madame Vernet determined to return to Paris by the next train. Léontine and Papa Bouchard, after an interview of recriminations, returned to the garden. At the same time De Meneval, having soon succeeded at the sanatorium in establishing his identity, came back enraged, but still afraid to expose the truth about the diamond necklace.

Suspecting that Madame Vernet would take the next train for Paris, Papa Bouchard, De Meneval, and Léontine were each anxious to get back to Paris before the others, and each tried to conceal this intention from the rest. The rattle of the approaching train was heard, and all made a rush for it, only to find the train running past the station, leaving them in a state of great perplexity and agitation.

The following week was one of the deepest anxiety for all concerned. Elise's suspicions were aroused; and although Pierre stood loyally by his master, and gave various plausible reasons to account for M. Paul's mysterious absences from his rooms on his anxious search for Madame Vernet and the necklace, Elise became convinced that something was wrong in M. Paul's new apartment.

Bouchard himself wrote imploring letters to Madame Vernet, increasing his offer of money for the return of the paste necklace.

Meanwhile, Léontine and De Meneval had each been in agony lest the other find out that the diamond necklace, as they supposed, was in pawn. Although Léontine supposed that the necklace in her possession was merely a fine imitation, its appearance of genuineness puzzled her.

At last, one afternoon, she determined to take it to the jeweler from whom it had been bought and to ask his opinion of it. The jeweler informed her that it was the original necklace of very fine stones, and well worth the forty thousand francs De Meneval had paid for it. Léontine, astonished, determined to confess everything to her husband. It happened that this was the evening Madame Vernet had appointed for Bouchard to meet her again at the Pigeon House to receive the paste necklace and to hand over in return a check for four thousand francs.

Bouchard and Pierre had just left the apartment when Elise turned up, determined to find out the truth about the mysterious goings-on of her husband and his master. The concierge proved willing to talk and told of the visit of Madame Vernet to Bouchard's apartment, and the frequent excursions of Bouchard and Pierre to Melun. Elise returned to Mademoiselle Céleste, poured out the story of M. Paul's and Pierre's delinquencies, and proposed that she and Mademoiselle Céleste should at once go to Melun and catch the culprits.

On the particular evening, De Meneval, not expecting his wife, was giving a little supper to the young ladies of the ballet. His soldier servant was putting the last touches to the table and arranging the bouquets with cards addressed to " The Sprightly Aglia," " Olga, Queen of the Dance," and " Louise of the Fairy Foot."

Arriving at Melun, Léontine went to her husband's quarters and saw the festive preparations. De Meneval had always sworn that he spent his evenings studying military tactics, except when he was looking at her picture and longing for her, consequently she was very indignant at what she saw, and determined to be revenged on him by passing herself off to the other guests as a dancer, which would certainly annoy her husband.

The first person to arrive was Major Fallière, a punctilious bachelor officer, known as "old P.M.P," the Pink of Military Propriety.

Léontine roguishly introduced herself as "Satanita, Queen of the Harem-Scarem." Major Fallière, in spite of his propriety, gaily chucked her under the chin, and she retaliated, much to his discomfiture, by chucking him under the chin. But she was so charming that the Major soon forgave her, and they entered into conversation.

"Now," said Léontine, seating herself beside Fallière, "what do you think of our host, Victor de Meneval?"

"One of the best fellows in the world," responded Fallière.

"Devoted to his wife, eh?"

"Yes. I never have seen her, but I hear she is a charming creature, and Victor is truly attached to her."

"This looks like it, doesn't it?" cried Léontine, pointing to the supper-table.

"I don't see that it doesn't," replied Fallière. "I happen to know that De Meneval has had a good deal to trouble him lately, and I advised him to give a little supper—it's dull out here, you know."

"*You* advised him to give a little supper! And how about his wife?"

"Oh," answered the Major easily, "she would probably make an awful row if she knew it, but she'll never know it. De Meneval has coached me; I know exactly what to tell Léontine when I meet her. We have mapped out our campaign and have a large assortment of lies, expressly for Léontine's consumption, and she will swallow every one of them."

"But I tell you she will not."

"How do you know? Are you a clairvoyant?"

"No," replied Léontine, rising, her whole face sparkling with impish delight. "I am Léontine, Madame de Meneval, wife of your friend, Victor de Meneval. Yonder is my picture. Here am I."

Fallière stared at Léontine, glared wildly about him, and then made a dash for the door, from which Léontine, laughing, dragged him back. Then she confided to Fallière her perplexity over her necklace and her husband, and her indignation when, on coming out to Melun to confess to him, she found he had prepared a festivity for the young ladies of the Pigeon House. She desired to punish him, and Fallière agreed to help her.

On the sideboard were some bottles of mineral water and on the floor was a wine-cooler full of bottles of champagne. Léontine transferred the labels from two of the champagne bottles to the apollinaris bottles, and then put the latter in the wine-cooler.

"I think I can drink at least a quart of apollinaris," she said.

"And I'll see that you get apollinaris every time," replied Fallière laughing.

"And I'm Satanita, and I shall act Satanita until I have made Victor sorry enough he ever played me any tricks."

"Oh, no, you won't!" said Major Fallière. "At the first sign of distress on his part you will throw the whole business to the winds, fall on his neck, and implore his forgiveness."

They were interrupted by a sound of scuffling, mingled with shrieks of laughter. The door flew open, revealing three remarkably pretty girls—Aglia, Olga, and Louise—dragging in an elderly gentleman by main force and his coat-tails. The gentleman was resisting mildly, but with no great vigor, and it was evident he was not averse to the roguish company in which he found himself. And the elderly gentleman was—Papa Bouchard!

Puffing, alarmed, but laughing in spite of himself, Papa Bouchard was saying:

"Young ladies, young ladies, I really cannot remain, as you insist, to supper. I do not even know the name of the host on this occasion. I am here this evening with my servant merely for the purpose of completing a business transaction."

A chorus of "Oh!" and "Ah!" saluted this speech, and Aglia, his chief tormentor, asked solemnly:

"Is your engagement with a lady or a gentleman?"

And when, in the innocence of his soul, he replied, "It is with a lady," each of the "Pouters," as the young ladies of the Pigeon House were called, pretended to fall over in a dead faint.

At this moment Papa Bouchard's eye fell on Léontine. He was disconcerted, but said in a stern voice:

"May I ask what you are doing here in this company?"

To which Léontine, with pert gaiety, replied:

"And may I ask what *you* are doing here in this company?"

"I," said Bouchard, with dignity, "am here by accident, and by the violence of these young women."

"Oh, what a fib!" cried Olga. "The old duffer begged us to let him come. We tried to shake him off but we couldn't."

Bouchard, astounded at such duplicity, glared at them, but the only satisfaction he got was a fillip on the nose from Aglia. He indignantly turned his back on these traducers, and again opened fire on Léontine.

"I am amazed at your temerity. What shall I say to Captain de Meneval when I see him to-morrow morning?"

"Anything you like," was Léontine's laughing reply.

"Léontine de Meneval," roared Papa Bouchard, "do you know me, your guardian and trustee?"

"No, I don't," responded Léontine nonchalantly. "I never saw you before."

Papa Bouchard, quite beside himself, turned to Major Fallière:

"Sir," he said solemnly, "you wear the uniform of an officer, and I presume you are a gentleman. Believe me, this lady is the wife of a brother officer of yours, Captain de Meneval. The truest kindness you can do him or her is to persuade her to leave this scene of dissipation and return at once to Paris with me."

"O-o-o-o-h!" shrieked the three impish girls in chorus. "What an outrageous proposition! And she says she never saw the man before!"

Papa Bouchard, still appealing to Major Fallière, continued:

"Perhaps this misguided girl has not told you that she is Madame Victor de Meneval."

"She told me," quietly replied Major Fallière, "that she was Satanita, a singer and dancer."

Bouchard dropped limply on the sofa and groaned. But now a jaunty step was heard on the stair. Aglia ran forward and opened the door, and in stepped the smiling De Meneval.

Papa Bouchard felt a sensation of triumph at Captain de Meneval's entrance. *He*, at least, would not dare to deride and defy him. But before Monsieur Bouchard could open his mouth Aglia burst forth, pointing to the old gentleman:

"Of all the impudent men I ever saw, this excels! What do you think? As soon as he found we were coming here to supper, he hung on to us and declared there was nothing he liked so well as a gay little party; that he could drink so much champagne he was called the Champagne Tank; and actually forced himself in here, although we tried to keep him out. Didn't we, girls?"

Papa Bouchard, thoroughly exasperated, said to De Meneval:

"You, of course, do not and cannot believe a word these young women say concerning my presence here to-night."

De Meneval, very much alarmed, and dreading to catch Léontine's eye, retained wit enough to assume the worst and to accept no explanation.

"Monsieur Bouchard," he said coldly, "you are asking a little too much of me when you wish me to believe your testimony against that of three ladies."

But De Meneval had troubles of his own to attend to then. He walked over to Léontine, and assuming an air of forced gaiety, such as a man puts on when he anticipates a wigging from the wife of his bosom, said in a low tone:

"Delighted you happened to arrive, my love, and what do you think of the Pouters?"

"I think they are very jolly girls," promptly responded Léontine; "but as I am another uninvited guest, I thought it best to tell Major Fallière and the others that I, too, am a singer and dancer—Satanita, I call myself."

"And you did not immediately inform them that you are my wife?" hissed De Meneval.

"No, I am Satanita—good name, isn't it?—for this evening. And if you say I am your wife I shall simply deny it. Satanita I am, and Satanita I shall be, and I shall live up to the name—of that you may be sure."

De Meneval was undecided whether to laugh or to shoot himself, and then there was a move of the whole party toward the supper-table. Fallière had got hold of the two apollinaris bottles, and filled Léontine's glass.

As the supper progressed, De Meneval grew almost frantic over the spectacle his dear little Léontine was making of herself. For she not only managed to drink innumerable glasses of apollinaris, but she sang, she even danced. She paraded up and down the room, singing, in her sweet, saucy voice, impromptu stanzas:

"Oh, I am the Widow Cliquot, Cliquot,
I live at the Château Margaux, Margaux,
My coachman's name is Pommery Sec,
My footman's name is Piper Heidsieck,
Moët-et-Chandon are my span,

And when Moët and Chandon go lame,
I drive Mumm and Roederer!"

This almost drove De Meneval to distraction, but a roar of applause, in which all joined except her husband and Papa Bouchard, encouraged Léontine to continue:

"This is the way in Champagne Land!
Oh, Champagne Land is dear to me,
But Champagne Land is queer to me.
There the lobsters grow on trees,
There you find a mine of cheese;
The oysters walk,
The cocktails talk,
And the *pâté de foies gras* builds his nest
In the hedge where the anchovy paste grows best."

This was too much for poor De Meneval, and rising from the table, with tears in his eyes, he cried:

"My friends, I beg of you to leave me. This lady who calls herself Satanita is my wife. I never have seen her act in this manner before. It is my duty as well as my privilege to shield her, and I wish to say that if any person, man or woman, ever mentions what her unfortunate conduct to-night has been a life will be forfeited, for I swear to shoot any man who dares to breathe one word against her, and any woman who does it may reckon on my vengeance."

This was too much for Léontine. Just as Major Fallière had predicted, at the first sign of repentance on De Meneval's part she forgot all her resolutions to punish him, and falling into his arms, she exclaimed in her own sweet natural voice:

"You dear, chivalrous angel! I haven't touched champagne —it is nothing but apollinaris, and I am your own true, devoted Léontine."

At that moment the door opened softly and in walked Madame Vernet. She advanced with downcast eyes, and said timidly:

"I knocked, and thought I heard someone say 'Come in.' I do not know on whose hospitality I am trespassing, but I saw Monsieur Bouchard enter half an hour ago, and as I must see him on a matter of business, I venture to ask a word with him here."

M. Bouchard, at the sight of her, seemed about to collapse. Not so Captain de Meneval. He rose at once and said, with an ironical bow:

"Madame Vernet, you are trespassing on the hospitality of Captain de Meneval, the gentleman you adopted as a brother about ten days ago and handed over as a dangerous lunatic to Dr. Delcasse."

At this Madame Vernet assumed an attitude more shrinking, more timid than before, and falling on M. Bouchard's shoulder, cried:

"Dear Paul, protect me from this dreadful person!"

Bouchard, looking the picture of despair, said feebly:

"Go away! go away!"

"Is that the way you speak to your own Adèle!" cried Madame Vernet, burying her head in Bouchard's bosom and bursting into tears. "Oh, what a change within one short week! Last week it was nothing but 'Dearest Adèle, when will you name the day?'"

"It is false!" wailed M. Bouchard, trying to escape from Madame Vernet.

"Do you pretend to deny," she sobbed, "that only a week ago you gave me this?" She took from her pocket the paste necklace, and at the sight of it a shock like a galvanic battery ran down the backbones of De Meneval and Léontine.

Then De Meneval, walking coolly up to her, suddenly took the necklace out of her hand, saying:

"This is the property of my wife, and as such I take possession of it, and call on you, Monsieur Bouchard, to make an explanation."

Bouchard was so delighted to realize that the De Menevals had the necklace and Pierre the four thousand francs, that his countenance changed, and he said:

"I am overjoyed to make an explanation. This necklace is paste, and the one Léontine has is real. You may remember, De Meneval, you came to my apartment a week ago last Monday evening, bringing Léontine's real diamond necklace with you. You told me that when you bought it for her you bought also an imitation one for seventy-five francs, which you kept a secret from Léontine, and that you had, still unknown to Léontine, put the paste one in place of the real one; and you threatened if I did not advance money to pay a large bill you owed at the Pigeon House, to take the necklace to the pawnbroker."

De Meneval turned to Léontine, and, knowing what was coming, said with a sickly smile:

"Dearest, will you forgive me?"

"Indeed I will!" replied Léontine, who knew more of what was coming than did De Meneval.

"Hardly were you gone," continued Bouchard, assuming his oracular manner, which sat rather awkwardly on him, as Madame Vernet persisted in nestling on his shoulder, "when in came Léontine, and for the same purpose—money or the pawnbroker. It occurred to me that she could not be trusted with any necklace on which she thought money could be raised, so I gave her back her own necklace, and told her it was paste. Then, just as I had got rid of her, in came this lady—" Here Papa Bouchard made a desperate effort to shake off Madame Vernet, but that diffident person only clung to him more affectionately—"picked up the necklace, clasped it round her neck, and walked off with it, and I have spent the most miserable week of my life trying to get it back. I had arranged to give her four thousand francs for it. If I could find that rascal Pierre I could prove all I say."

As if in answer to his name, the door burst open, and in rushed Pierre, pale and breathless.

"Monsieur!" he cried to Bouchard, "all is discovered, and we are in the greatest danger. My wife Elise found out everything from the concierge in the Rue Bassano this evening. She went back to Mademoiselle Bouchard, and both of them took the train for Melun to capture us. I ran into them at the foot of the stairs. They are on the stairs now."

The next instant in walked Mademoiselle Céleste Bouchard and Elise, whose disordered apparel gave evidence of the perturbation of mind in which they had prepared to travel.

The amazing sight that met their eyes was M. Bouchard apparently submitting willingly to Madame Vernet's endearments, while the lady herself sobbed upon his breast.

Mademoiselle Bouchard, panting and trembling with wrath and horror, sank into a chair. Elise exclaimed:

"When you, Mademoiselle, have finished with Monsieur Bouchard, I'll dispose of Pierre.   Oh, the rascal!"

Pierre, like his master, was dumb before the accuser.

Poor M. Bouchard was a pitiable sight, and the De Menevals, Major Fallière, and the three girls were heartless enough to go into convulsions of silent mirth at his predicament.

"Paul," cried Mademoiselle Céleste, "stop those shocking demonstrations toward that person and explain your conduct to me."

"My dear Céleste," replied Papa Bouchard weakly, "if you could induce this lady to stop *her* demonstrations I should be the happiest man on earth.   And there's no explanation to give. I'm the helpless victim of a designing woman."

At which Madame Vernet screamed and said, trying to kiss him:

"I will forgive you, my own Paul!"

Apparently Madame Vernet was mistress of the situation, but here the cool, the resolute Major Fallière, came to the rescue. Going up to Madame Vernet, he said:

"You seem to have lost sight of the little incident of representing my friend, Captain de Meneval, as your brother and a dangerous lunatic, and the trick you played on Dr. Delcasse. Now, I happen to know that Dr. Delcasse is determined to punish you if he can find you, and unless you immediately quit these quarters and leave Melun I shall inform Dr. Delcasse of your whereabouts, and you will have a visit from the police."

Madame Vernet, seeing she had met her match, disengaged herself from M. Bouchard, and said with great innocence:

"I don't really understand what you mean.   But, being naturally a very diffident and retiring person, I shall certainly leave this censorious and unsympathetic company."

At this Fallière ceremoniously showed her out of the room. Mademoiselle Bouchard then rose majestically, and said to M. Bouchard:

"And you, Paul, will seek refuge and protection in the house of your sister in the Rue Clarisse, where you spent thirty happy and peaceful years."

M. Bouchard, the image of despair, looked round him. Captain de Meneval and Léontine were in fits of laughter.   The three girls were tittering; the grim Major was smiling broadly. Even a worm will turn, and so did M. Bouchard.

"I am sorry, my dear Céleste," he said in a voice he vainly endeavored to make cool and debonair, "but what you suggest is impossible. I have taken my apartment for a year. I—I shall remain in the Rue Bassano!"

Mademoiselle Bouchard, defeated, was speechless. Not so Elise. Walking up to Pierre, she seized him and bawled:

"No excuses shall keep you from the Rue Clarisse. I promise you that you shall have a very different time there from your present life—running out here to the Pigeon House and making a show and scandal of yourself."

"No, Elise," firmly replied Pierre, who had more real courage than his master, "I promised Mademoiselle Bouchard I never would desert Monsieur. I cannot break my word."

Mademoiselle Bouchard realized she was beaten. So did Elise. They rose slowly. De Meneval ran into the next room and, bringing out a cage that held the redoubtable Pierrot, put it into Mademoiselle Bouchard's hand.

"There, dear Aunt Céleste," he cried, "is your consoler. I offered to buy him from the proprietor of the Pigeon House, but the man said he would give me the bird for nothing; in fact, he would pay to get rid of him. He was driving away the customers of the Pigeon House by his horrible language."

"At least," said Mademoiselle Bouchard solemnly, "if men are renegades, there is something of the same sex that is faithful and grateful. No doubt this poor bird is happy at escaping from the dissipated atmosphere of the Pigeon House to the sweet seclusion of the Rue Clarisse."

But—horror of horrors!—the instant the wicked Pierrot found himself going in the direction of the door, he broke out into the most outrageous denunciations of the two ladies. Shrieks, demoniac laughter, yells, oaths, and slang of the worst description poured from him. He actually forced open the door of the cage and bit furiously at Mademoiselle Céleste and Elise, and shrieked:

"Go to the devil, you bow-legged old rapscallions!"

But the two respectable elderly persons so infamously described were already fleeing.

Elise cried out, as they ran down-stairs:

"The only safe thing to do, Mademoiselle, is to keep everything masculine out of our apartment. They are all alike—men and parrots—they are never so happy as when they are lying to us. So let them go—Monsieur, Pierre, and Pierrot—the wretches! and trust to retributive justice to overtake them!"

But neither M. Bouchard nor Pierre seemed to fear the blindfolded lady with the sword. They were at that moment capering with glee, and Pierre was shouting:

"I wouldn't go back to the Rue Clarisse for a million of monkeys!"

And Papa Bouchard was saying:

"I have a confession to make. It is this: that I like a gay life, and, as this worthy fellow says, I would not go back to the Rue Clarisse for a million of monkeys. Victor, when next you have a little party of Pouters on hand, don't forget your Papa Bouchard."

"Indeed I won't," cried De Meneval, "and Fallière and I will promise to get twenty of the best fellows in the regiment and take you on the biggest lark you ever heard of in your life!"

"But pray don't forget, Pierre," said Papa Bouchard, "that we won't go back to the Rue Clarisse!"

"No!" shrieked Pierre, capering in ecstasy. "We won't go back to the Rue Clarisse!"

And Pierrot yelled as if inspired: "We won't go back to the Rue Clarisse! We're free! we're free! Gay dogs are we!"

MATILDE SERAO

(SIGNORA EDUARDO SCARFOGLIO)

(Greece, 1856)

THE CONQUEST OF ROME (1889)

(*La Conquista di Roma*)

This story was written by the versatile and favorite Italian author as a relaxation from her journalistic work on the *Corriere di Napoli*, of which she is the founder and editor. It is greatly admired as a faithful picture of modern Roman social and political life, and its only accurate translation into English forms one volume of *The Literature of Italy* series, published by the National Alumni.

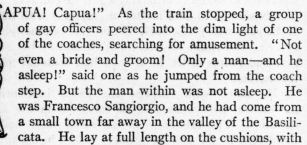 APUA! Capua!" As the train stopped, a group of gay officers peered into the dim light of one of the coaches, searching for amusement. "Not even a bride and groom! Only a man—and he asleep!" said one as he jumped from the coach step. But the man within was not asleep. He was Francesco Sangiorgio, and he had come from a small town far away in the valley of the Basilicata. He lay at full length on the cushions, with closed eyes, one hand within his coat clutching and caressing a little gold medal, which bore an idolized inscription: *Francesco Sangiorgio, XIVe Legislatura*. He was trying to forget his ten years of sordid legal practise; the black cross over the grave of the old deputy he had succeeded seemed to signify that his political triumph had been aided by Death.

The human cargo of histories and passions with which he was journeying was sleeping. Half in fear, half in vague, agitated longing, he remained awake and watchful. Yes, Rome was calling him! He clutched his precious medal, knowing that at last he could respond. The lonely landscape filled him with a longing for companionship. Unformed desires were in his mind; he saw in the great, gray station at dawn only colorless shapes of bustling humanity, but above the din he felt a strong consciousness of the great presence of Rome.

Sangiorgio's interest and taste in religion, in churches, and in architecture was provincial. The first morning's drive after his arrival was unimpressive to him, except for the one thing of interest to a deputy—the House of Parliament. But he was content; although unknown in the cafés and shops, he could see the crowds of *bourgeois* and elegant attachés at session and reception. As for all the signs of the dead past, they were nothing to him. He thought only of the future, and in rosy dreams beheld himself a central figure therein.

The newly sworn deputies soon became his friends. In his search for lodgings, his heart felt the chill of sordid, selfish Rome. With the instinct of a man fine as well as strong up to that time, he decided to take a grimy, ugly suite, with tattered, bespattered draperies, rather than the higher-priced lodgings where the desirability of having a private entrance for "special" friends seemed to be a matter of emphasis with the landladies. If he did not particularly notice the commonplace "tidies" covering the chairs and tables of the untidy but subtle women that had rooms to let, he at least had no mind for the women themselves.

He noted with surprise the jaded inattention and the mechanical performance of all functions in the assemblies of deputies. The crudeness of his rustic taste had made him indifferent to the glaring primary colors in cheap furnishings; but he was soon aware of the delicate shades of difference in Roman life, and awoke to a comprehension of its feminine puzzles, its half-hinted revelations showing how corrupt beneath was that which showed a fair outside. Even Christmas seemed unlike that day of sincere rites and yule-log celebration in his own part of the country, beside the hearth of his old parents, left by him almost without regret. A procession of veterans on the way to Garibaldi's home, which he followed until he met a Parliamentary colleague, interested him. But this fellow-deputy scorned any ceremony or sentiment. They smacked of the rawness of youth, he said, and of the folly of poetry. He thanked God he never had written any poetry! No, nor babbled in silly, tedious speeches, he added, in reply to Sangiorgio's questions, who was surprised at the listlessness of the ladies driving by in carriages, the indifference of the workmen and students pausing to listen to a fragile orator making a speech which should have been an eloquent reminder of the great events of 1848.

Giustini, the Tuscan deputy, who surprised Sangiorgio with his cynicism, tore the veil from the quiet city, the sight of which impressed the younger man as they stood looking down upon it and watching the passing carriages.

"Do not believe that Rome is quiet," said the Tuscan; "her women, her artists, her workers, her citizens and merrymakers, slumber not. Nor even down in those great palaces decorated by Michelangelo do curate, priest, monk or seminarist sleep. They love, hate, struggle, live for themselves, for the Church, and for the Pope! Do you say Rome has no beliefs? All is mystery: we have no beliefs—not even there in that furnace where our hearts and desires are burned up." The Tuscan pointed to the Montecitorio Palace (the House of Parliament) visible on the dusky horizon. "Once I, too, believed in Rome, and dreamed of her love, but she yields to no one. You must steel yourself against her inexorable heart—it is like *the heart of a woman who does not know how to love*, but who has seen everything and knows everything. But there must be something, someone in the world, that one day will come to trouble that serenity. He that would conquer Rome must dominate her, conquer her, and avenge the thousands of the vanquished who have touched her walls without being able to subjugate her. Yes, someone must conquer the superb city of Rome!"

"I will!" said Francesco Sangiorgio.

The Prime Minister, a man built on the common model for public servants, who can work sixteen hours a day, had just ended a dry statistical report when Sangiorgio made his maiden parliamentary speech. It was earnest, free from figures and oratory, and at once interested the gallery, where the ladies were, as well as the parties of the Right, the Left, and the Center.

It was a frank criticism of existing methods of government, a plea for the humble townspeople and the peasant. He showed that he knew the life of the provinces and evinced a human tenderness that was not merely a display of Southern oratory. The deputy from the barren district of the Basilicata made a hit that went straight to the heart. His address was only a plea against an added tax on salt, but it showed clearly what a heavy burden to the peasantry such a tax would be.

A handsome woman in the gallery, to whom he had been introduced in passing, the Countess Elena Fiammanti, was so charmed with the new orator that she sent in her card to him the next day at the Chamber. He made his way through the crowd of anxious or disappointed visitors in the anteroom that were forever begging for interviews with deputy or minister, and went outside to receive her congratulations. With some surprise he found himself first seated beside her in her carriage, then before a bright fire in her luxurious house. Her jewels, her brilliant yet furtive eyes, her dress, the soft lamps, rich colors, and studied elegance of this fastidious woman, the coffee served, the freedom to smoke, talk, or listen, gave a delightful sense of ease to the deputy from the country. She liked not solitude or books. "Nor do other women," she said. "They pretend a great deal, but they should follow the only way—take the gifts the gods provide and not expect too much!"

"That philosophy applies to love also," said Sangiorgio.

"Particularly to love," said Elena quickly.

In spite of the flattery of her words and actions, his judgment for some time was as cool as if he had come fresh from his bleak native hills. But, added to the natural intoxication of the day for him, the pose, the figure, the dress of the Countess at last asserted an alluring power, which veiled the slight vulgarity of her free actions and her cynical words:

"One hundred thousand lire for a true man or a faithful woman! Of course there are virtuous women—cold women, who do not know how to love. Now Donna Angelica, the wife of the Minister, is absolutely virtuous. Do you know her?"

"Yes—that is—by sight," Sangiorgio murmured.

Then in a rich, passionate, yet exquisite voice, sometimes soft, then powerful, like the woman herself, she sang to him, until the day ended in unresisting yielding to new emotions and surroundings.

Later in the summer an unusual stir arose in the Chamber. News of socialistic discussions and uprisings came up. Amid all the three hundred and fifty deputies no one seemed so cold, so distant as the deputy from the Basilicata. In the gallery the presence of a certain lady of rank indicated, like a barometer, an approaching crisis—and the fall of a cabinet. Again Francesco, in plain, direct accusations, swayed the Chamber. Without smile or gesture, he showed how unsystematic had been all recently enacted measures, and how negligent of his duties had been the Prime Minister. Sangiorgio's name was spoken of everywhere as that of a rising man.

On the day when the remains of Victor Emmanuel were to be removed to the Pantheon he gazed long, amid the gloom, the blue flames, and white tapers, at the pearly pallor of a sad, devout face. Music, incense, lips moving in prayer made him feel an impelling adoration for this woman, lost in a sort of voluptuousness of grief. To him she seemed a part of the service, and he wept; this woman, of whom the Countess Elena had spoken sneeringly, but whom he had admired with almost reverential respect, seemed to him the embodiment of all the tenderness, poetry, and religious sentiment heretofore lacking in his own life. She was Donna Angelica, wife of Silvio Vargas, Minister of the Interior, whose penetrating voice and shrewd speeches attested his seasoned mental vigor, though physically he suggested approaching senility. Angelica's soft, young roundness and slenderness formed a strong contrast to this old oak stick. Soon after this the elderly Minister made the acquaintance of Sangiorgio; he liked the young deputy and was more than willing, at his own house and in the Chamber, to assign to him the office of entertainer or escort to the neglected wife. But it was evident that the lady disliked not only politics but politicians. She complained that whenever her husband was at home their house seemed like an exchange or a commercial establishment in its reception of public men, who came and went continually, and took all the Minister's time.

The visits of the audacious Countess Fiammanti to Sangiorgio might well be forgotten by him under the absorbing spell of this new friend, with her purity of life, her scorn of false standards, her sacrifice of personal feeling to the power which her husband feverishly sought. While Sangiorgio was with her, her beauty, the fresh flowers she always carried, the imagined details of her life in her own rooms, where she often remained unmolested even by servants, were his absorbing study, and even when away from her, plunged in the whirl of public affairs, he could not wholly forget them.

One night there was a ball at the Quirinal, and through the dazzling, mystical scene of beauty, where bejeweled women, displaying snowy skins and glittering fabrics, sensuous music, and softened lights made a rich blending, he followed her. At last, after the royal presentations, he had the chance to feel how sweet, pure, and elegant she was, as she went with him through the crush of the ball seeking her husband in order to go home. But Silvio Vargas had to talk with men important to his plans, and he requested Sangiorgio to accompany his wife home. With what joy Sangiorgio obeyed, and what happiness it was to see her leaning back in the carriage, pure, colorless, serene, in her snowy draperies and simple, elegant white mantle, with diamonds gleaming in her dark hair like stars in a midnight sky.

Angelica sat near him motionless, in sweet, half-smiling silence, but at times she met her lover's eyes with the timid glance of a girl. What was passing beneath that mask of reserve? Did it conceal ardent dreams, sad thoughts, warm desires? Did that heart ever throb violently, or was it steeped in perpetual repose? He could not answer his own queries, and she remained enveloped in the mystery of her serenity.

But between those two beings—she, chaste, calm, religious, he, plunged in an abyss of intoxicating emotion—glided a third— Love!

Sangiorgio grew to feel that this was the love that touches the deeps of destiny. At Carnival time he was in no mood for the silly, brutal frolics common to those celebrations. He sought the park to meet Angelica. She came, half reluctantly, yet drawn despite herself.

"A man must have courage to keep his conscience," she told him in that interview. When he asked her plainly why they might not love, she leaned over the parapet, and, pointing to the noisy crowd below, said: "*They* will not let us! Besides, one should not love too late. Had we met five years earlier—before I married Silvio!" After being congealed by life with that glacier, could there be for her any sunlight? She had not even had a child to keep her heart warm—nothing but the long arctic night of association with a man of one idea—political ambition.

This self-centering of her woman's grief was to Sangiorgio a new phase of femininity. He begged only to be her devoted friend, only to have her trust, her confidence. But she had no faith in his promises, in spite of his assuring her that he loved her with a love unlike that of ordinary men. He refused to bid her a long farewell at the park gate, though she left him lonely amid the thousand carnival lamps, looking on at unshared joys.

After he had met her several times out on the desolate campagna a fear of malicious gossip from an ill-natured deputy, who was a friend of Silvio's and had caught a glimpse of them at one of these meetings, made her very reluctant to see Sangiorgio any more in public places. She often kept him waiting in a fever of impatience which left him as soon as she appeared; sometimes she failed to keep their appointments. He was humble, not daring to say anything that would cause pain. With the dumb but passionate patience of some natures he watched her gather the wild spring flowers, almost wishing that he might eat of those poisonous red berries, which would end his pain. Instead of doing this he laid away a cluster of them with a bit of her gown and a dried spray of lily-of-the-valley that she had worn. She was his Beatrice, his princess, his lady of the ivory tower.

In spite of all the inconvenience and danger of their meetings, for a long time Angelica would not see her lover at any more secluded place.

Finally one night at the opera she consented to let her lover find some rendezvous of comfort and security. In his own sordid lodgings a fever of desire possessed him: where should the rooms be? What could be worthy of his divinity?

Now that matters had taken this important turn Sangiorgio let his constituents and Parliament take care of themselves, while he looked for an apartment. At last he found one; it was tasteful, not too ornate; everything was in perfect harmony of shape and color. There was a charming drawing-room in soft brown tones. A bedroom in heavenly blue, with star-flecked ceiling, a dainty dressing-room in cream—all these were completed in four days. The eager lover wondered whether his lady might not think the effect perhaps a little too voluptuous. He felt dimly conscious that the *ensemble* suggested an idea altogether too material for a creature so divine.

But, after all his trouble, and the expense and debt he had assumed, Angelica held back. The apartment was in a street he liked—the Piazza di Spagna—but she would not relieve Sangiorgio's agony of expectation by saying what day or hour she might visit it. "Some time I will go!" was her only answer to his pleading. She disregarded his entire life, which day by day became devoted merely to useless vigils at the shrine where he hoped to install her as goddess. He passed hours of impatient idleness in the luxurious nest, leaving food untasted, official reports unfinished, friends and public duties ignored, all of which was noticed by his colleagues, some of whom began to criticize him severely. He bought flowers and firewood daily, but daily the wood and his hopes were both consumed to ashes. Nor could he, as heretofore, see her at her home, seek her at social functions, or find her in the ladies' gallery in Parliament.

But on a glorious first of May she came at last, saying: "I have delayed a long time, but I could not help it!"

She hardly noticed the flowers which he strewed over her dainty gray dress, or the great passion of relief that shone in his face. She wanted a friend, she said; she longed to cry out in her loneliness; she would come again. She stayed only a short time, going, as she came, with an air of innocence, as if this were an ordinary call upon another woman. Incidentally she asked whether he ever had cared for Elena Fiammanti—a woman of good heart, she thought, despite the gossip about her. Her promise to return within five days caused Sangiorgio to resume his parliamentary duties. But he took his papers mechanically; he could not get hold of what the speakers were talking about! Yes, he had been ill, he replied to one who questioned him as to his long absence and worn appearance. Walking and smoking in the corridors brought no return of interest; in weariness he returned to his old, ugly apartment, where even the Countess

Elena had recoiled at the greasy, frayed coverings and had tucked roses in various places to relieve the sordid surroundings. But he longed to lean his face on the chair that had been pressed by Angelica's head, and soon reëntered the nest in the Piazza di Spagna.

Although he felt that no reliance could be placed on her promises, a bitter tenderness was all Sangiorgio could feel when he saw Angelica again. All her other claims took precedence of his. She came at odd hours, unexpectedly, refusing to observe any fixed engagement. When she did visit the nest Sangiorgio listened to her confidences, to her detailed accounts of her tastes, her early life, and her present social affairs. The tender idealism of a true man for woman colored and exalted for him her lightest word. She talked of her moral widowhood, her indifference, and her enforced isolation from her husband. With veins on fire he listened to little tales of her habits and her home occupations. No one ever entered her sanctuary, she said; her dressing-room, where she preferred to dress her own hair, was never visited even by babbling servants. But her icy little air of inconsolable sadness held her lover always at a certain distance, in spite of the wild words that filled his thoughts but never passed his lips.

Angelica complained one day of the dull, endless routine of social life, and innocently suggested that he and she should go early some day into the country and take breakfast together, like children on a picnic? Sangiorgio reproached her with trying to torment him with such suggestions, but apparently she did not understand. She grew into the habit of calling often, at last, with no thought whatever, no idea, of the deeper dreamings of the man.

Yet he was only a man, after all! This cruel game of restraint was too much for any mortal. And when one day she offered to let down her hair to show its full beauty, he, knowing his limit of self-control, protested, saying: "I could not endure it!" But she only laughed like a girl, took the shell combs out and let down the splendid mass. With her usual little half smile she asked whether she might step into the bedchamber to rearrange it. In silence he watched her enter that room for the first time. But she did not look at the mirror. Her glance was caught at once by the blue quilt on the couch, bearing her own initial, A, embroidered in silver thread. With a startled cry she looked deep into Sangiorgio's eyes and therein read the truth. Silently she fastened up her hair, put on her hat, gathered up her gloves and flowers, and left him without a backward look.

One evening soon after this, when the ushers were putting out the lights of the Chamber after sessions, Silvio Vargas spoke to Sangiorgio in the porch of the Montecitorio.

"I wish to speak with you," he said.

"Very well; shall we go to your office?"

"No; to your home, if you please."

The Honorable Francesco Sangiorgio felt that through this man spoke the voice of Fate.

As he was about to lead Vargas toward his shabby bachelor rooms the Minister said, "That way?" in a tone of surprise. "Certainly," Francesco replied.

"But do you not live in the Piazza di Spagna?" Vargas inquired. Sangiorgio assented coldly, and with no emotion evident took Vargas to that nest of luxury. After both men were seated a slight pause ensued, which Sangiorgio broke by saying: "I am waiting, Silvio Vargas."

"I am thinking, Sangiorgio, how irresistible must be your desire to kill me."

"Almost irresistible—yes."

"But I am old! Death will come soon; can you not wait? You might be my son; would you kill your old father for his wealth? We will not fight, for we should only seem ridiculous. I even like you. Angelica is as a daughter to me. She has told me all; though I could not soothe her when she confessed that she had been to see you fifteen times. It was not fifteen but eighteen times, however. You remember that I am the Minister of the Interior and have means of obtaining accurate information. But you are right to love each other. After the fortieth year men have other passions than love. It is I who follow an illusion. You are wise. I am the fool—at seventy!"

Sangiorgio hid his face in self-reproach while he listened.

"Besides," the Minister continued, as if alone and musing

aloud, "that great power called man is ruled by a supreme law; it says: 'Do this and nothing else if you do not wish to sink into mediocrity. Have a singular passion, one sole ideal.' Love, science, politics, art—the highest expressions of human passion —are overmastering. Each would require the whole force of one being. You cannot embrace all. A man cannot be a lover and at the same time a true scientist, an artist, or a politician, without falling from greatness. He must choose; great passions are selfish; they demand great sacrifices."

After bitter reflection Francesco demanded sharply: "What is the wish of Signora Vargas?"

"That you leave Rome! And do not write to her," Vargas replied.

"Does she suffer?"

"She has suffered."

"May I ask whether you compel her to do this?"

"She acts of her own free will, Sangiorgio. She relies on your love and asks you to do this!"

"Very well, I will not return. Farewell, Silvio Vargas!"

"Farewell, Sangiorgio."

They parted under the portico. Sangiorgio turned back for one word more: "You knew that I loved Angelica and that she came here; how was it that you feared nothing?"

"Because I know my wife!" Vargas said significantly.

Sangiorgio understood. Like the husband, the lover now knew Angelica—*the woman that knew not how to love!*

While the House was still in session the deputy stole to the Speaker's private rooms. From there he sent in a letter to the House tendering his resignation, giving ill health as a reason. The reply came: they would give him three months for rest. Again he wrote, saying that his request must be final. The usher returned: his resignation had been accepted with regrets.

And this was the end! He was vanquished. How thin and valueless the little medal felt now! He had no wish to shake hands in farewell, to exchange parting words. He had no desire for food. He went to his dusty, shabby old rooms, reeking in midsummer heat, with a tumult in his brain. He threw himself face down upon the bed, utterly relaxed in his misery. His debts—even Rome, the scene of his dreams of conquest—were only a part of the general ruin of his hopes.

To and fro on the railway platform a man with the unseeing eyes of a somnambulist was pacing. He had not enough money to buy a first-class ticket, but he did not care about that. He stumbled against others and took his second-class seat mechanically when the guard called. He was bound for a remote village in the Basilicata. As the train moved he appeared to waken. He sprang to the coach door. Wistfully he gazed back upon Rome, the imperial mistress—dark, immense, overwhelming, upon her seven hills shining with dazzling lights—where he had left his shattered dreams of her glorious conquest. Then he sank back upon the seat like one smitten with death, for, in very truth, through the wile of a woman, Rome had conquered him!

GEORGE BERNARD SHAW

(Ireland, 1856)

THE IRRATIONAL KNOT (1880)

In a preface to the American edition of this novel, in 1905, Mr. Shaw says it was written by him in London in 1880, a few years after he had exported himself thither from his native Dublin. He was twenty-four years old when he wrote it, and it was his second novel. All the London publishers, and some American ones, refused to publish it, and it was brought out by Mrs. Annie Besant, as a serial, in her small propagandist magazine. Mr. Shaw admits that he was extremely "raw and inexperienced in the English side of the life portrayed," and hardly blames the publishers for declining the book, if "its defects and not its qualities were what deterred them." Mr. Shaw fantastically disavows his present self (1905) as its author, since physiologists declare that the substance of the body changes entirely every eight years; and, consequently, it was written by his literary great-grandfather. Though even his recollection of this ancestor is obscured by the lies a man tells to himself about himself, he remembers well that the novel was written on very cheap paper, and that he constrained his natural indolence to writing five pages of this demy in quarto each day until the work was finished. He refreshed himself during the task by hearing Bizet's *Carmen*, which was then new in London. His own experience in the National Telephone Company in London helped him, and he was also a skilful accompanist on the piano. Mr. Shaw declines to recommend anyone to read *The Irrational Knot*, which he thinks is one of those heaps of spoiled material that every apprenticement involves. But he hastens to say that, as some who have read *Man and Superman* have actually told him that *Cashel Byron's Profession* was his best work, there may be a public for even *The Irrational Knot*.

N an untidy apartment on the first floor of a house in York Road, Lambeth, a muscular, well-developed young Irishman of thirty, with tanned face and auburn hair, was tying a white tie. Concentrated and calm, he did even this with no fumbling. A handsome young woman, with dark eyes and olive complexion, was standing, in her petticoat and red silk stays, before a glass on the mantelpiece, arranging her black hair. On concluding her task, she snatched up a pink program and read off the numbers of a concert "for the People" to be given

that evening, at Wandsworth, by the Countess of Carbury, making caustic comments upon the selections. Conolly, being now ready to go out, picked it delicately from her fingers and left the room. His sister damned him very heartily, and when she was dressed she sent for a cab and was driven to the Prince's Theater, Soho.

At the concert Conolly met the Society artists and their friends: Miss Marian Lind, a beautiful young woman with light-brown hair and gentle gray eyes; Miss Elinor McQuinch, her cousin, who was lean, black-eyed and restless; Marmaduke Lind, Marian's cousin also, droll and red-haired; Rev. George Lind, her brother, the fashionable incumbent of a church in Belgravia; a literary, snobbish woman, Mrs. Leith Fairfax, and Sholto Douglas, a tall, dark, handsome young man, who was rather patronizing.

Conolly was made conscious by these swells of the fact that he "worked" in Lord Jasper Carbury's electrical laboratory; but Miss Lind, for whom he played an accompaniment when her friend Elinor found she had forgotten the music, was rather cordial. They all had perforce to admire his excellent barytone voice. He explained to Miss Lind that his grandfather had been a great *buffo*, and that his father was for years connected with the theater. He himself had served an apprenticeship of six years to an electrical engineer in America, and it was his ambition to invent a cheap electro-motor. Lord Jasper Carbury's fad was electricity.

After the concert, as it was only ten, Marmaduke Lind proposed to Conolly that they should drop in at the Bijou and hear Lalage Virtue in a new burlesque, promising to introduce him to the lady later. Mr. Lind was somewhat surprised to find that Conolly was the young woman's brother, while the young woman was surprised and not a little irritated to learn that her friend's name was Marmaduke Lind, and not Marmaduke Sharp. She declined to go to supper. When Conolly had bidden his sister good night after their return home, he turned back and remarked: "He must be the Marmaduke Lind who is to marry Lady Constance Carbury, my noble pupil's sister."

"It matters very little whom he marries," she retorted sharply.

"If he saw the working of perfect frankness without affection, and perfect liberty without refinement between us, he might be led to conclude that it means a great deal," said her brother.

Mr. Reginald Harrington Lind, Marian's father, was the fourth son of a younger brother of the Earl of Carbury. He married the heiress of a Lancashire cotton-spinner. She eloped, on the eve of her fourth confinement, with a professor of spiritualism, and died, leaving Lind seven thousand pounds a year. He did not marry again. The elder boy ultimately entered the army, and the other, George, entered the Church. Marian had lived in a perpetual round of visits to her relatives while the boys were being educated. Elinor McQuinch was a favorite of Marian's, and when Mr. Lind took a house at Westbourne Terrace, Paddington, she was invited to stay with them, which she was glad to do, for she was idolatrously attached to Marian. At the time of the Wandsworth concert she had been her companion four years.

The day following that concert Sholto Douglas called on Marian and in his highly conscious manner asked her to marry him, which she declined to do. Marmaduke also called, learned that Lady Constance Carbury would be in town the following week, and later, after a very stormy interview with Lalage Virtue, concluded by suggesting a private marriage until he should be a little more on his feet.

"*Marry* you! Catch me! No collar round my neck. I can support myself well enough without that. But don't look so dazed. What difference does it make to *you?*"

"But—" He stopped, bewildered, and gazed at her.

"Get out, you great goose!" she retorted, and springing out of the hansom in which they had come, darted into the theater.

In August Marian and Elinor were guests at Lady Carbury's. Jasper, her son, had prohibited any visitors but friends, as he wished to devote himself to his electrical investigations.

The Reverend George came to the Carburys' not long after this, with the news that Marmaduke had taken a cottage in West Kensington and was living there with a young woman. This was rather annoying, since there was a sort of virtual understanding that he was to marry Lady Constance, who was more than willing and who had a jealous, exacting temperament.

Marian bethought her that Edward Conolly might see Marmaduke and let him know that his interests and the family peace demanded that he should come to the Carburys' and give up this liaison. Conolly understood, of course, that the young actress who was living with Marmaduke was his sister Susanna. He called at Laurel Lodge and delivered Marian's message. As Marmaduke was felicitating himself that Conolly had not seen his sister, Conolly remarked, as he was holding Lind's hand in parting:

"If I may ask, how is Susanna?"

Susanna appeared before the stupefied Marmaduke was able to ejaculate a word, and Conolly said:

"I have been admiring the villa, Susanna. It is better than our place at Lambeth. You won't mind my hurrying away: I have a great deal to do in town. Good-by; good-by, Mr. Lind."

Marmaduke told Susanna he had to go down to Carbury for a few days, and this precipitated a quarrel; so that they parted in anger.

Marian's feelings may be imagined when she learned from Marmaduke who it was that she had selected as her ambassador to him. When she saw Conolly she apologized for what she had done, and was amazed to see with what coolness he advanced his views on the subject. He regarded Susanna's case quite objectively. He himself was to leave Carbury. When he raised his hat on parting, Marian, with a smile, put out her hand. He took it for the first time, looked at her gravely for a moment, and left her.

Two years later Conolly had perfected his electric motor, and a company was formed in which Marian's father and Lord Carbury were directors. Sholto Douglas had returned from his long exile, wearing a fine, glossy, black beard. Susanna had presented Marmaduke with a little daughter. His family had threatened to disinherit him, but he had checked that move by declaring that if they did he would marry the lady.

One May morning Marian received a characteristic letter from Edward Conolly in which he asked her to become his wife. He felt bound to tell her that, while he never would interfere in any way with her actions so far as they concerned herself, he was prejudiced against religions of all sorts.

"I will not go through a ceremony in any church, nor will I permit my wife to teach my children to know Christianity in any other way than that in which an educated Englishman knows Buddhism."

He requested Marian to give him her decision at the Academy about four the following day. She met him there, and became his promised wife.

Mrs. Leith Fairfax, by her ingenious meddling, had in the mean time convinced Sholto Douglas that Marian was in love with him. Later, when he met Marian, some covert allusions of hers to a surprising condition of sentiment in which she found herself further confirmed, apparently, Mrs. Fairfax's statements. Douglas spoke to Mr. Lind on the subject soon afterward, when dining at Mr. Lind's, and his rage, as well as Mr. Lind's, may be imagined when Marian, seeing what an unpleasant mistake existed in the mind of each of them, declared her engagement to Conolly. Mr. Lind imperiously ordered Marian to go to her room.

"I wish I were under Mr. Conolly's protection now," she said, flushed and indignant, as she obeyed.

Mr. Lind had an interview with Conolly the next day at the offices of the Conolly Electro-Motor Company. He learned a great deal about his future son-in-law, and he also learned that he could not prevent his marrying his daughter. He married her, in fact, very soon after this. Mrs. Conolly used to accompany him in his trips to English places where he went to establish offices of the company, and after this had been pretty well accomplished, they traveled on the Continent.

Nearly eighteen months later, when Nelly McQuinch came to pay Marian a visit at Holland Park, after their return to London, she soon realized that there was some peculiar disaffection on Marian's part toward her husband. He did not consult Marian as he had done in the beginning. Marian warned Elinor not to say anything to Ned that could make any coldness between them.

"He is so clever that he would at once conjecture from your sarcastic remarks just what I have been saying about him to you. I am clinging to him with all my heart and soul, and you must help me, Nelly."

At this time affairs with Marmaduke and Susanna were pretty bad. The woman had become a dipsomaniac, and was constantly intoxicating herself with champagne. Marmaduke was unable to prevent her drinking, and he dreaded the influence of such a spectacle on his little three-year-old daughter, Lucy. Conolly had calmly advised Susanna to get a barrel of brandy, and condense the process of killing herself into a few days. His sister had accepted an American engagement, as her London vogue was greatly impaired by her intemperate life. She did not mean to leave the stage until she was forced to. In the mean time Sholto Douglas frequented the Conollys' house a good deal.

In October Marian visited friends in Sark. One evening Conolly was surprised by a call from Mrs. Leith Fairfax, who had been in Sark, and had come with the amiable purpose of stirring up Conolly by remarks about the attentions Marian was receiving at Sark, especially from Sholto Douglas. She advised his going down there. He received her insinuations with such perfect self-possession and entire lack of resentment, or even disapproval, that the lady broke down and declared that her only wish had been to save Marian. Whereupon Conolly's *sang-froid* vanished and he said with entire frankness:

"My dear Mrs. Fairfax, I am now deeply and sincerely obliged to you"; and he kissed her hand with all the grace of a man of the world.

After her departure the Reverend George arrived, evidently, as soon appeared, on a like mission. To him Conolly said:

"If you go down there, you will find that Douglas is in love with my wife. She knows it, has told me that he is, and rather likes it. Every married woman requires a holiday from her husband occasionally, even when he suits her perfectly. If Marian had been educated rightly she would be a strong woman as well as an amiable one. I pity her. She may turn for relief to love or to religion. For her sake I hope it may be the first, as the less permanent of the two evils. The difference between us is neither her fault nor mine, and no explanations can remove it."

It was not long after Marian's return from Sark before Conolly had to take a hurried business trip to Glasgow. On his return to his home he found Nelly McQuinch there and a brief letter from Marian, which he read to her distressed friend. It ran thus:

"Our marriage was a mistake. I am going away with Douglas to the other side of the world. It is all I can do to mend matters. Pray forget me."

Then Conolly, dropping his wonted half-playful manner in speaking to ladies, spoke out clearly and fully.

"I have asked myself once or twice how long the condition into which Marian and I had lapsed would keep up. Since the end had to come I am not sorry that it has, though I regret the manner of it. Instead of eloping with Douglas in the conventional way, we could have obtained a divorce without any scandal. I never have made any claims on her since she found out that she didn't care for me. When I married Marian I realized that for me to marry into her class was a *mésalliance*. I am a worker, and I admit no loafing aristocrat as my equal. The man at the bench who does his work the best he can is my equal. I soon began to feel that Marian's lungs could not breathe the air on which I subsist. My love for her is over. She would have to be born over—a thing that can happen—to bring us into sympathy again. Now you have the story from my point of view. I shall apply for a divorce; I shall not be heard crying out misery and disgrace; I have nothing to say against her, and I do not think she has anything to say against me."

When Conolly was left alone he ate his dinner, played on the organ until nearly midnight, took a short walk, and then went to bed and was soon asleep.

On Christmas day Miss McQuinch received a letter from Marian in New York, in which she admitted she had made an utter fool of herself.

"I wish I were back with Ned again," she wrote. "Sholto is a—I don't know what epithet is fair. But Ned, as usual, was right in his estimate of him. His reserves of talent (Sholto's) existed only in our imagination. As he has sacrificed his prospects for me, I cannot honorably desert him. But my only hope is that he will tire of me, when he will have no remorse in departing." In the inevitable postscript, Marian mentioned that

Lalage Virtue, Ned's sister, had failed completely in America. Her dissipated habits had spoiled any chance for success.

One January afternoon the break came in New York. In an irritable moment Douglas insulted the woman who had left her husband for him.

"Good-by," she said, stepping quietly to the electric button in the hotel room and pressing it. "I will never see you again if I can help it. If you follow me, or persecute me in any way, I will seek the protection of the police as Mrs. Conolly. I despise you more than anyone on earth."

He snatched up his coat and hat. As he was leaving the waiter appeared. Douglas pointed at Marian and said:

"I will not be accountable for that woman's expenses from this time forth. You can keep her at your own risk, or turn her into the streets to pursue her profession, as you please." With this he departed.

Marian counted her money. She had a little more than one hundred dollars. She called on a New York woman whose acquaintance she had made on the steamer, and confided the state of things to her. Mrs. Crawford put herself out for a relative of the Earl of Carbury, and Marian found herself in two small rooms, in an unfashionable quarter. A woman who was fond of drink lived on the same floor, but Marian did not let that deter her. She was too anxious to be settled somewhere cheaply until she could hear from a cablegram she had sent to England to Elinor McQuinch: "Separated. Write to new address. Have I forfeited my money?"

As she was going to her room she heard a husky voice calling to the maid: "Eliza! *Eli'*-za!" Marian started. There was something familiar in the tones, but she could not place them. That night, as she was going to her bedroom, she saw a woman coming down the stairs. Her black hair had tumbled down over a crimson satin dressing-gown, which was stained very badly. The once fine face had a thirsty, reckless leer that filled Marian with loathing. The woman almost screamed as she saw her. Then she exclaimed: "Mrs. Ned!" To Marian's look of astonishment, she replied:

"I'm your sister-in-law. Perhaps you didn't know you had one. I was as good-looking as you once. Don't drink, Mrs.

Ned. Champagne leads to brandy; and brandy to—" Susanna indicated herself with a grimace. "Did Ned send you here? How is Marmaduke? He wasn't blameless like Ned, but he was a nice sort to get along with." She then obtained from Marian a promise to come and see her the following day.

Not long afterward Susanna was in such a state that Mrs. Kemp asked Marian to step in and try to quiet her.

She found Susanna in a querulous but reminiscent mood. When she spoke to her about Lucy Susanna said it was a relief to have the child off her hands.

"I wonder whether I shall get any ease before there is an end of me?" she exclaimed peevishly.

"Perhaps the end for you on earth may be a good beginning for you somewhere else, Susanna."

"Thank you! That is a nice, cheerful turn to the conversation, isn't it? I've got to take my chance, anyhow, and I can't be much worse off than I am now. Stay till I go to sleep, will you?"

Marian sat listening to her moaning respiration for half an hour. Then she went to her room to get her writing-desk. She heard Susanna stirring, then the clink of a bottle and a heavy fall. She rushed back to find Susanna on her hands and knees near the stove. She rose, her face streaming with blood from a wound in her temple, and then tumbled forward. Marian fainted. When she came to and asked the doctor how Susanna was, he said:

"It's all over with her. It's just as well. She would have died a worse death but for this accident."

When Marian explained to him her own state of health, he asked a few questions, and then told her she might expect to be a mother in a few months.

Marian's despair at the thought that a reconciliation with her husband was now impossible showed her how homesick she really was. She was not disposed to go near Susanna, now that any aid was impossible; but the thought that Conolly might think this unfeeling led her to do so. She found Susanna decently laid out, with the maid's rosary and crucifix on her breast, while a statue of the Blessed Virgin and lighted candles were on a table at her side.

Marian went to Mrs. Crawford's and spent the evening there. After she had been home in her room for a while she heard a sound up-stairs, in Susanna's room. She nerved herself to go there, and when she opened the door she found her husband sitting by his sister's body. He started violently. She closed the door and stood facing him.

"Marian, here—" he indicated the bed—"is an end of hypocrisies. Let us have the truth now. Say something real to me. You never told me the truth, because you never told yourself the truth."

"Had we not better go down-stairs?" she said.

He acquiesced, and when in her room he asked: "Now, about the future. Will you give the life at Holland Park another trial?"

"It is good of you to offer to take me back, I know. If I decline to come, will it disappoint you, Ned?"

"I am prepared to adapt myself to either circumstances."

"Yes. I forget. You foresee everything," she said, with some bitterness.

"No. I only face what I see. That is the reason you do not like living with me. Good-by. Do not look troubled. We shall meet again often, I hope; but to-night makes an end of the irrational knot."

"Good night." She proffered her hand, rather forlornly.

"One folly more," he said, taking her in his arms and kissing her. "If such a moment could be eternal, we never should say good-by. As it is, we are wise not to tempt Fortune by asking for such another."

"You are too wise, Ned," she said, letting him replace her gently in the chair.

"It is impossible to be too wise, dearest," he replied, and turned unhesitatingly and left her.

CASHEL BYRON'S PROFESSION (1882)

With this novel the author published a dramatic version in blank verse. Another dramatization, in prose, was made by Stanislaus Stange and was played in 1906.

IN her twenty-fifth year Lydia Carew found herself the independent possessor of Wiltstoken Castle, an annual income of about forty thousand pounds, and a reputation for vast learning and exquisite culture. She had spent several years traveling with her father, a man of active mind and bad digestion, with a taste for sociology, science in general and the fine arts, on which subjects he had written books and earned a reputation as a critic and philosopher. As he was very irritable and fastidious, Lydia in assisting him had learned self-control and endurance and acquired a habit of independent mental activity.

After Mr. Carew's death, which occurred in his daughter's twenty-fifth year, Lydia found a letter in which he told her something of his separation from her mother. After expressing his affection for her, he said:

"Some day, I expect and hope, you will marry. You will then have an opportunity of making an irremediable mistake, against the possibility of which no advice of mine or subtlety of yours can guard you. If you fail in this remember that your father, after suffering a bitter and complete disappointment in his wife, yet came to regard his marriage as the happiest event of his career. Beware of men who have read more than they have worked, or who love to read better than to work. Beware of artists of all sorts, except very great artists. Self-satisfied workmen who have learned their business well, whether they be chancellors of the exchequer or farmers, I recommend to you as, on the whole, the most tolerable class of men I have met."

In the May that followed Mr. Carew's death Lydia went to

227

Wiltstoken Castle, and wandering about the park one day found herself in a long avenue of green turf. Suddenly she realized that this must be the elm vista whose privacy was stringently insisted upon by an invalid tenant to whom Warren Lodge and the elm vista had been let before her decision to spend the spring at Wiltstoken. She hastened toward an opening and came into the sunlight, then stopped, dazzled by an apparition, which she at first took to be a beautiful statue, but presently recognized, with a glow of delight, as a living man. He was clad in a jersey and knee-breeches of white, and his arms shone like those of a gladiator. It came into Lydia's mind that she had disturbed an antique god in his sylvan haunt. Then she perceived another man, who looked like a groom and was contemplating his companion as a groom might look upon an exceptionally fine horse. He was the first to see Lydia, and the statue-man, following his sinister look, stared with undisguised admiration at the small, graceful woman, with the glorious ruddy gold hair, who turned and went away quietly through the trees.

On her way back Lydia almost believed that the godlike figure was only the Hermes of Praxiteles changed by a daydream into reality, and the groom one of those incongruities characteristic of dreams; and she dwelt on her vision with a pleasure she would not have ventured to indulge had it concerned a creature of flesh and blood.

The next evening Lydia's cousin, Lucian Webber, dined at the castle; and she proposed that she and her companion, Alice Goff, should walk to the station with him. On the platform they saw Lord Worthington and a young man whom Lydia recognized as the Hermes of yesterday modernized. He carried himself smartly, balancing himself so accurately that he seemed to have no weight. His expression was self-satisfied and good-humored. But—! Lydia felt that there was a "but" somewhere; that he must be something more than a handsome, powerful, and light-hearted young man.

She asked Lord Worthington, in case his friend were her tenant, whom he had recommended, to present him. Lord Worthington hesitated; then, his eyes twinkling mischievously, said:

"Mr. Cashel Byron, Miss Carew."

When they left the station he said:

"I saw you in the park yesterday and I thought you were a ghost. But my trai—my man—saw you too."

"Strange!" replied Lydia. "I had the same fancy about you. I thought you a statue."

"A statue!"

"You do not seem flattered."

"It is not flattering to be taken for a lump of stone," he replied ruefully. Lydia looked at him thoughtfully. Here was a man whom she had mistaken for the finest image of manly strength and beauty in the world; and he was so devoid of artistic culture that he held a statue to be a distasteful lump of stone.

He interested her, and she concluded that he was a gentleman unaccustomed to society. She thought he had some occupation, for he did not seem like an idler, yet he did not fit into any ordinary profession; and there was something formidable in him that gave her an unaccountable thrill of pleasure.

Cashel Byron was a prize-fighter. He was the son of a beautiful and successful Shakespearian actress known as Adelaide Gisborne. Mrs. Byron had alternately spoiled and bullied Cashel until he had come to regard her with sullen defiance; and as he grew the lack of subtlety and imagination that made him unable to act up to her in her maternal rôle and his sulky endurance of her endearments, displeased her; and she sent him to school. There, being compelled to defend himself, he became the best fighter among the boys; but his distaste for books and his wretched standing as a student caused many complaints to be made to his mother. When he was seventeen he found that she intended him to remain at Moncrief House two years longer; therefore he ran away and reached Melbourne, where he became assistant in a gymnasium conducted by Ned Skene, ex-champion of England and the colonies. Cashel was unfitted by his education and circumstances for anything better than the profession into which Skene launched him; and in that he soon became celebrated. He had recently come to England from America, and was training at Warren Lodge for a fight in which Lord Worthington was interested.

Cashel had fallen in love with Lydia the instant that she

appeared before him in the park. Though he had been popular with the young women whom Mrs. Skene knew in Melbourne, he had disliked them; for, though his mother had made it impossible for him to be very fond of her, she had nevertheless given him his ideal of what a woman should be; and to him Lydia seemed an angel as she appeared among the trees. He took every opportunity to see her, but would not tell her his profession, and even asked her not to try to find out. He was little more than a boy at heart, and his simplicity made him as much an enigma to Lydia as was she to him by her learning and her attitude toward him. One day when they met in London she declared that he was an enigma to her, and he replied mournfully:

"I'm a pretty plain enigma, I should think. I would rather have you than any woman in the world; but you're too rich and grand for me. If I can't have the satisfaction of marrying you, I may as well have the satisfaction of telling you so."

Lydia forbade such a subject, though it brought a faint color to her cheeks and she wondered at the novel sensation. Still she allowed him to attend her Fridays until her cousin Lucian told her of Cashel's profession. Lydia realized that Cashel had obtruded his profession upon her at their every meeting; but she, ignorant of the very existence of such a calling, had understood nothing.

The day that Cashel received her note saying that she had discovered his secret, and that he must not come again, he went to see her. In response to her query as to whether he could not find some nobler occupation, he declared flatly that he could not; but he said he should retire after the next match, and he asked Lydia to marry him, saying that he should be worth five hundred a year and he presumed she had as much more. Lydia told him he was mistaken as to the amount of her income, and when he heard the actual sum Cashel became very red.

"I see," he said, in a voice broken by mortification, "I have been making a fool of myself," and he turned to go.

"It does not follow that you should go at once," said Lydia, betraying nervousness for the first time. "I am grateful to you because you have sought me for my own sake, knowing nothing of my wealth."

"I should think not," groaned Cashel. "Your wealth is a

settler for me. I hope, Miss Carew, that you'll excuse me for making such an ass of myself. It's all my blessed innocence; I never was taught any better."

"I have no quarrel with you save for hiding the truth."

"If only you hadn't been kind to me," said Cashel. "I think the reason I love you so much is that you're the only person that is not afraid of me. And you knew I was afraid of you; yet you were as good as gold."

He asked whether he should never see her again, and Lydia told him never as the prize-fighter, and at last Cashel said:

"I never was happier in my life, though I'm crying inside all the time. I'll have a try for you yet. Good-by. No," he added, turning from her proffered hand, "I daren't touch it; I should eat you afterward." And he ran out of the room.

Lydia took from her desk her father's last letter, and sat looking at it.

"It would be a strange thing, father, if your paragon should turn aside from her friends, the artists, philosophers, and statesmen, to give herself to an illiterate prize-fighter. I felt a pang of absolute despair when he replied to my forty thousand pounds a year with an unanswerable good-by."

It happened at this time that Mrs. Byron returned to London from a long tour of America and the colonies. She had been almost forgotten in London, while she had grown rich playing in the provinces the half-dozen characters in which she was most effective. A certain actor-manager was about to make an elaborate presentation of *King John* and engaged Mrs. Byron, or Adelaide Gisborne, to play Constance; and he requested Lydia to allow her to inspect a certain scrap of vellum containing an illumined picture of Lady Constance, which Mr. Carew had bought. Accordingly Mrs. Byron one day called, and Lydia was convinced by the first look at her eyes, by the first sound of her voice, that she was Cashel's mother. Apart from her interest in Cashel's mother, Lydia was attracted and amused by her guest's odd acquirements and unreasonable character and felt the charm of her personality. She surprised herself at last in the act of speculating whether she could ever make Cashel love her as his father must have loved her visitor.

There was then in England an African king about to be

restored to his kingdom, which England had stolen a few years before and found useless. He was difficult to amuse or impress; and finally a grand assault-at-arms was arranged for his entertainment, to which Lydia asked Lord Worthington to take her. The show progressed through several phases of skilled violence, and Lydia's mind wandered farther and farther from the place, until suddenly she saw a dreadful-looking man coming toward her across the arena, a man with a hideous head and enormous hands and feet, though otherwise well made. Then, looking again, she saw Cashel, exactly as she had seen him at Wiltstoken for the first time, approaching the ring with an indifferent air.

"A god coming down to compete with a gladiator!" whispered Lord Worthington eagerly. "If he could go into society looking like that the women—"

"Hush!" said Lydia, as if his words were intolerable.

The two men drew on gloves, and the master of ceremonies shouted: "Paradise, a professor. Cashel Byron, a professor. Time!" Of the two men Paradise shocked Lydia least; for in Cashel's relentless watching there was something infernal. Cashel played with his opponent until Paradise lost all pretense of good humor, tore off his gloves, and leaped upon Cashel before he could remove his; and the two men laid hold of one another. There was a roar of indignation when Paradise seized Cashel's shoulder in his teeth as they struggled for a throw. Then Cashel threw Paradise, and a distracting wrangle followed. Cashel seemed to have no self-control and outswore and outwrangled everyone, until Lord Worthington dropped into the ring and whispered to him. Then Cashel suddenly subsided, pale and ashamed.

Lydia declared that she had seen enough, and went home. The following day she returned to Wiltstoken. There she remained till autumn, preparing her father's letters and memoirs for publication, using Warren Lodge for a study. On the twelfth of August she noticed that the roads beyond the meadows were thronged. The forenoon passed away peacefully until suddenly there was a rustle and a swift footstep without. Then Cashel rushed in and stopped, stupefied at Lydia's presence. He was dressed in a pea-jacket too small for him which showed that he wore nothing underneath it, and white knee-breeches, grass-stained. On his face was a mask of sweat, dust, and blood. Underneath his left eye was a mound of bluish flesh as large as a walnut. His jaw and cheek were severely bruised, and his lip was cut through at one corner.

"I didn't know there was anyone here," he said in a hoarse whisper. "The police are after me. I have fought for an hour and run over a mile, and I'm dead beat. Let me hide in the back room, and tell them you haven't seen anyone—will you?"

"You ask me to shelter you," said Lydia sternly. "What have you done?"

"I've been fighting, and it's illegal. You don't want to see me in prison, do you? Confound Paradise, a steam-hammer wouldn't kill him!"

"Go," said Lydia, with uncontrollable disgust. "How dare you come to me?"

"Very well," said Cashel, panting heavily, "I'll go."

As he spoke he opened the door; but involuntarily shut it immediately, for a crowd of men, police and others, were hurrying through the elm vista. Cashel cast a half-piteous, half-desperate glance around, which Lydia could not resist.

"Quick!" she cried, opening one of the inner doors. "Go in there."

He slunk in submissively, and when the policeman entered and asked whether she had seen anyone pass she pointed out a glade across which she had seen Cashel run, unrecognized, before he had come to the door. They had Paradise, who was a shocking spectacle, and Lydia told the sergeant to take him to the castle, where they might all obtain refreshment. When the last straggler had disappeared Cashel cautiously entered, looking cold and anxious.

"Are they all gone? Where are you going? Won't you speak to me?"

"Just this," she replied with passion. "Let me never see you again. The very foundations of my life are loosened: I have told a lie. Even your wild-beast handiwork is a less evil than the bringing of a falsehood into the world. Keep the hiding-place I have given you. I never will enter it again."

Cashel, appalled, shrank back and neither stirred nor spoke

as she left the lodge; then he went out and gave himself up to the police.

The idea that she had disjointed the whole framework of things by creating a false belief filled Lydia's mind and pressed heavily upon her. The one conviction that she had brought out of her reading, observing, reflecting, and living was that concealment of a truth must produce mischief. She resumed her work next day with shaken nerves and a longing for society; but she resolved to conquer her loneliness and work more diligently.

One afternoon Mrs. Skene came to see her, to plead for Cashel, who, she declared, was moping and fretting over what Lydia had said to him and his arrest.

"In what way did you expect to relieve Mr. Byron's mind by visiting me? Did he ask you to come?"

"He'd have died first. Why won't you marry him, miss?"

"Because I don't choose to, Mrs. Skene," said Lydia with perfect good humor.

Mrs. Skene urged her to consider and told her of Cashel's good qualities. "How happy you ought to be, miss, a gentleman born and bred, champion of the world, sober, honest, spotless as the unborn babe, and mad in love with you."

"I must take time to consider what you have so eloquently urged, Mrs. Skene. You have produced a great effect on me," said Lydia, with an irrepressible smile.

"If I might just tell him——"

"Nothing. I can only assure you that you have softened the hard opinion I had of Mr. Byron's actions." Then, after considering, she said she could not see how he could have acted otherwise than he did; but she made Mrs. Skene promise to tell him nothing for a fortnight, after which she might tell him what she pleased.

As Mrs. Skene was going, Lydia said:

"Does Mr. Byron ever *think?*"

"Think!" said Mrs. Skene emphatically. "Never! There isn't a more cheerful lad in existence."

Lydia, in searching her father's books, came upon a volume of poems open at a page that had evidently lain open often before.

"What would I give for a heart of flesh to warm me through
    Instead of this heart of stone, ice-cold whatever I do;
    Hard and cold and small, of all hearts most of all."

Lydia read and reread the lines. "If such a doubt as that
haunted my father it will haunt me, unless I settle what is to be
my heart's business now and forever. If it be possible for a
child of mine to escape this curse of autovivisection, it must in-
herit its immunity from its father—from the man of emotion
who never thinks, and not from the woman of introspection who
cannot help thinking. Be it so."

Before many days Lydia summoned Cashel to her house to
bring about a meeting there with his mother—a surprise to them
both. Cashel at first received his mother's embraces and expressions of admiration and affection with his old schoolboy
sullenness; but after Lydia had left them he interrupted Mrs.
Byron's raptures with the suggestion that perhaps she could
help him, and told her of his love for Lydia. At first she was
contemptuous at the idea of his aspiring to Miss Carew's hand.
Then after a few moments' consideration she said:

"After all, I do not see why you should not. When your
uncle dies I suppose you will succeed to the Dorsetshire
property."

"I heir to a property?"

"Yes, to old Bingley Byron."

"Well, I am blowed! But—supposing he is my uncle, am I
his lawful heir?"

"My dearest child, nothing can be clearer than your title."

"Well," said Cashel, blushing, "a lot of people used to make
out that you weren't married at all."

"What!" exclaimed Mrs. Byron indignantly. "Oh, they
dare not say so!"

"Tell me one thing, though, mamma. Was my father a
gentleman?"

"Of course."

"Then I am as good as any of the swells that think themselves her equals?"

"You are perfectly well connected by your mother's side,
Cashel. The Byrons are only commoners; but even they are
one of the oldest county families in England."

Cashel in excitement questioned her eagerly as to the value of the property to which he was heir; then he asked her to go and let him speak to Lydia alone. When he had seen her to the door he stole up-stairs to the library, where he found Lydia reading.

"She's gone," he said.

Lydia looked up at him, saw with a spasm of terror what was coming, and said with an effort: "I hope you have not quarreled."

"Lord bless you, no. I asked her to go away because I wished to be alone with you. She's told me a whole heap of things about myself. My birth is all right: I'm heir to a county family that came over with the Conqueror, and I shall have a decent income. Won't you marry me? I'm not such a fool as you think; and—you're fond of me in a sort of way, ain't you?"

"Yes, I'm fond of you in a sort of way. But have you considered that henceforth you will be an idle man, and that I shall always be a busy woman, preoccupied with work that may appear very dull to you?"

"I won't be idle. There's lots of things I can do besides boxing. And I won't expect you to give up your whole life to me. So long as you are mine, and nobody else's, I'll be content. And I'll be yours and nobody else's. You do whatever you like; and I'll do whatever you like. You have a conscience; so I know that whatever you like will be the best thing. Come!"

Lydia looked around as if for a means of escape.

"It can't be," said Cashel pathetically, "that you are afraid of me because I was a prize-fighter."

"No; I'm afraid of myself; afraid of the future; afraid *for* you. But my mind is already made up. When I brought about this meeting between you and your mother I determined to marry you if you asked me again."

She stood up quietly and waited. The rough hardihood of the ring fell from him like a garment; he blushed deeply, and did not know what to do. Nor did she; but without willing it she came a step nearer to him and turned up her face toward his. He, nearly blind with confusion, put his arms about her and kissed her.

"Cashel," she said, "we are the silliest lovers in the world, I believe—we know nothing about it.   Are you really fond of me?"

She recovered herself immediately and seeing that he remained shy and was evidently anxious to go, presently asked him to leave her, though she was surprised to feel a faint pang of disappointment when he consented.

To her cousin's remonstrances she listened patiently, and then tried to explain to him that the phenix of modern culture and natural endowment, as he characterized her, was attracted by a man who never had been guilty of self-analysis, who complained when he was annoyed, and exulted when he was glad, who was honest and brave, strong and beautiful, whose face was neither thoughtful, nor poetic, nor wearied, nor doubting, nor old, nor self-conscious, but that of a pagan god, assured of eternal youth, and disqualified from comprehending *Faust*.

When Lucian admitted that he could not understand all this, she said:

"The truth is this: I practically believe in the doctrine of heredity; and as my body is frail and my brain morbidly active, I think my impulse toward a man strong in body and untroubled in mind is trustworthy.   You can understand that."

In after years, when she had leisure to consider the matter at all, it seemed to Lydia that, on the whole, she had chosen wisely.   Cashel's admiration for his wife survived the ardor of his first love.   He succeeded his uncle shortly after his marriage, and was elected to Parliament, where he soon acquired reputation by the popularity of his own views and the extent of his wife's information, which he retailed at second-hand.

Lydia led a busy life, and wrote some learned monographs and a work on education.   The children inherited her acuteness and refinement with their father's robustness and aversion to study.   They were a success, and she soon came to regard Cashel as one of them.   The care of her family left her little time to think about herself, or about the fact that when the illusion of her love passed away Cashel fell in her estimation.

MARY WOLLSTONECRAFT GODWIN SHELLEY

(England, 1798–1851)

FRANKENSTEIN: OR, THE MODERN PROMETHEUS
(1816)

This romance was the result of an agreement between Lord Byron, Polidori, Shelley, and his wife that each should try his hand at writing a ghost-story. They were spending the summer of 1816 as neighbors in Switzerland and certain volumes of that class of literature, translated from French and from German, had fallen into their hands. Byron began a tale, a fragment of which was afterward printed at the end of his *Mazeppa*, and Shelley began one founded on his early life. Polidori's, also, never was completed. Mrs. Shelley's endeavor alone saw the light, and in a shape that bids fair to live as one of the weirdest conceptions in our language. It is strange to note how well-nigh universally the term "Frankenstein" is misused, by even intelligent persons, as describing some hideous monster; whereas Frankenstein is the name of the hero and supposed narrator of the story, and not of his terrible creation.

Letter to Mrs. Saville, England

YOU will be rejoiced to hear that no disaster has befallen our expedition, but a strange adventure, which cannot fail to interest you. Last Monday, when our ship was surrounded by ice, we perceived a low sledge, drawn by dogs, pass us, going northward. It appeared to contain a man, apparently of gigantic stature, and we watched him until he vanished in the distance. On the following day the ice had broken up, and a second sledge came drifting toward us on a huge cake. Only one of the dogs remained alive, and the man who sat beside him was nearly dead from cold and exposure. We took the poor fellow aboard and revived him, and, during the days that followed, his remarkable intelligence, gentleness, and refinement, together with a deep-seated grief that oppressed him, made us come to regard him with warm affection. He had inquired about the other sledge and its occupant; in fact, he had even refused our aid until informed that we, also, were bound north. Naturally, though I was deeply curious, I did not seek to probe his grief, but one day, when I spoke enthusiastically of the discoveries that might lie before us, he said: "Unhappy man! Do you share my madness? Have you drunk also of the intoxicating draught? Hear me—let me reveal my tale, and you will dash the cup from your lips!" He fulfilled his promise thus:

I am named Victor Frankenstein and am, by birth, a Genevese. My father was a syndic of that city, and my mother died when I was seventeen years of age, leaving, besides myself, two younger boys and an adopted daughter of nearly my own age to whom I had always been tenderly attached. Elizabeth was more than worthy of the love I felt for her, and the wishes of my parents, as well as the inclinations of both of us, had long pointed toward her becoming my wife.

As a boy I had been interested in philosophy and in recondite studies, having run across, by chance, the works of Cornelius Agrippa, Paracelsus, and other searchers for the elixir of life and the philosopher's stone.

When, after my mother's death, I was sent to the University of Ingolstadt, the vanity of the aims of these early investigators had become evident to me, and I turned eagerly to the study of chemistry, as offering possibilities little less marvelous.

My progress was rapid; the structure of the human frame became a subject of deep interest to me, and I often asked myself whence proceeded the principle of life, without which our organization would be an inert mass.

Thus absorbed, I carefully investigated everything that might throw light on my studies. I delved deep in the secrets of the charnel-house, analyzing all the minutiæ of causation as exemplified in the change from life to death and death to life, until, from the midst of this darkness, a sudden light broke upon me— a light so brilliant and wondrous, yet so simple, that I became dizzy with the immensity of the prospect. I found myself capable of bestowing animation upon lifeless matter.

With this power in my hands, I felt no rest until I could employ it in the creation of a human being, and, that the minuteness of the structure might hinder me as little as possible, I resolved that he should be of gigantic stature.

Who can conceive the variety of feelings that filled me when, after incredible toils, I saw before me a creature fashioned like a man and took measures to infuse the spark of being into it? But when I saw the dull, yellow eyes open, and the straight, black lips writhe back, I realized the horror of the thing I had done.

His limbs were in proportion, and I had selected his features as beautiful; but when life came to them I saw that I had created a monster of such hideousness that, unable to endure his aspect, I rushed madly from the house. A mummy endowed with animation could not be so frightful.

Wandering in the streets, I was overjoyed to meet my dearest friend, Henry Clerval, who had come unannounced to Ingolstadt, but I could not bring myself to tell him of my awful achievement. When we returned to my house, though, I found, to my relief, that the being I had come to detest had fled. A serious illness now prostrated me, and when, through Clerval's care, I recovered, my former studies had become repulsive to me.

A letter received from home some time after my recovery filled me with wo. My youngest brother, William, a lovely child, had been found strangled, and a servant of our family, Justine, who was really more one of us than a servant, had been charged with the murder.

I hurried to Geneva, and as I drew near the town I saw, during a terrific tempest that broke out, the very demon I had created. He was hanging among the rocks of the nearly perpendicular ascent of Mont Salève, and quickly disappeared; but an awful thought oppressed me. None but he could have destroyed the innocent child, and I felt myself, in effect, a murderer. I found it impossible, though, to prove my suspicions true, and my anguish was increased when, despite all our efforts, poor Justine was convicted and executed for the crime.

After these painful events I fell into a condition of the deepest despair, and buried myself in the valleys of the Alps, whence, ascending one day to the summit of Montanvert, I suddenly beheld my terrible creation.

"Devil," I exclaimed, "do you dare approach me? and do you not fear the vengeance of my arm wreaked on your miserable head?"

"I expected this reception," said the demon. "All men hate the wretched; how, then, must I be hated, who am miserable beyond all living things! Yet you, my creator, detest and spurn me, your creature, to whom you are bound by ties only dissoluble by the annihilation of one of us. Do your duty toward me, and I will do mine toward you and the rest of mankind. If you refuse, I will glut the maw of death until it be satiated with the blood of your remaining friends."

He evaded my rage and demanded that I should be calm and hear his story, until, despite my horror and loathing, I was forced to listen.

Then he told of his awakening and of his wanderings: how, with the love of mankind in his heart, he had learned their speech and sought to do them good, until, repelled at every point, assailed, wounded by those whose benefactor he had been, his friendliness had given place to hatred, and an overmastering desire for vengeance had taken possession of him.

Thus inspired, yet yearning above all for companionship, he had found my poor brother and tried to carry him away, but the child struggled violently.

"Hideous monster!" he cried, "let me go. My papa is the syndic—he is Monsieur Frankenstein!"

Thus the creature realized that his captive was akin to me, whom he regarded as his enemy, and driven to despair by the epithets of loathing, he grasped the little throat to silence them. In a moment poor William lay dead at his feet.

He told how he gazed on his victim with exultation and hellish triumph, realizing that he, too, could create desolation; and then, escaping from the scene, he had found the sleeping Justine and thrust into her bosom a miniature he had taken from my brother, the discovery of which caused her conviction.

Now he demanded that I should create a female, a creature like himself, to be his companion, and he swore that if I would do so he would become well disposed once more toward mankind and would disappear forever in the wilderness of uninhabited lands.

I refused with indignation, despite his pleadings and threats, and yet I could not but feel there was much justice in his claim. At last, influenced by this consideration and the hope that he would keep his promise and take himself from the sight of men, I yielded and agreed to do as he desired.

I journeyed north with my friend Clerval, intending to leave him in Scotland and withdraw to a remote spot where I should be uninterrupted in my repulsive task; and before my departure it had been settled that, on my return, I was to marry my dear Elizabeth.

Having parted from Clerval, I hastened to one of the most distant Orkneys and set about the work I had agreed to do. I had advanced far toward its completion; but, as I sat one evening in the miserable hut that served as my laboratory, I fell to reasoning that I had no right to turn forth upon the world another creature of such fiendish malignity as him I had already made. I distrusted his promises; I had no certainty that the woman might not refuse his companionship, and the possibility of their perpetuating their awful race was a curse that no selfish motives could justify me in inflicting on my kind.

While in this mood I saw at my window the ghastly face of the demon. It expressed the utmost malice and treachery, and, trembling with passion, I tore to pieces the thing on which I was engaged. He tried in vain to persuade me to begin again, but I was firm, and he rushed away, breathing destruction and vengeance.

"I shall be with you on your marriage night!" he shrieked, and, springing into a small boat, escaped.

A few days later, while sailing in my skiff, I was carried out to sea and finally wrecked upon the coast of Ireland. Much to my surprise, the natives received me with every sign of detestation, and I soon found I was accused of the murder of a young man who had been found strangled on the beach. Judge of my horror and despair when I saw the body and recognized Henry Clerval! The demon had resumed his fiendish work, and, though I was soon freed from prison, on proof of my innocence, there seemed to be no happiness possible for me.

Returning to Geneva, I could not refuse to marry my beloved Elizabeth; yet I dreaded the threat of the fiend that he would be with me on my marriage night, when, I imagined, he contemplated my murder.

As the time drew near my heart sank, but I took every care to protect myself. At last I was married to the woman I loved, and we set out on our wedding-journey. We stopped at a little inn at ——, and, fearful lest my enemy might attack me in my wife's presence, I went to search for him, prepared to defend myself.

A scream from the room to which Elizabeth had retired awoke me to a terrible realization of the revenge he had planned; and, rushing madly back, I found her murdered as had been my brother and my friend.

Great God! why did I not then expire? but life is obstinate. All efforts to take the murderer failed, and my story, which I at last brought myself to reveal to the magistrate, was received, I could see, as being but the fiction of a disordered mind.

Then I devoted myself to the task of hunting down and slaying the creature who had caused all this wo. I felt bound to free humanity from the awful presence and the peril I had brought upon it. He fled; I pursued until, as you know, you found me, exhausted and helpless.

Letter to Mrs. Saville, England

You have read this strange and terrific story, Margaret. Frankenstein died to-day, urging me to fulfil his mission. Great God! what a scene has just taken place! I entered the cabin where his body lay. Over him hung a form I cannot find words to describe; gigantic—hideous. As he turned to go I saw such misery in his face as I could not have dreamed of.

"This is also my victim!" he exclaimed. "Oh, Frankenstein! generous and self-devoted being! what does it avail that I now ask thee to pardon me?"

"Your repentance," I said, "is now superfluous. If you had listened to the voice of conscience Frankenstein would still have lived."

He told me how his soul had wavered between love, despair, revenge and remorse, through which his fate had driven him to this awful consummation, and with my hatred was mingled something of pity.

"Fear not that I shall be the instrument of further mischief," he said. "Soon I shall die. I shall ascend my funeral pile triumphantly and exult in the agony of the torturing flames. My ashes will be swept into the sea by the winds. My spirit will sleep in peace."

He sprang from the cabin window upon the ice-raft and was borne away by the waves and lost in darkness and distance.

ELIZABETH SARA SHEPPARD

(England, 1830–1862)

CHARLES AUCHESTER (1853)

The interest in this story as a novel of musical life is enhanced by the fact that in the character of Seraphael, who plays a leading part in the story, the author has described the immortal Felix Mendelssohn-Bartholdy and given a graphic picture of his times and the furor of idolatry that pursued this romantic composer. Of this story Benjamin Disraeli wrote, in a letter to the young author: "No greater book will ever be written upon music, and it will one day be recognized as the imaginative classic of that divine art."

 WAS born of an English father and of a Franco-German mother in whose veins ran some strain of Hebrew blood, and my early life was spent in an interior city of England, where my father had made an honorable name, but less fortune, in commercial pursuits. Musical sense ran in the family, except in my eldest sister, Clotilde, who was clever, but in other ways. Millicent, with keen sensibilities, possessed a voice thrilling with the tenderness of the wood-dove's note, though it was limited in range. In my own case nature gave an accuracy of ear infallible in the subtlest *nuances* of sound, with an intuitive insight which subjected me to constant torment in listening to amateurs, long before I knew much about the art or science of music. Indeed, my thoughts were not then turned to the profession of music, passionately as I loved it, for commercialism had promised to swallow me as it had swallowed my brother Fred.

The great music-festival, in which *The Creation* and *The Messiah* were to be rendered with larger chorus and orchestra than usual, was only three weeks off, and I could not help lingering about the ticket-office, though guinea prices were far beyond our reach. One day a gentleman, whom everybody seemed to know there, spoke to me, and told me I had "a violin face." I confessed my longings, and he took me to his quaint little house, and there I sang for him, at which he showed much surprise and pleasure. He was Mr. Lenhart Davy, a professor of music who was drilling a part of the chorus, and he promised to place me among the altos at the festival. He took me home and secured my mother's consent. Thenceforward I was in his class, and I met among the members a charming girl with an exquisite voice, Mademoiselle Benette, several years my senior, who would also be an alto in the chorus. We had hard daily rehearsal, and finally the great day arrived.

Everything was ready, orchestra and chorus in place, and an immense audience. But no conductor arrived. The great virtuoso, Milans-Andre, who was then setting musical Europe afire, had been originally expected, but he could not come, and Mr. St. Mechel was to wield the bâton. After a little it was made known that he had broken his arm, and the Chairman of the Board expressed the hope that some professor present might volunteer. Silence, some hisses, an uneasy stir, and I hoped that Lenhart Davy, who sat among the basses, would offer. Then came a gliding form, as it were floating through the air, and sprang to the conductor's stand before the open score, bâton in hand. His slender fingers, his face, his form seemed to quiver with electrical energy as he stretched forth his arms, and the orchestra thrilled with the gesture. That performance was inspiration, not interpretation. Every voice, every instrument, was touched with divine fire. He was young, slight, could hardly have numbered twenty years, "but the heights of eternity were foreshadowed in the forehead's marble dreams." Such a day of musical elysium the city never had known before; and rapture was blended with wonder at the sudden disappearance of the stranger as abruptly as he came. Who could it be? Not Milans-Andre, having changed his mind?—for he was known to be touring Europe. It was a nine-days' wonder.

In the music-class I often turned to my young lady, whose voice was a true contralto—more soft than deep, more distilling than low, her sweet face in singing shining in a glory not its own, the most ardent musical intention brooding on the eyes, the lips, the brow. Near us sat, also, a young girl with great yellow eyes, who sang with careless ease, and had a slender figure of serpentine litheness. She was learning a little music while her training as a danseuse was in progress. My master often told me that my vocation would not be singing, but an instrument, probably the violin; yet I never had shown much talent for playing. I sometimes visited Mademoiselle Benette and practised with her at her home. She made her living in part by the most exquisite embroidery, was a ward of Mr. Davy, who had brought her from Germany as a little child, and she hoped some day to sing on the stage.

The next important event in my career was participation in a musical party at the Redferns', a rich family of the vicinity, where I was to sing in a quartet. Here I met Santonio, the great violinist, who looked at me keenly and turned to Mr. Davy with:

"It will not be alto long; his arm and hand are ready-made for me."

Whereat I wondered and could have worshiped him, for the violin had begun to haunt all my dreams. When he played, I knew as soon as I heard him draw the first quickening chord, quivering to my heart—I knew that the violin must become my master or I its own.

Miss Lawrence, a wealthy young lady, distinguished for her devotion to and patronage of music, played in the concert with him. She came to me afterward and spoke of the great Incognito, to whom she had noticed me carrying a glass of water at the festival; and she told Clara Benette and me of an adventure in Scotland. An unknown person had stolen into her summer cottage in her absence and left on her piano the score of a wonderful composition, *Heather and Honeysuckle*, and that was what she had played as her solo. I met Miss Lawrence again at Clara Benette's, whither she had sent for me to come, and we talked much of my newly aroused musical ambition. When, a few days later, a violin arrived for me as a gift, which Davy said was a genuine Amati (a fairy fiddle, which I loved better than even the Stradivarius that I afterward possessed), and at the same time a beautiful piano came to Miss Benette, all knew that Miss Lawrence must have been the donor.

The dayspring of my destiny had come, and it had been decided that I should go to Germany for musical study. Santonio wrote to my mother, advising the Cecilia School at Lorbaarstadt and offering to take charge of me on my journey, which hastened my departure.

On the journey I was informed that at first I should be under the same master under whom he had once studied, and also as, he said, had my Chevalier of the festival, for he guessed who that must be, knowing the characteristics of every conductor in Europe, though he did not reveal his surmise. There I was to remain until old enough to enter the school. Six months speedily passed under the iron rule of old Aronach, whose eccentric manner hid a genial heart, and I made progress enough to satisfy even that exacting disciplinarian. Of two other pupils, little Starwood Burney, a gentle boy, became my friend, while Iskar, who had a hard, superficial brilliance, I detested.

On the opening day of the Cecilia examinations a stranger called, asking for me, for the young violinist who had come at Christmas time; and when Starwood described him my heart thrilled with a delightful premonition. The vision came to me with a dazzling blindness, and I staggered in the arms of my adored Incognito. We talked much, in English and in German, as he took me to the Cecilia School. I remarked on his perfect English, and he answered in German:

"That is nothing, because we can have no real language. I make myself think in all. I dream first in this and then in that, so that, amid the floating fragments, as in the strange mixture we call an orchestra, some accent may be expressed from the many voices, of the language of our unknown home."

We entered the exhibition hall, where diplomas and medals were being dispensed by Milans-Andre. As we looked, one beautiful girl received her medal with a little gesture of disdain, as if resenting a reward for a service of love. I saw my companion's eye dilate at the instant, and a flash of color as if a radiance from the sun. When the distribution was over Milans-Andre went to the piano and began to play with a splendor of tone, but then a rushing noise arose like the thunder of an irrepressible enthusiasm. Something had happened. One came through a side door and carried my companion away. I

saw him move down the aisle amid the mad *vivas* of the multitude, mount the platform and go to the piano, which the great
Milans-Andre had been compelled to quit. Then from under
magic fingers rolled such a wonderful *Song of the People* that the
multitude, stilled to an ecstatic calm, seemed to live and breathe
in the golden notes.

When the disconcerted Imperial Pianist—for such Milans-
Andre had been lately nominated—was permitted to finish his
brilliant concerto, a voice summoned me from reverie: "Come,
Carlo mein," and we went to the refreshment-tables in the gardens. There we noticed the haughty girl-medalist on whom
my companion, just acclaimed by the vast audience as Seraphael,
fixed again a rapt gaze. What a marvelous resemblance between them in mold and expression of face! It was as if the
same celestial fire permeated their veins, the same insurgent
longings lifted their feet from the ground.

Seraphael took me to Aronach and made my peace with him,
for I had come without the master's permission. It was full of
delicious humor, the love and devotion of the great teacher
jarred by the bright vagaries of Seraphael's Ariel-like moods,
which seemed the sheen of summer lightning about Aronach's
sterner mental habit.

The Chevalier departed, and I was duly admitted to the
Cecilia and placed under the first violin as teacher, who gave me
special attention, as he had had such injunction laid on him by
Seraphael, who, I learned, was the dominating power in the
school, though he was there but little. He, the favorite of kings
and courts, already the great composer, though little more than a
boy in years, followed solely his artistic impulse, which led him
to the noblest ideals; for, as Aronach told me, he was the idolized
heir of a family of great wealth.

I soon became acquainted with the Cerinthia family—for
that was the name of the "magic maiden," as Chevalier Seraphael described her—which was of Italian stock. Maria and
I became warm friends, and I found no wonder that her bright
and aspiring spirit had so irresistibly reminded me of soul-
kinship to my idol Seraphael. Something like a shock accompanied Maria's revelation to me one day that Florimond Anastase, my violin teacher, who had been to my heart an austere

and reserved nature, was her beloved and would become her husband by and by. The romance that had begotten that tie I knew not till later. Did the Chevalier know? She said she never had been able to tell him. Why should this have cast a shadow over me? Her communion with Seraphael had been on a loftier plane than love and marriage; for she longed to create music herself, and not to sing it. Her little sister Josephine would have the great power of interpretation, as my own instinct told me when I heard her sing, though her voice itself was then as crude and sour as a green whortleberry.

I was selected to play first violin with Anastase in a new orchestral work by Seraphael, which the composer would conduct, with his great relatives present. My fear shrank from the test, but I struggled resolutely with the task; and when the day arrived, after much rehearsal, I had won the full approval of a severe critic. How was I rewarded for all by the visit of Lenhart Davy and his bride, who was my favorite sister Millicent!—a wooing and marriage that had been kept secret from me. The wonderful *Mer de Glace*, with its lucidity of orchestration, airy splendor, and a closing movement that rose to sublimity, left the audience spellbound in a trance for a minute or two; but when they came to themselves with thunders of applause, Seraphael had vanished. That was always his way. I saw him again in the gardens, and then he invited me and my dear ones to his birthday party at the Glückhaus, a quaint old place which he had bought and renovated.

Anastase told me, when I went to see Maria Cerinthia that evening, that Seraphael had written a birthday piece in the form of a two-act fairy opera; and that he wished me to sing counterpart to Maria, who would be Titania. My singing was rusty, but the Chevalier had quoted Aronach's word, that my voice was like my violin, and that sufficed, as his will. The opera was produced in the wild, forest-like gardens of the Glückhaus, and Seraphael himself was the Ariel. At the end of it the Chevalier brought Maria an ice and playfully fed her with it. Anastase entered and glanced with a swift coldness, saying:

"That weight of hair will tire you; let me fasten it up for you, Maria; and then we need detain no one, for Carl, I see, is ready."

The expression, voice, intonation, the air of right, told a story, and Seraphael's fingers were icy cold as he led me out by the hand, to and through the house buzzing with joyous talk, and up to his own place. An awful paleness marbled his face. The voice trembled like a breaking harp-string as he said, after many minutes:

"You know what I wished. May you never suffer as I do now. The sorrow is, that never on earth or in heaven will she wish to be mine now."

There the subject was dropped. Afterward Maria, in walking with me, said with a childish *naïveté* inseparable from her deep womanliness, describing her feeling for Florimond Anastase by the law of comparison:

"I cannot imagine wishing to marry the Chevalier. It would abase the power of worship in my soul—it would cloud my idea of heaven—it would crush all my life within me. I should be transported into a place where the water was all light, and I could not drink—the air was all fire to wither me. I should flee from myself in him, and in fleeing die." She told me that three years before, the family—her father, a music-teacher, then living—being in financial straits, had been assisted by Anastase, who was engaged as first violin in a Paris orchestra; and that they had grown to care deeply for each other. It was through him, too, that arrangements had been made to live at Lorbaarstadt.

Seraphael was now on one of his frequent musical progresses, and my friend Starwood Burney, who had been taken in special charge after I told the Chevalier that the boy's soul was in the piano, not in the fiddle, was with him. My life was one of steady practise and study, my sweetest solace in the companionship of Maria Cerinthia. Her soul was bent on writing a symphony—she had secretly composed several of the movements, indeed—and no one knew of it but myself. She gave me the score, of which I tried the violin part and thought it very beautiful, though it was identical in style with the genius of Seraphael. Maria said that sometimes his very image seemed to be present, inspiring her with his deep eyes—indeed, guiding hers with his very hand. Maria became pale and thin, her beauty etherealized to an unearthly intensity as the months passed; and when

I hinted to Florimond my fears his face clouded, but he could see only a slight indisposition.

When Seraphael returned, I placed in his hands, though without Maria's consent, the symphony score for examination; and as his wonderful fingers finished their interpretation there was an outburst of passionate joy:

"It is terrible, *Carlo mein*, to think that this work might have perished; and I embrace thee for having secured me its possession. It must and shall be finished. The work is of Heaven's own. What earthly inspiration could have taught her strains like these? They are of a priestess and a prophetess. She has soared beyond us all."

She had indeed caught the very soul of Seraphael in its most celestial mood; and her rapture at the approval of the mighty musician speedily enabled her to complete the symphony. The perfect orchestra, which Maria herself conducted on the night of performance, gave the marvelous first movement with thrill-ing power, as if the souls of all of us were winging upward to God. Then strangely, suddenly, her arm fell powerless—her pallor quickened to crimson—her brow grew warm with a burst-ing, blood-red blush—she sank to the floor upon her side, silently as in the south wind a leaf just flutters and is at rest; nor was there a sound through the stricken orchestra as Florimond raised her and carried her from us in his arms. That virgin sym-phony was buried in her virgin grave.

The long absence of Seraphael from the school after that great shock—Anastase himself, too, had gone—made my years of further stay at Cecilia unimportant, aside from the study of technic. But when I returned to England I found that Se-raphael was not only not forgotten but had grown greatly in musical glory, to a height surpassing all competition in the field of his great art. I taught the violin and helped Lenhart Davy to reorganize the orchestra of my native city. My quiet life, however, found excitement in the reported coming of Seraphael to England that summer, and in a letter from Clara Benette, now become famous in Italy as Benetta Benedetta, to Davy. She apprised him that she had accepted a London engagement for the season, and on her arrival I lost no time in going to London to see her. I found her domiciled in a quaint old house in a beautiful suburb, a genuine *rus in urbe*. I found her the same, though with her ineffable childhood of spirit enshrined in perfect womanhood, and with her Laura Lemark, the dancing sylph of the flaming yellow eyes, incarnating the most vivid contrast, now a famous though most capricious artist. A more unexpected delight was that of meeting Seraphael, who had arrived, without any flourish of trumpets, at the house of Miss Lawrence. He carried me away with him, and the next day his longing to live in the country suggested the vicinity of Clara Benette's charming retreat, and there we found a suitable hermitage.

Seraphael's acquaintance and his residence near by quickly ripened into an intimacy to the character of which I was almost blind, just as I had been to his feeling for Maria. He spent much time at Clara's cottage; but also at another shrine of tone-worship, the brilliant salon of Miss Lawrence, whose great wealth consecrated itself to musical culture, he received the homage due to the demigod. That gracious lady, whom the fairies had endowed with all the gifts of artistry, had with Seraphael's consent embodied his marvel of personality on canvas. There were two other countenances, their figures half veiled in cloud, one on either side of the central splendor. One face was dread and glorious, a self-sealed seraph; the other mild and awful, informed with steadfast beauty; and in their shadowy hands a crown of stars was held over Seraphael's head. I knew them for Beethoven and Bach. When she showed me this great presentment of the world's verdict, she told me in confidence that the new oratorio, which Seraphael had brought with him, would be produced in Westminster Abbey, with the greatest musicians in London to take part in chorus and orchestra. I did not know then that Clara Benette would be its greatest interpreter.

When I saw Clara next I could not repress my curiosity as to what she thought of my idol. She did not answer that, but told me something strange, that Seraphael had implored her not to accept any agreement for the stage, but to leave in his hands the arrangement of her future. She could not surmise what it meant, nor could I.

The wonderful performance in the Abbey revealed a *chef-*

d'œuvre of such tonal beauty and spiritual uplift as ravished the musical world. Clara arose to sing to a violoncello obligato and ocean-like pianissimo of the orchestra. Deeper, stiller than the violoncello notes, hers seemed surcharged with a revelation beyond all sound.

That night Laura Lemark came to my room, in defiance of all conventionality—we were staying at the Lawrence house— and in an outburst of mad weeping confessed her passion for Seraphael, her bitter jealousy of her friend and benefactress. Even then I was not quite prepared for the revelation from Clara, who told me, when next I saw her, that Seraphael had asked her to be his wife.

This twain, so perfectly fitted to belong to each other, became one and departed for their own life of mutual devotion and content in Germany or Italy, as the mood came. I labored with Davy in the apostleship of provincial work. Christmas season came, and with material a little crude and obdurate we had worked hard to prepare *The Messiah*. The first part was somewhat cold, and as we were waiting in place to begin again, Davy with a rapturous expression came to the front and announced that Chevalier Seraphael, unexpectedly arrived from Germany, would conduct the second part. This was immediately followed by the ethereal power of the hierarch, and the first wave of the time-stick melted and transfused every instrumentalist and singer with uplifting magic, which made the performance a celestial hymn transcending words. Clara had insisted on his coming, though she needed his tenderest care. He told us about his perfect life with the beloved one; yet he said his own career here would not be long, however consummate its earthly bliss. He departed, and three months later a brief letter informed us that Clara had given him twin sons. The July festival, the great musical climax of the year, was approaching, and Seraphael, who had written for us several exclusive compositions, came to conduct the rehearsals. He was recalled by the message that his children were very ill. A fortnight later a letter from Clara contained the tidings that their children had been recalled; and too soon another followed, saying that Seraphael was himself stricken, and asking that I would come to them at once. My arrival was greeted by the tolling of minster bells that clanged their story with iron strokes on my heart. I was convulsed with grief and agitation; but her face was ecstatically calm in its rapt expression. She said:

"After I left you with him—when his arms were around me; when he kissed me, when his tenderness oppressed me—I felt raised to God. No heart was ever so pure, so overflowing with the light of heaven. I can only believe that I have been in heaven."

She had been his earthly angel, even as he had been her heavenly seraph.

JOSEPH HENRY SHORTHOUSE

(England, 1834–1903)

JOHN INGLESANT (1881)

In the preface to a new edition of this novel the author characterizes it as an attempt at a species of literature which he believes has not had justice done to it, though it is capable of great things—philosophical romance. "Amid the tangled web of a life's story," he says, "I have endeavored to trace some distinct threads—the conflict between culture and fanaticism, the analysis and character of sin, the subjective influence of the Christian Mythos," defining Mythos as "Eternal Truth manifested in phenomena." The story is supposedly arranged by one Geoffrey Monk, from manuscripts found in the library at Lydiard, the residence of a Roman Catholic gentleman in Shropshire.

JOHN INGLESANT'S great-grandfather had been in his youth a follower of Thomas Cromwell, who had employed him in the suppression of the Priory of Westacre; and he had received a grant of the Priory from Henry VIII. Though he and his son and grandson were at heart Catholics, they confirmed outwardly to the State Church.

John and his twin brother Eustace were born in 1622. In 1629 Eustace, the heir, was taken to London to be a page at court. John was placed four years later under the care of a schoolmaster who had an easy and attractive way of teaching, was a Greek scholar and Platonist, a Rosicrucian, and a believer in alchemy and astrology. He found John an apt pupil, "mild of spirit and very susceptible of fascination, strangely given to superstition and romance, of an inventive imagination, though not a retentive memory, given to day-dreaming and metaphysical speculation." John gained considerable facility in reading Greek and Latin, imbibed that mysterious Platonic philosophy which seemed to become, when seen through the rays of Christianity, a foreshadowing of it, and adopted eagerly his master's Rosicrucian theories.

After three years he was recalled to Westacre, where he found his father and his brother and a stranger who regarded him kindly with a peculiar look, penetrating and alluring at the same time, and who, after talking with him and hearing him read Plato, said to his father:

"The lad is apt—indeed, more so than any of us could have dreamed; no fitter soil, I could wager, we could have found in England."

Events were then occurring of which John was ignorant, but which were soon to close about him and involve him in a labyrinth from which he may be said never to have issued during his life.

Between 1630 and 1640 the Catholics enjoyed great freedom in England, of which advantage was taken to gain converts and confirm uncertain members. Among them were two parties, one viewing the English Church and Archbishop Laud with hatred, the other believing that little was needed to bring the Established Church to submission to the Papal See. To this latter party Mr. Eustace Inglesant belonged; and he was in constant communication with leaders in both churches. The value of emissaries in the confidence of both sides was obvious; and Mr. Inglesant judged his son John peculiarly fitted by temperament to be trained for such an office.

To Father St. Clare—a Jesuit missionary priest of unbounded devotion to his order, unflinching courage, scholarly attainments, and elegant and fascinating manners—the idea commended itself; and he took up his abode at Westacre, carrying on his work in adjoining counties and educating John, over whom he gained great influence. But he made no effort to draw the boy from the National Church, rather took pains to prevent such a result, knowing that if once the enthusiastic nature of his pupil became attached to Roman doctrine he would be useless as a mediator.

About two years later, John's heart beat high with excitement and delight when Father St. Clare told him that they were to go to London, where he would open to him the position of parties and the crisis of affairs in which he was to play his part—

to a great extent, alone.   On their arrival in London he became
a page in the Queen's household, and here he devoted his
leisure to reading, interesting himself chiefly in religious books,
especially of the High Church party.   In his mind he was still
devoted, though in a halting and imperfect manner, to the pursuit of the spiritual life and purity, which had always attracted
him; and he lost no opportunity for consulting on these mysterious subjects any who, he thought, would sympathize with
his ideas.

With this object he visited a religious house at Little Gidding,
called the "Protestant Nunnery," founded by Nicholas Ferrar,
one of whose friends and frequent visitors was Richard Cra-
shaw, the poet.   On this and subsequent visits he met the
founder's niece, Mary Collet, with whom he fell in love.   But
both felt that they had work laid out for them and a path in
which to follow the divine call.

The next year Mr. Inglesant died.   John was kept from
joining the Roman Church by two influences: that of Father
St. Clare, and the remembrance of the sacrament at Little Gidding, which had had the greatest effect on his imaginative
nature and filled his mind with light and sweetness and peace
unspeakable.   Closely connected with it was the thought of
Mary Collet; for, looking upon her pure beauty, he felt as if he
had already gained the beatific vision.

But at times his enthusiasm was checked by such thoughts
as these: How do I know that this divine life within me is anything but an opinion formed from what I have heard and read?
How do I know that there is any such thing as a divine life?

John was very active in procuring evidence for the defense
of Archbishop Laud when his trial was coming on, so that, as
Father St. Clare intended, his name became as closely associated with Laud's party as it had been with that of the Queen
and the Jesuits by his connection with them.   When the Archbishop was executed John attended him to the scaffold.

After this he spent at Gidding the last peaceful hours he was
to know for a long time.   Letting Mary go out of his life, and
with her the bloom and freshness of youth that he was never to
know again, he answered the summons of the Jesuit.

In the low ebb of royal affairs after Naseby, the King had

consented to an agreement with the Irish which the Duke of Ormond and Lord Glamorgan were negotiating, the King to make certain concessions and receive a large force from Ireland. On account of English prejudice, the negotiations had to be carried on secretly.

In an interview with Inglesant, Charles signed in his presence a few lines which he was to carry to the King's agents; but he was made to understand that in case of difficulty the King would deny all knowledge of the matter. He found that it was most important that Lord Biron, in command of Chester, should be prepared for the reception of Irish troops, in order that he might not surrender. Lord Biron appeared dissatisfied with the communication; and when a rumor came that Lord Glamorgan had been arrested in Ireland for concluding without the King's sanction a treaty with Irish rebels and Catholics, he questioned Inglesant, who declared that the letter he had shown was a forgery.

Lord Biron surrendered Chester to the Parliamentary leader. Inglesant was arrested on the charge of treason, and on examination declared that the letter was a forgery, a part of a plot with the Roman Catholics, whose envoy Lord Glamorgan was. He was sent to the Tower, and at the end of a year was tried and condemned to be hanged for high treason. As he mounted the steps of the scaffold a week later, he saw a dense crowd of heads and heard a roar of indignation, contempt, hatred, and cries of " Give over the Jesuit to us!" "Throw over the Irish murderer!"

For a moment his senses reeled; then, hardening himself, he faced the crowd calmly. He had been indifferent before, only wishing the ordeal to be over; now he became angry, fierce, contemptuous; hated, he hated again. Then a paper was offered him, and he was told that if he would sign the true evidence he should be set free. Rejecting the paper, he said:

"These good people are impatient for the final act; do not keep them any longer."

There was a pause, a signal was given that caused the soldiers to break ranks and mingle with the crowd, and Inglesant was hurried into a house and through back entries and yards to the river, and so to the Tower, while the mob expressed its disappointment in maddened yells and a shower of stones.

After the trial and execution of the King, Eustace brought a warrant for John's liberation. In the light of his brother's love, John's whole nature, crushed and lacerated during his long imprisonment, seemed to heal itself and expand; but he never wholly recovered from the strain of those years; and an added shock was destined to influence his future. As the brothers were on their way to Oulton, belonging to Eustace's wife, Eustace was murdered by one Malvolti, an Italian enemy.

Remaining at Oulton, John gradually regained strength and calmness of mind, and began to adapt himself to a course of religious life from which he never altogether departed, notwithstanding some doubts of his own and some attempts of others to divert him from it. The peculiar form that Christianity assumed in his mind may be described as Christianity without the Bible (of most of which he was profoundly ignorant), without doctrine or dogma of any kind, and concentrated on what may be called the idea of Christ; that is, a lively conception of and attraction to the person of the Saviour. This idea—which came to him first in the sacrament at Gidding—being purely intellectual, would no doubt be inefficient and transitory were it not for its unique and mysterious power of attraction.

The transient calm of this existence was disturbed by an absorbing desire for revenge on his brother's murderer. In the search for this man he went in 1651 to Paris, where he was well received by the fugitive Royalists. It appears that then he was formally received into the Catholic Church, though there is proof that he attended services at the Anglican chapel.

Answering a message one day from a certain convent, he found there Mary Collet, who had heard accidentally of his presence in Paris. She was dying of a fever, wasted to a shadow— only her wonderful eyes the same as he remembered them. She told him of her sufferings and hardships after leaving Gidding; she had been preparing to take the veil, but never would take it now. As she spoke, the old familiar glamour that shed such holy radiance at Gidding seemed to fill the little room. The light of heaven that entered the open window was lost in the diviner rays that shone from her face into the depths of his being.

His whole nature was shaken to its foundation by her death, and life became more holy and solemn than ever. He desired to listen to the Divine voice, but it seemed silent. He consulted a Benedictine who had been a leader at Oxford, telling him of his early attraction to mysticism, of his failures and discouragements, his studies and pagan sympathies.

"Come with me," said Cressy. "In our home you shall engage in no study that is any delight or effort to the intellect, which would be fatal to you; you shall teach children, visit the poor, and perform duties of the household—and all for Christ. In this path you shall find the satisfaction of the heavenly walk until you come unto the perfect day."

Cressy's words impressed Inglesant, but failed to carry the absolute conviction of the heavenly call. And yet, when he had rejected the Benedictine's advice and departed for Italy, where he hoped to find the murderer, an idea took possession of him that he had turned his back upon Christ; and he was the more confirmed in this belief because the purpose of revenge had so strong a hold upon him.

In Italy the study of art and Italian music opened a new life to him. But he saw much of the distress occasioned by bad government, and wished to satisfy himself on some points before becoming involved in any political action.

In his second year there, he met in Florence Lauretta, a daughter of the Conte di Visalvo, toward whom he felt a singular attraction; but with it he was conscious of a half-formed fear, a sense of glamour and peril, of an alluring force independent of his will. After several weeks, during which they met repeatedly, Lauretta left Florence. Inglesant, who never had recovered entirely from the effects of his prison life, and seemed sometimes to be walking as in a dream, unable to distinguish the real from the seeming, now fell into a fever, which intensified this condition. When he had partly recovered from bodily weakness he set out for Rome with Cardinal Rinuccini, noting that the nearer he approached the capital the more wretched did the country appear.

In Rome he was attracted to Molinos, a Spanish priest who had gained great influence by his mystical doctrine of communion with the Divine through contemplation. Conversation with the mystic enabled Inglesant to take some of the old pleasure in the light of heaven and the occurrences of life. Moreover, under the influence of Rome his tone of thought was considerably modified; in the midst of so much religion his attention was diverted from the religious side of life.

The first commission given to him as an agent of the Jesuits came in a request from the Superior of the English Jesuits that he should go to the court of the Duke of Umbria, an old man without heirs, who had virtually made over the succession to the Pope, but had not formally ratified it. Devoting all his thought to religion, he welcomed everyone who could help him to any clearness in the vision of the future life. A Lutheran had gained some influence over him, and Inglesant was to counteract this and hasten the completion of the act of succession.

There were pleasant features in the prospect of this mission —the study of the Duke's mental condition, and the luxurious life in a palace noted for its art treasures; but the part he was expected to play tallied exactly with the scheme he imagined was developing for his spiritual destruction. Yet the habit of implicit obedience impelled him to accept the commission.

So winning were Inglesant's appearance and manner that the Duke regarded him with great favor. Inglesant's conscience revolted at the thought of persuading the Duke to a course which his judgment told him might not be conducive to the welfare of the people; and the subject of the succession never was mentioned between them.

About a month after his arrival the Duke gave him a fief in the Apennines carrying a small revenue and the title Cavaliere, saying that he did it with the full approval of the Fathers. This convinced Inglesant that the deed had been signed, and that he was believed to have been instrumental in bringing about the result.

He returned to Rome, and after the death of Pope Innocent X he attended Cardinal Chigi, who after a protracted session of the conclave was elected Pope. He was exhausted in body by the long attendance; and the tone of his spirit was impaired by the intrigue and hypocrisy of which he had been a witness and partaker. He felt himself again the sport of the fiend who was plotting his destruction by some terrible crime of which he was the agent and Malvolti the cause. But two attempts on his life by this man worked a change that strengthened and clarified his spirit. His superstitious dread of his brother's murderer left him. He felt that the Lord had still some work for him to do, even though he lived always on the verge of delirium, in a condition where a little additional pressure upon a nerve might estrange him altogether from reason.

On the morning of Ash Wednesday he was kneeling in utter prostration of spirit at the steps of the high altar in the Lateran to receive the ashes, and the priest began, "*Memento, homo, quia pulvis es*"—when a sudden thrill made him raise his eyes. Opposite him knelt Lauretta, her lustrous eyes fixed upon him in inexpressible tenderness. The thought and presence of heaven vanished; the roses and loves of earth alone remained.

His marriage was arranged soon afterward. One day in a lonely pass he met Malvolti, who had been reduced to beggary by the defeat of the party of Cardinal Barberini. He knelt before Inglesant and begged for his life. Then the cruel light faded from Inglesant's eyes, and he let his enemy go.

Three years with his wife in the Castello di San Giorgio passed peacefully; but neither was fitted by habit or education for a retired country life, and time hung somewhat heavily on the spirits of both. Lauretta was troubled about her brother, the Cavaliere di Guardino, a notorious debauchee, who had been ruined by the election of Chigi and had disappeared. The life of romance and excitement, combined with a certain spiritual Quixotism, which Inglesant had long followed, had rendered any other uncongenial to him. So when the plague was raging in the south, to comfort Lauretta he went to search for the Cavaliere, whom after many days he found dying.

When he returned to his home he found that the plague had done its work there also. His little boy lay dead upon his couch, and beside it, on the marble floor, lay Lauretta, dead too, and uncared for.

In Rome again Inglesant joined Molinos, whose following included thousands of the best natures in the city. But when the reputation of the Quietists was at its height, the Jesuits and the Benedictines took alarm; Molinos was arrested, and before the end of a month more than two hundred Molinists crowded the prisons of the Inquisition. What of the future for them? Was this gate of Paradise to be forever closed, and the petty details of a formal service to be the only food for their souls?

Inglesant declined to leave Rome, as his friends urged him to do. He desired to find a way by which the highest spiritual walk and the purest condition of spiritual worship might be possible within the Church of Rome. Moreover, a life of intrigue and policy had from training and severe practise become a passion and a necessity with him.

From the General of the Jesuits he vainly demanded for himself and his friends spiritual freedom, the freedom of silence, promising that no change in doctrine would be asked, no proselytes sought; in truth, but one thing was desired—the sacrament without confession.

In time the majority of the imprisoned Quietists were released; but the party was utterly crushed, and Molinos, from being a popular idol, became an object of hatred and contempt. On false charges of hypocrisy and lewd courses, he was sentenced to life-imprisonment. Inglesant spoke with him on the day of his condemnation. He himself was arrested and confined in the Castle of St. Angelo, having been detected in giving a packet to the prisoner, which a masked lady in the crowd had asked him to do.

A fortnight later he was visited by the General, who said, after some conversation about the cause of his arrest:

"You have deserved well of the Order, which is not ungrateful. You look upon the prosecution of Molinos as an act of intolerable tyranny, and are eager to enter upon a crusade in behalf of religious freedom. You have considered this freedom only as the right of the educated and refined. Reflect that to grant it to them and not to the populace is impossible. You are standing at the junction of two roads—individual license, and obedience to authority. There is no permanent resting-place between unquestioning obedience and absolute unbelief. I am convinced that you are an invaluable agent of the Society; but here in Rome we require agents of a lower type. I recommend you to return to England; and I hope you will take with you no unpleasant recollections of Rome and of the poor Fathers of Jesus, who wish you well."

He spoke with so much feeling that Inglesant could but assure him that he felt nothing but gratitude toward him and reverence for the city, "the mother of the world."

Little is known of Inglesant's life after his return to England, save through an imperfect letter describing the writer's meeting with him.

"The first sight of Mr. Inglesant pleased me very much. His expression was lofty and abstracted, his manner courteous almost to excess; yet he seemed a man habitually superior to his company. When I asked his opinion of the Romish system, and whether he preferred it to that of the English Church, I saw at once that his whole life and being was in this question. He said, in part:

"'This is the supreme conflict of all; it is between the noblest parts of man's nature, arrayed against each other. On one side, obedience and faith; on the other, freedom and the reason. . . . The Church of Rome has ever traded upon the highest instincts of humanity, upon its faith and love, its passionate remorse, its self-abnegation and denial, its imagination and yearning after the unseen. It has based its system upon the profoundest truths, and played the part of human tyranny, greed, and cruelty. Mankind will do wrong if it allows to drop out of existence, merely because the position on which it stands seems to be illogical, an agency by which the devotional instincts of human nature are enabled to exist side by side with the rational. The English Church offers the supernatural to all who choose to come. Thanks to circumstances which the founders of our church did not contemplate, the way is open to its altars barred by no confession, no human priest.'

"Through a discussion of truth Mr. Inglesant came to speak of the ideal life, and concluded:

"'Let us, above all, hold fast by the law of life we feel within. This was the method Christ followed; and He won the world by placing Himself in harmony with that law of gradual development which the Divine wisdom has planned. Let us follow in His steps and we shall attain the ideal life; and, without waiting for our "mortal passage," tread the free and spacious streets of that Jerusalem which is above.'"

HENRYK SIENKIEWICZ

(Poland, 1845)

QUO VADIS (1895)

This, the latest novel by this author, has achieved a world-wide success, running through many editions in England, the United States, France, and Poland. It was dramatized for the English stage.

PETRONIUS, the arbiter of fashion in Rome, woke at midday, greatly wearied. He was enjoying himself in his private baths (which the Emperor admitted were superior to his own), when young Marcus Vinicius was announced. Marcus was the son of Petronius's oldest sister, who had married a man of consular dignity. Marcus being handsome and athletic, Petronius cherished for him a sentiment which as nearly approached affection as he was able to feel. He gave orders that Vinicius should be admitted, and questioned him as to the progress of the war in Asia, from which the young man had just returned, while Vinicius joined him in the bath and the luxurious attention of the slaves for the care of the body which followed. At last Vinicius explained to his uncle the special errand on which he had come, and asked advice. He had put his arm out of joint, outside the city, and Aulus Plautius, coming by at the moment, had taken him to his house, where the skilful slave-physician had restored him to health. There he had fallen in love with the ward of Plautius, a young girl of incomparable beauty, who was called Lygia because she came of the Lygian nation, though her own barbarian name was Callina. The girl was a king's daughter, or something of that sort. The commander of the legions of the Danube had exacted from the Lygians a promise not to cross the boundary; and in confirmation of their promise

266

the Lygians had given hostages, among them Lygia, the daughter of their leader, and her mother. After the fall of their king they vanished, leaving the hostages in captivity; and, his widow having died soon afterward, the little Lygia had eventually been entrusted to Pomponia Græcina, the wife of Aulus Plautius, a most dignified and respected matron. Moreover, Vinicius had slept one night in the temple of Mopsus, in order to have a prophetic dream, and Mopsus had appeared to him, declaring that through love a great change would take place in his life. He had made a beginning of expressing his feelings to Lygia; but instead of replying she had drawn on the sand by the fountain, with a reed, the figure of a fish, looked at him, then down at the figure, then back at him; and had fled without a word.

Vinicius entreated his uncle to plead for him; and Petronius having gladly consented, they betook themselves to the house of Aulus Plautius. Aulus was very wealthy but sedate, and his wife, Pomponia, a rarely virtuous woman in the Rome of those days, had been suspected of entertaining "that Eastern superstition which consists in honoring a certain Chrestos," as Petronius explained to Vinicius on their way, and had been tried by a domestic tribunal and acquitted. While Vinicius wooed Lygia in words that found an echo in her maiden breast, Petronius watched her, and decided that she was not only as beautiful as Aurora and the spirit of Spring, but had something quite uncommon about her.

Petronius did not dare to speak openly to Lygia's guardians concerning his errand; but he bethought himself of a method whereby Vinicius could obtain her, either as a slave or as a wife, Vinicius honorably desiring the latter. He held a confidential conversation with Nero, in consequence of which, two days later, a centurion at the head of several score of Pretorian soldiers appeared at the house of Plautius and demanded that Lygia be surrendered to them, Nero having decided that he and the Senate were the proper guardians of a State hostage. Aulus and Pomponia were forced to submit, though with profound grief; but they gave the young girl a retinue of slaves befitting her rank. Among them was a tall, broad-shouldered Lygian known in the house as Ursus, who had escorted Lygia and her mother to the camp of the Romans, and who now besought permission to accompany his young mistress. How he would be able to watch over and protect her at the palace he could not say; but iron broke in his hands as if it were wood. Pomponia, being a Christian, like Lygia, chose the girl's retinue exclusively among the adherents of the new faith. Aulus Plautius divined that this catastrophe had happened through Petronius, and cursed the day in which Vinicius had entered his house; for, he said, those men were seeking not a hostage but a concubine. He resolved to go directly to Nero, though he feared his visit would be of no avail. He was not admitted to the presence of Nero; but he returned home somewhat encouraged, because a visit to Vinicius proved to him that the young man knew nothing of the matter, and was indignantly eager to rescue Lygia.

Petronius had asked Nero to take the girl from Aulus and give her to Vinicius. She had been taken to the palace; but Petronius calculated on the girl's beauty arousing the jealousy of Poppæa, Nero's wife, who would promptly send her to Vinicius. This arrangement was for the sake of preserving appearances. Meanwhile, Lygia was safe under the protection of Acte, a former favorite of Nero, favorable to Christianity, to whom Pomponia had written. Feeling thus sure of her, Vinicius, while intoxicated at the imperial feast which Lygia was forced to attend, behaved disrespectfully to her, told her that Nero had given her to him, and that she was to be brought to his house on the morrow at dusk, and kissed her passionately. The gigantic Ursus repelled him, and rescued the girl, who refused to allow him to force his way past the palace guards and carry her home lest Nero's wrath should slay Aulus and Pomponia in revenge. It was decided, after consultation with Acte, that Ursus should go to Bishop Linus and entreat him to despatch Christians to take Lygia away from Vinicius. She could then become concealed among the Christians outside of the city, and Aulus and Pomponia, being able to prove their ignorance of her whereabouts, would be safe from Nero's wrath. Ursus was to wait with the Christians for Lygia.

The next afternoon, while Acte and Lygia were in the gardens, the Empress Poppæa appeared, accompanied by her infant child in the arms of its nurse. Poppæa was seized with mad jealousy as she beheld Lygia's beauty; but she softened when Lygia begged her not to allow her to be given as a slave to Vinicius (as Nero had promised), but to return her to Pomponia. With an evil smile, Poppæa declared that the girl should become the slave of Vinicius that very day, and passed on. As she did so the infant began to wail, no one knew for what reason.

When Vinicius's freedman, with an escort, came for Lygia at dusk, the girl, firm in her faith that God would rescue her, went with him unresistingly. Vinicius had decked his house in green, prepared a great feast, and was anxiously awaiting her, in company with Petronius, when a slave rushed in and reported that the girl had been snatched away from them by strangers, after a bloody conflict which had left several of Vinicius's people dead and many wounded. Vinicius slew the slave who brought the news, ordered all his slaves flogged, and rushed madly forth to find Lygia. The thought that Nero himself might have taken her made his heart sink within him, and for the first time he realized how he loved her. The next morning he went to the palace to find out the truth. Acte assured him that Lygia was not there; that Nero had not left the cradle of his child, who had been ill since the day before. The black nurse had declared that the child was bewitched by that strange woman (meaning Lygia), and if it died Poppæa would certainly accuse the girl of witchcraft; and then, wherever she was, there would be no rescue for her. Therefore, until the royal infant should recover, Acte advised Vinicius not to mention Lygia to Nero; and she told him that Lygia loved him, reproaching him for getting her away from Aulus and Pomponia by stratagem, instead of asking for her, the daughter of a king, in honorable marriage, of her guardians. Lygia had hoped he would rescue her from the palace and restore her to them. Her love for and trust in him had been evident as she spoke of this. Vinicius's wrath was now turned against Petronius. Had it not been for him, Lygia would now be his betrothed, and no danger would be hanging over her dear head.

The slaves of Petronius and Vinicius, who watched the gates and searched the city, were unable to find the slightest trace of Lygia. Petronius sent for a Greek physician and soothsayer, recommended to him by his beautiful slave, Eunice, as certain to find her. This Chilo Chilonides, a man of repulsive, even ridiculous aspect, confidently undertook the task, declaring that he already knew she had been rescued by her slave, who must have found aid among slaves, coreligionists. His plan was to find out what the religion was, worm himself into the confidence of its adherents, and discover the secret of her whereabouts. He inquired whether Petronius and Vinicius had ever seen Pomponia and Lygia making signs to each other, signs intelligible to them alone. Vinicius mentioned the fish that Lygia had sketched on the sand; and Chilo departed.

In a week the royal infant was dead, and Petronius, cleverly managing Nero through his grief, persuaded him to go to Antium (the child's birthplace), calculating that this would not only divert his mind from all possible thought of Lygia in that connection, but would also afford them greater freedom to seek her. Chilo presently reported that the fish was the secret symbol of the Christians; that Lygia herself belonged to that religion, and Christians had carried her away. By drawing a fish, he had won the confidence of an old slave who was weeping over his son. The old man had painfully collected the money to buy his son's freedom; and the master had taken the money and withheld the freedom. He had learned that slaves, many of whom were Christians, among them this man's son, unloaded stones every night from boats on the Tiber. He had represented that he was a Christian recently arrived from Naples, whose letters of recommendation to the brethren in Rome had been stolen from him on the way; and he suggested a means of earning the eternal gratitude and entire confidence of the old man, Euricius.

Accordingly, Vinicius gave Chilo money to purchase the freedom of Euricius's son; and made sure of his honesty by following and watching him. Chilo's search was prolonged and ardent; but nowhere did he see Lygia, or hear of her, in the Christian gathering which he frequented. He learned, however, that a great teacher of the Christians, Paul of Tarsus, was imprisoned in Rome; and that the supreme priest of the whole sect, who had been a disciple of Christ, might arrive in the city at any moment. Great meetings were sure to follow the arrival of this man, since all the Christians desired to see and hear him.

It would be easy for him to take Vinicius with him to these crowded meetings, where they would be certain to find Lygia. The great difficulty in the way was an elderly Christian, Glaucus by name, with whom Chilo had once journeyed from Naples, and whom he had betrayed, robbing him of his family and property, and leaving him for dead in a field. Glaucus had recovered from his wounds, and Chilo, having seen him among the Christians, was so terrified lest his victim should see him that he persuaded Vinicius to give him a large sum to get Glaucus assassinated. He represented to Euricius and his son, who were devoted to him since the redemption of the latter from slavery, that he needed some strong, courageous men to ward off danger from all Christians. The son suggested a herculean Christian who worked for a baker, and brought the two together. The giant's Christian name was Urban. To him Chilo plausibly explained that there was a Judas among the brethren who intended to deliver over Christ's flock to the wolves, and must be destroyed. Urban did not know Glaucus; but he said that all the thousands of Christians in Rome would assemble on the following night, at Ostranium, the cemetery of the Christians, outside of the city gates, to listen to a great apostle of Christ. The brethren would point out Glaucus to him there. To Vinicius Chilo reported that he had found Ursus, who had promised to kill Glaucus at Ostranium, where Lygia would surely be found. Vinicius could follow Ursus to Lygia's dwelling, or have him arrested as the murderer of Glaucus, and forced to confess where he had hidden her.

In preparation, Vinicius sent for Croton, an ex-gladiator, who was to deal with Ursus and carry off Lygia; and well armed, wearing Gallic cloaks, and hoods that concealed their faces, they set out for the gathering, Chilo having secured the passwords. To this meeting without the gate the Apostle Peter came, as had been anticipated, and his preaching of universal love and forgiveness of injuries amazed Vinicius, while Chilo took courage in the thought that even if Urban followed it, and refused to kill Glaucus, his own life would be safe from the latter. Peter's narrative of the Resurrection was beginning to make an impression on Vinicius when Chilo pointed out to him Ursus accompanied by Lygia, only a few paces distant. Warned by

Chilo that people were beginning to stare at them because they were the only persons who had not removed their hoods, Vinicius and his companions withdrew, and waited outside the cemetery for the girl, who emerged escorted by Ursus and several others, one, apparently, being the Apostle Peter. When, after a long walk, Ursus, Lygia and an old man entered a house in a narrow lane, the three men followed, after some delay, and found within a little garden containing a small house, from which Ursus emerged to wash vegetables at the fountain.

Vinicius ordered Croton to kill Ursus, overconfident of his gladiator's strength, and himself rushed to Lygia, and seizing her in his arms, was making for the entrance, when the girl cried to her protector, "Kill not!" and Ursus, dropping the dying Croton, tore Lygia from him. Then the earth turned round with him, and the light of day died in his eyes. Chilo, who was hiding behind the corner house outside, watching curiously, was terrified to see Ursus come forth, with Croton's body in his arms, and went his way toward the river. After long debating with himself what was the safest and most profitable course for him to pursue, he decided to send Euricius in the evening to Lygia's house to make inquiries; meanwhile, he slunk home and slept until he was aroused by a messenger who summoned him to Vinicius.

When Vinicius came to his senses, he found himself tended by Lygia, Ursus, Crispus, and the old man Glaucus. Ursus had wounded his head by thrusting him against a wall, and his arms (which he had put out to save himself from falling) had been broken and put out of joint. They were about to leave the house (after dressing his wounds) for fear of persecution, and to save Lygia from him. But he reassured them on the score of Croton's death, and his own intentions, and prevailed on them to remain and allow him to remain also, until his arm should heal. He sent for Chilo in order to despatch to his home a letter saying that he was gone to Beneventum. Chilo, however reluctant, could not refuse to come, Ursus being the forceful messenger. Ursus did not recognize him as the man who had incited him to murder Glaucus; but on his arrival Glaucus knew him at once, and proclaimed his character to all present; whereupon Ursus realized the truth and seized him. Vinicius did not intervene, but the Apostle Peter reminded Glaucus of the precept to forgive enemies. Vinicius was as much astonished at Christian doctrine and practise as Chilo; but during his illness, nursed by Lygia and Ursus, he learned to appreciate many of the Christian teachings, and to regard Lygia in a different light, with more love and far more respect than before. He also learned from Ursus certain details of Lygia's ancestry and fortunes which showed him that she could occupy, as his wife, the highest possible position at the imperial court. That Lygia loved him he was able to convince himself on many occasions; and he was increasingly impressed with the beauty of the Christian life.

Lygia, discovering her unconquerable love for Vinicius, begged Crispus to let her leave his house, frankly telling him the reason; and Crispus, a severe old man, consented, finding no word of forgiveness for a love that he regarded as sinful, since it was bestowed on a heathen, an adherent of Nero. But the Apostle Peter rebuked him, quoting the marriage at Cana, and upheld Lygia, encouraging her to hope that Vinicius might be converted. Nevertheless, Lygia went away secretly, leaving near Vinicius's bed a cross made of twigs, which he thenceforth cherished.

On returning to his house Vinicius found, to his surprise, that his character seemed to have undergone a change. He used his slaves and people gently, and felt ready to accept Christianity, having learned from Glaucus about the scene between Crispus, Peter and Lygia. Chilo, unexpectedly appearing, told Vinicius that Lygia was living in the house of Bishop Linus, and that, as Ursus went to work at night, the house might be surrounded and Lygia seized during his absence. Vinicius, though sorely tempted, refused, and seeking out the Apostle Peter, told him and his fellows that, although he knew Lygia's whereabouts, he had come to ask her of them, pledging himself to begin the study of Christianity himself, as well as not to impede Lygia in her faith. Now he must go to Antium, with the imperial court, at Nero's command; but he entreated the apostle to let him see Lygia before his departure. Peter sent for the girl, and having questioned her as to her love, in the presence of Vinicius, and received her assurance, blessed them as they knelt before him. And Lygia, as she walked with Vinicius in the garden, confessed that she had loved him from the first, and, had he taken her back to the house of Aulus from the Palatine, she would have told her protectors of her love, and allayed their wrath against him.

When Nero, at Antium, shut himself up for days to compose songs, Vinicius made a hurried visit to Rome and Lygia. He was now ready to receive baptism, he told the young girl; but Paul of Tarsus had advised him to receive it at the hands of Peter. Moreover, he wished her to be present, and that Pomponia should be his godmother. After their marriage, he said, they would go to live in Sicily, whither Aulus had long since resolved to withdraw. His estate was near that of Aulus, and they would found a colony of Christians. Returning to Antium, Vinicius pined. Petronius, taking advantage of Nero's amiability (which he had cleverly aroused by flattery), reminded the Emperor of his promise about the young man and Lygia, and induced him to order Vinicius to proceed forthwith to Rome and marry her.

With glad haste the young man set out; but on approaching Rome found it in flames, set by Nero's instigation and hint, if not by direct command. With infinite difficulty, and almost at the cost of his life, he made his way to the house of Linus, in the Trans-Tiber district, only to learn that Linus and Lygia had gone, two days before, to Ostranium, where Peter was to baptize a whole company of confessors to the faith. Vinicius (guided by Chilo, whom he had accidentally encountered) found the Apostle Peter, who led him to a hut where dwelt the ill and feeble Linus, Lygia, and the faithful Ursus. On the way he had begged Peter to baptize him, and he now swore to stand by the brethren in the day of trouble. Whereupon Peter baptized him, while the shouts of fighting and the roar of the burning city were audible outside.

Nero, on returning to Rome, found the people in savage mood, not likely to be appeased by the food that had been distributed. At the instigation of Poppæa—herself cleverly instigated—he was persuaded that the Christians were enemies of the human race, of the city, and of himself, whom they never had recognized as a god. His conviction was confirmed by the news that Poppæa gleaned from the treacherous Chilo, that when the God of the Christians was crucified He had promised to come to the world again after Rome should have been destroyed by fire, and give Christians dominion over all the earth. Chilo also told the manner of Croton's death, denounced Aulus, Pomponia, Lygia, and Vinicius as Christians (out of revenge for Vinicius's once having threatened to have him flogged, and in spite of the enormous sums of money he had received from him), and promised to deliver up Peter, Linus, and thousands of others. Poppæa, whose jealous eye had correctly estimated the supreme beauty of Lygia, seized her opportunity, and revived the accusation of witchcraft exercised upon her dead child.

Thus the fate of the Christians was settled. It was decided to lay the blame of Rome's destruction upon them. Petronius warned Vinicius that the pursuit might begin at any moment, that persecutions and tortures awaited them; Vinicius must not pause for questions, but take weapons, a purse of gold, a handful of Christians, and flee instantly with Lygia beyond the Alps or to Africa, or even rescue the girl by force if need be. He arrived too late: Lygia had already been seized and cast into the Mamertine prison. Emissaries had also been despatched about the city to arouse the populace, who promptly began to demand that the Christians be thrown to the lions. Yielding to this apparently popular demand, Nero determined to furnish such a spectacle as never had been seen and could not be imagined. In the greatest haste, a new and vast circus was constructed of wood, and the Christians were to contend with divers wild beasts as the chief feature of the entertainment. By dint of money and the friendly aid of Christians among the guards, Vinicius tried to save Lygia. One torture she escaped through falling ill, providentially, with the prison fever. Her appearance in the amphitheater was at least postponed; and Petronius proposed to Vinicius a plan of rescue. Lygia was to be placed in a coffin and carried out at night, as if for burial. Vinicius adopted the suggestion, and through the Christian son of the woman with whom Lygia had lodged (who had hired himself to carry out corpses, that he might aid his fellow-Christians) he arranged that on arriving at the "Putrid Pits" the coffin was to be consigned to persons who would be waiting with a litter. But before midnight on that day Lygia and Ursus were removed to the Esquiline prison. Petronius divined that this had been done to prevent her dying of the fever, and so escaping the amphitheater to which she had been condemned; and he did not even try to console the unhappy Vinicius.

Vinicius now lost hope of saving Lygia: Christ alone could do that, for the Esquiline prison was far better guarded than the Tullianum. His sole hope now was to see her in prison. With this end in view, he bribed the overseer of the Putrid Pits with an enormous sum of money to enroll him among the servants who were sent nightly to prison for corpses. The chances of his being recognized were small; he wore the garb of a slave, and the prisons were badly lighted. Moreover, no one would suspect that the son of one Consul and the grandson of another would be found in such a position. Appointed to the most difficult and dangerous detail, which had to visit the prisons at night, he eventually discovered Ursus and Lygia, and proposed that the young girl should envelop herself in a mantle and pass out with his countersign. But Ursus declared that not only was she too feeble to stand, but she loved Vinicius and would not allow him to sacrifice himself. Nevertheless, their interviews strengthened both Lygia and Vinicius in their love and faith, although Lygia had given up all hope, while her lover was persuaded that rescue would come. At the end of three days the overseer refused to admit Vinicius, as the prisons would be full that night of soldiers and officials who were to conduct the remaining Christians to Nero's gardens, and he feared to risk his own life through having Vinicius recognized. Vinicius stood by the gate to watch the prisoners as they were led forth. Lygia and Ursus were not among them.

After the burning alive in the gardens of a large number of Christians as living torches, the populace began to be sated with blood. Chilo, who had seen Glaucus burning there, and after a conversation with Paul of Tarsus had been baptized on that dreadful day, had died the death of a martyr for refusing to declare that the Christians had fired Rome. The people were beginning to believe in their innocence. Petronius cleverly endeavored to induce Nero to command Vinicius's marriage to Lygia, the latter, as hostage, not being lawfully subject to imprisonment; but one of his rivals and enemies thwarted him.

Nero was persuaded to make of Vinicius's suffering a tragedy to delight himself, and this his followers knew, though the exact nature of the torture planned for Lygia was a secret. A night spectacle at the Circus was ordered. Every eye was turned on the unhappy lover, who could not absent himself, Nero having expressly commanded his presence. Ursus, unarmed, entered the arena. Then a door opened and an enormous German aurochs rushed in, with Lygia, naked, bound to his head between the horns. Ursus understood. After a terrible struggle he succeeded in killing the aurochs with his naked hands, unbound the unconscious Lygia, and bearing her aloft on his outstretched arms he first held her silently up before Nero, then made the circuit of the arena, showing her to the spectators, and dumbly begging for her life.

Vinicius, leaping over the barrier, ran to Lygia, and flung his toga over her; then tore apart the tunic on his breast, and displayed the scars from the wounds he had received in the Armenian war, stretching out his hands to the audience in entreaty. The enthusiasm knew no bounds. Nero hesitated and halted. The audience were seized with uncontrollable rage, and began to shout: "Matricide! Incendiary!" The people were absolute lords in the Circus. Nero began to be seriously alarmed, and gave the sign for mercy, which evoked thunderous applause. Lygia was carefully carried to the house of Petronius, where she recovered consciousness during the night. Petronius skilfully tied the hands of his enemy, for the time being, by suggesting to Nero that he write a poem about the maiden who, at the command of the Lord of the World, had been freed from the horns of the aurochs and given to her lover. But he advised Vinicius to take Lygia to Sicily (whither Aulus Plautius had already removed), as soon as she was able to travel, since his special enemy was capable of employing poison—not out of hatred to either Vinicius or Lygia, but to him, Petronius.

Twice the Apostle Peter came to the house of Petronius to see the young pair; but soon Petronius warned him that his presence and that of Paul, in the city, had been discovered at the Palatine (where it had hitherto been supposed that they had perished in the conflagration), and it had been determined to seize them, at all costs, and so root out the last remnants of the hated new religion.   Peter hesitated long to abandon his post; but, strenuously urged by all the Christians, he finally consented to flee until a more favorable season.   He set forth; but on the Appian Way he beheld a vision: Christ coming to meet him, in heavenly radiance.   The Apostle fell with his face to the earth, and cried: *"Quo Vadis, Domine?"*   ("Whither goest Thou, Lord?")   A sad, sweet voice replied: "If thou desert my people, I am going to Rome to be crucified a second time."   Peter lay so long that his guide thought he had swooned or was dead.   But at last he rose, and turned back toward Rome, where, that same evening, he told the assembled Christians that he had seen the Lord. Afterward he went undauntedly to crucifixion, prophesying, as he went, that the heathen temples should become Christian temples, and Rome the capital of Christendom.   That same day, also, Paul of Tarsus was executed, manfully confessing the faith.

Vinicius and Lygia went, after their marriage, to Sicily, whence Vinicius wrote to Petronius of his happiness.   Petronius received the letter at Cumæ, whither he had gone with Nero and the court.   He was out of favor.   As Nero daily sank to the rôle of a comedian, a buffoon, and a charioteer, he could no longer endure the elegant patrician, especially as Petronius maintained silence and no longer praised.   Petronius's special enemy had at last won the ascendant; and many envied the wealth and splendid works of art of the former arbiter of fashion.   Petronius was lost.   Afraid to attack him in Rome, where the populace admired him, Nero invited him to Cumæ, imprisoning his servants in Rome, and surrounding his house with Pretorian guards.   Petronius understood.   He wrote a farewell letter to Vinicius and Lygia; and then, on the evening before the centurion was to come with his death-sentence, he assembled about him all his friends at a magnificent banquet.   At the end he read to them an insulting, plain-spoken letter that he had prepared for Nero, then had his Greek physician open a vein in his arm, and calmly died, to the sound of music.   His favorite, Eunice, a beautiful slave whom he had freed and who loved him, had her veins opened, and died with him.

The blood of the martyrs was the seed of the Church; and Nero's persecutions caused the Christians to multiply marvelously in numbers, and to wax fervent in the faith.

WILLIAM GILMORE SIMMS

(United States, 1806–1870)

THE YEMASSEE (1835)

The author of this Indian romance was the historian of South Carolina, and his State's history furnished him with material for the story. It deals entirely with colonial life in the Carolinas at the period when Charles Craven was Governor of the Province, and clearly delineates him, under an assumed name, as the savior of the Colony from destruction by the powerful Indian tribes that flourished near the coast, in combination with the hostile Spaniards from St. Augustine.

ITHIN a mile of the Council Town of the Yemassee Nation, Pocotaligo, dwelt Sanutee, one of the chiefs of that powerful tribe of Indians on the Carolina coast in the sixteenth and seventeenth centuries. As he left the low door of his lodge, to go hunting, his wife Matiwan questioned him about his return. He answered that he was going to hunt the deer in the far swamps; and it would be dark before his return. Then she asked after the one son of their union, the young chief Occonestoga. The chief, turning to Matiwan, replied that he knew him no longer as their son; that he was possessed of the bad spirit, which may have to serve the good spirit at times, but does so reluctantly. "No! Matiwan must not be the mother of a dog."

The chief crossed the river in his canoe and struck a trail that led toward the white settlement, though avoiding it. He saw the encroachments of the whites, and was willing to change the peace policy of his nation to one of hostility. He examined the blockhouse, which, now without defenders, was at the extreme limits of the treaty boundary of the white settlements. He then went to the river, and saw a vessel in midstream and two sailors rowing away from it. After this he turned home-ward.

While circling about a swamp his dog struck the trail of a deer, and soon a fine buck came on the trail, when an arrow pierced its side; yet it kept on running until the report of a rifle sounded from the wood, when the animal fell. The dog dashed at the throat of the deer. The hunter from the wood, apparently a seaman, in trying to drive him off, was attacked by the animal, whose ferocity he could only quell by killing it.

Sanutee, seeing the death of his dog, sprang at the hunter, and a fight ensued, until the chief was at the mercy of the sailor. The latter had raised his knife to slay, when he was arrested by a powerful hand. He turned fiercely, only to look into the muzzle of a rifle. The man behind him was English, tall, straight as an arrow, and with features combining manliness and beauty.

"Put up your knife, good Pepperbox. Would you strike the great chief of the Yemassees, the best friend of the English?"

"Who are you?" retorted the sailor.

"Suppose, fair master, I don't choose to say, what then?" asked the Englishman.

At this moment another chief of the Yemassee, Ishiagaska, appeared on the scene, and Harrison, for so he was called, disappeared in the forest. As soon as he was out of sight of the Indians and the sailor he despatched his negro, Hector, to see whether the seaman accompanied the Indians. Reaching the river, he looked at a craft in midstream, and was convinced that it was a Spanish vessel, and probably laden with arms and ammunition for the Indians. The Spanish, in common with the Indians, were jealous of the English settlements on the coast, and Harrison was on the alert for signs of hostility.

As he stood on the bank, a boat carrying two brothers, Graysons, came within hail, and he arranged with them to meet him at the blockhouse the next morning. When he had gone, one of the brothers, Hugh, declared his enmity against this man, Harrison, and said he would not attend the appointed meeting.

Harrison went to the cottage of the old parson, Matthews the Puritan, and as he entered he met the pretty daughter, Bess, to whom he spoke in the terms of an accepted lover. "Am I never to know the secret of your long absences?" she said.

The old parson came in soon, but treated his guest with formal coolness, for he was hostile to the Church of England and to the proprietary government of the Colonies. Neither was Matthews in the confidence of Harrison, and when he inquired about the duties that caused his continued absence from Charleston, where recently he had sought him in vain, the captain gave him no satisfactory reply, but said he should soon know all. He had asked the hand of his daughter, Bess, while yet a comparative stranger, and Matthews thus far had withheld his consent. He said he must know more of this man who would marry his daughter, and furthermore, there were other objections. "What other objections? Speak!" demanded Harrison.

"Levity—profane words—singing of mirthful songs, and light bandying of wit," the old man enumerated.

"You will give your consent when I come for her after I have performed duties that will reveal to you both my character and my mission," replied Harrison. He then warned the parson that mischief was afoot among the Yemassees, and that he, with his family, should be ready to retreat to the lower blockhouse.

When Harrison had left the sailor and the two Indians in the forest, the former told the chiefs that the vessel in the river was from the Spaniards, who had sent them, through him, a belt of wampum, which he took from his breast-pocket, and which was the signet of treaties between the Indians and their allies. The chiefs examined the belt carefully, deriving satisfaction as they discovered one figure after another, and found the different signets thereon.

"He promises to find the arms if you find the men," the sailor explained. By the treaty, the sailor said, he was to have all the slaves captured in war, or he would do nothing for them.

In the midst of their deliberations, Hector, Harrison's slave, was detected concealed in the edge of the wood, and they captured him and carried him to the vessel in the river. The two chiefs then arranged for a council of the chiefs of the various tribes the following day. A Spanish force was on its way overland, and when it should be heard from, the captain of the vessel was to attack the settlements on the river, and a general massacre, by the Indians, was to take place.

The Council House at Pocotaligo was filled the following day. Sanutee, the head chief, realized his critical position, since other chiefs, seeing his popularity, were jealous of his power. For this reason he had formed a conspiracy to involve the nation in war with the settlements. He arrived in Pocotaligo just in time. Commissioners from the English settlements were there, and had distributed many gifts to the chiefs. They wished to buy more land, and they had bribed the chiefs with bright-colored garments and gewgaws to obtain their consent. Sanutee and two or three others fiercely opposed selling more lands; but they were voted down by the majority, and a treaty was ratified. The last of the chiefs assenting to the treaty was Occonestoga, son of Sanutee, whom the old warrior had disowned. When the son spoke he was somewhat intoxicated, and when he sat down his infuriated father would have tomahawked him had he not been forcibly prevented.

Because of this defeat within the council, Sanutee determined to appeal to the people. He made an adroit speech to the popular assembly, and so aroused public sentiment that it was resolved to punish the members of the council who had favored the selling of more land. An attack was made on these members, when suddenly the prophet, Enoree Mattee, poured forth a wild rhythmic strain, according to which he was to cut the token from the arms of the chiefs, so that hereafter they must roam as outlaws.

The English commissioners had fled to the house of Granger, the English trader, living in Pocotaligo. A thousand Indians soon surrounded the house, demanding the treaty. But the commissioners refused to give it up, and would have been murdered if Granger's wife had not snatched it and thrown it out to the mob. The treaty being destroyed, the commissioners were permitted to depart. Harrison was at the blockhouse when they arrived there, and it was decided that they should go directly to Charleston with despatches that Harrison had prepared for the Government.

While they were talking, a boat containing three men came from the vessel to the shore, and Harrison resolved to hold these men until his slave Hector should be restored to him. He sounded a trumpet, which met with a dozen responses from the Green Foresters. The men in the boat rowed for the parson's cottage, and one of them entered the house and made himself known as Dick Chorley, once a boy-member of the parson's London congregation.

Those whom Harrison's horn brought to his side were his old followers in the Coosaw war. Under his orders they secured the two men in the boat, while he went directly to Parson Matthews's. There he found Dick Chorley and told him he knew Hector was a prisoner on the vessel. Chorley denied this, and then Harrison blew his trumpet and the Foresters came in. The exhibition of force, and the assurance that his boatmen were prisoners, brought Chorley to his senses. He wrote an order for Hector's delivery and the men soon returned with the negro.

Harrison informed Matthews of the insurrection at Pocotaligo, and again urged his retreat to the blockhouse, but in vain. As he went out he received word from Bess that she would meet him the next day in the grove of oaks, as he had requested. He then went to the blockhouse, which he ordered put in condition for a siege. Hector's information confirmed his own conjectures as to the character of the vessel.

Occonestoga, son of Sanutee, had fled from Pocotaligo as soon as he left the Council Hall, and had sought refuge in the blockhouse. That afternoon Bess Matthews went to the grove to meet Harrison, as appointed. While waiting she saw a huge rattlesnake directly in front of her. Its glittering eyes charmed her and held her powerless to move, until she fell insensible just as the reptile made its spring. At that moment an arrow pierced its head from the bow of the fugitive, Occonestoga. The reptile tried to regain its coil, but, failing, struck its fangs into its own body and died in convulsions by the side of the unconscious maiden. Harrison came at that instant, and, seeing the young chief trying to revive the girl, he would have struck him down, but glancing about him, he saw the reptile. When he discovered the arrow in its head he comprehended the situation and gave his heartfelt thanks to the Indian, as he lifted the unconscious form and carried her to her father's house.

Harrison next sent the young chief on a secret mission to Pocotaligo to ascertain the state of affairs there. This adventure he readily undertook, and was not long in reaching his father's wigwam, out of the door of which the old chief was just passing. Waiting until Sanutee was out of sight, he entered and found his mother, Matiwan, alone. She embraced him lovingly, but in a few moments, hearing footsteps, she hid him behind a pile of skins. Just then Sanutee entered and was resting by the fire when voices were heard. The cabin was surrounded, and the Indians came in, declaring that they had traced Occonestoga there.

At that instant the young chief sprang from his hiding-place, hatchet in hand, and, standing in the center of the lodge, desperately challenged them. Sanutee dashed toward him and would have struck him dead but for Matiwan. Then the hostile Indians surrounded Occonestoga, bore him out, and were about to perform the ceremony of expatriation, which would doom him to outlawry, when, rather than that this terrible sentence should be executed, Matiwan rushed in and smote him dead with a hatchet.

Harrison, anxious at not receiving any word from Occonestoga, mounted his horse and rode through the settlements, warning them of the threatening situation at Pocotaligo. He came to the cottage of Parson Matthews and hastened to the grove, where he met Bess and gave her an ardent greeting. He urged her to impress on her father the peril from the Indians, and told her about the vessel in the river; and she, in turn, informed him that it had moved some miles up the river within two or three hours, which added to his anxiety. Returning to the block-house, he found that the Indians had been visiting the vessel, taking off boxes and packages.

Everything now pointed to an early attack by the savages. Harrison tried in vain to enlist Granger, the trader, as a spy on the Indians at Pocotaligo and so determined to go himself. He instructed Hector that if he were not back by moonlight he was to put his hound, Dugdale, on his track. Then he mounted his horse and was off.

Meantime Hugh Grayson wandered through the woods to his cottage and found his mother at home alone. His deadly jealousy of Harrison, in the latter's relation to Bess, had made him moody, and his mother questioned him. Without answering, he went toward the door. She now begged him not to leave her alone, but still he made no reply. He left the house and followed the trail to the river. There he heard the tread of a horse, and, gazing through the gloaming, saw Harrison a short distance away. He cautiously drew nearer to him, and as the captain stretched himself on the ground he would have attacked him; but his resolution failed him. Harrison, discovering him, and surprised at his wild action, spoke to him kindly. While they were speaking, Hugh's brother, Walter, landed from his canoe, and Harrison, without speaking of Hugh's action, induced Hugh to take his (Harrison's) horse and remove his mother to the blockhouse, while Walter could help him along toward his destination. This plan was adopted, and he was soon on his way again up the river in the canoe. Walter landed him just below Pocotaligo, and there they parted.

Harrison, in passing through the woods, discovered several war-councils of different tribes. He examined the general camp at Pocotaligo from a secluded spot, and was satisfied that it indicated war. In order to stimulate the spirit of the warriors, they had secured a white man, an Irishman, as a victim, and tortured him with arrows and fire until he succeeded in breaking away from them. He darted for the woods at the point where Harrison lay concealed. There an Indian overtook the victim and beat his brains out at a blow. Harrison drew his knife and pierced the murderer to the heart; but before he could escape a dozen warriors surrounded him. The prophet of the tribe claimed him as his sacrifice. He was taken to the log cell of the town, and a guard was put over him. From this desperate plight he escaped, in the darkness of midnight, with the aid of Matiwan, the mother of Occonestoga, who rescued him because he reminded her of her dead son. He fled to the river, found a canoe, and made his way within a few miles of the blockhouse.

While Harrison, that night, was a prisoner, the Indian war-party distributed itself over the border country, pillaging and devastating. Captain Chorley, of the river-vessel, commanding his own men and a body of Indians, led in this murderous warfare. Another band was led by the chief, Ishiagaska, and this last force came to the cottage of Parson Matthews. The chief distributed his force behind shelters, he himself reconnoitering until he found an unlocked window, which he entered. This was Bess's room, and she lay asleep. He raised his knife to despatch her, when he received a blow from a heavy club wielded by the old parson. At this crisis Chorley, the sailor, entered on the scene and ordered the old chief to cease his attack. As he refused to do so, the sailor and his men surrounded the Indians and prevented the slaughter. Then Chorley, with the family as his prisoners, renewed his march.

In the absence of Harrison, Walter Grayson commanded at the blockhouse, where his force consisted of about twenty-five men. Hugh Grayson, equally brave with his brother, was out on Harrison's horse beating up recruits. After he had secured several Foresters he met reënforcements from Beaufort, and together they made their way toward the blockhouse.

Harrison, after his escape, traversed a region inhabited by his enemies, and while trying to evade them was attacked by two Indians. While he was fighting for his life, he heard the voice of his hound, and the next moment Dugdale seized one of the Indians by the throat; the other took to flight. When the dog had killed his antagonist, Harrison made haste toward the blockhouse. He had gone but a little distance when he and Dugdale came in the rear of a party of savages in fierce conflict with a band of Foresters. The baying of the hound led the Indians to believe that reënforcements were at hand against them, and, panic-stricken, they took to flight.

After much fighting, when the blockhouse was besieged and apparently doomed to destruction, the besiegers suddenly discovered that they were being ambushed from without. They sought to escape, but it was too late, for their path was effectually blocked by Hugh Grayson and his men. The defeat was as complete as any recorded in the annals of Indian warfare. Chorley, finding that he and his force could not contend alone, escaped to the river. He had Bess Matthews a prisoner; but as he was making for his vessel in a boat, with her secured, Harrison reached the shore, saw the situation, and with a shot from his rifle pierced the ruffian's heart. As the sailor fell into the water the boat was capsized. Harrison sprang into the water to rescue Bess, and was just in time to save her from drowning. The old father, in gratitude for the deed, freely surrendered her to the brave man who had saved her from worse than death.

Harrison's next enterprise was to take possession of the vessel; but before he could accomplish this the pirates set her on fire and abandoned her, and an explosion resulted in her complete destruction.

The time had now come for Gabriel Harrison to reveal himself to all with whom he had been associated; and when he said to the assemblage that he was Governor Craven, the Lord Palatine of Carolina, they were filled with wonder and admiration. He issued to Hugh Grayson the commission that made him the commander of all forces in the county of Granville. Grayson, accepting the office, proceeded to act on the plans of the Governor. Sanutee, with his force, was nearing Charleston, and his Spanish allies would soon unite with him. The Governor, therefore, hastened to that city and organized a force that soon numbered twelve hundred fighting men, with which he planned a campaign against the Indians before the Spaniards should reënforce them. Sanutee, seeing that he must give immediate battle or retreat, formed his camp on the banks of the Salkehatchie River, to avoid fighting until his allies arrived. But Governor Craven followed him, and camped within sight of the savages. He abandoned his camp before daylight, and concealed his men where their rifles commanded the camp, which was left undisturbed, as if occupied. The Indians, intent on surprising the Governor's force, attacked the camp before sunrise, when the whites, in turn, attacked them from their place of concealment, and nearly annihilated them. The Chief, Sanutee, lay dying in the woods when the Governor came upon him at early dawn, and Matiwan was there singing the death-song and performing the last Indian rites for the dying chieftain.

MAY SINCLAIR

(England, 18—)

THE DIVINE FIRE (1904)

This story was the author's first great success, and it has passed through many editions. The romantic hero is supposed to be drawn from a well-known figure in London literary life.

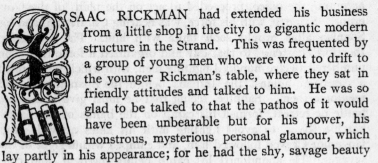

ISAAC RICKMAN had extended his business from a little shop in the city to a gigantic modern structure in the Strand. This was frequented by a group of young men who were wont to drift to the younger Rickman's table, where they sat in friendly attitudes and talked to him. He was so glad to be talked to that the pathos of it would have been unbearable but for his power, his monstrous, mysterious personal glamour, which lay partly in his appearance; for he had the shy, savage beauty of an animal untamed, uncaught.

They felt the tragedy of the disproportion between the young fellow and the shop, which in his soul he hated; and they felt terribly his one flaw: when excited he sometimes dropped—no, skipped—his aitches. He, Savage Keith Rickman, though only twenty-three, was a little poet about town. Some very modern poems, which he called *Saturnalia*, were appearing in *The Planet*, and he had finished a remarkable classic drama entitled *Helen in Leuce.*

When Keith was nine years old he had been discovered reading Greek in the shop by old Sir Joseph Harden, who had advised his father to give him a good education. This Rickman had done; for though he himself had sufficient knowledge for the trade in new books, he desired his son to have the expert knowledge necessary for successful traffic in second-hand books.

288

Keith, the genius, was discovered by Sir Joseph's nephew, Horace Jewdwine, an Oxford don, the most exacting and fastidious of men, whose entire nature was dominated by his critical faculty; therefore his disciple was not fed largely with praise. Keith looked up to him with simple, hero-worshiping fervor, with devotion untainted by any thought of material advantage.

"You've still got to find your formula. Not to have found your formula," Horace said solemnly to him one day, "is not to have found yourself."

Perhaps it was not to be wondered at if young Mr. Rickman had not yet found himself. There were, as he sorrowfully reflected, so many Mr. Rickmans. There were: Mr. Rickman of the shop, who served you with a certain remoteness, a noble apathy; Mr. Rickman the student and recluse, a humble and reverent person, who inhabited the insides of other men's books; Mr. Rickman the obscure writer of brilliant paragraphs, a fellow destitute of reverence and decency and everything except consummate impudence, a disconcerting humor and a startling style; Mr. Rickman the young man about town; Mr. Rickman the serene and perfect intelligence who sat above in judgment on them all; inextricably one with all these Rickmans was a certain apparently commonplace young man who lived in a Bloomsbury boarding-house and dropped his aitches. These six were liable at any moment to a visitation from a seventh Mr. Rickman, the genius, who might come in the form of a high god or of a demon, a consolation or a torment.

Shortly before Easter, 1892, Dicky Pilkington, financial agent, having a bill of sale from Sir Frederick Harden on the great Harden library, to fall due May 27th, offered to sell the library to Rickman. Therefore, when Sir Frederick's daughter sent to Rickman's for an expert to rearrange and catalogue the library before May 27th, when she was to go abroad, Isaac insisted upon Keith's doing the work, so that he might be able to estimate the value of the books.

For ten generations the men of the Harden family had been scholars. Then the Harden intellect encountered an insuperable obstacle in Sir Frederick, and by a freak of heredity it reappeared in Lucia, his daughter, not in its former austere and colorless form, but with a certain brilliance and passion, a touch of purely feminine uncertainty and charm.

Horace Jewdwine knew that if he could only make up his mind to something very definite and irretrievable, the great Harden library, with Court House, might one day be his. There was between him and Lucia a something altogether intangible and vague, understood to be an understanding. Lucia adored him; if she had not, he would have felt urged to something irretrievable and definite. His expressions of irritated astonishment at finding that there was no catalogue of the library had crystallized Lucia's vague intention of some time having the work done.

When Keith saw her and learned that she was ignorant of the coming sale, his conscience accused him of being there as a spy; and he protested vaguely, but yielded to Lucia's determination, and agreed to do the work with her assistance.

As they worked together, a frightful exaltation of the consciousness of self in him was yet pervaded, transcended, by his consciousness of her. Of her beauty he became every moment more aware. The intense quiet of her presence made his own appear noisy and intrusive; her finished courtesy seemed to place between them a fine but untransparent veil, dividing them more effectually than a barricade.

On Easter Sunday, when Keith was taking the holiday that Lucia had insisted upon, the wind scattered some leaves that he had been working upon, and among them Lucia found a printed slip bearing a sonnet with the headline *Helen in Leuce* and signed S. K. R. She had already identified Keith with the wonderful boy her grandfather had found; now she identified him with her cousin's discovery, the author of the drama that Horace had shown her, in which she had discerned the troubled pulse of youth, the passion of an imprisoned and tumultuous soul. She felt profoundly sorry for him, partly because he was not a gentleman. She never had seen anything like this inspired young cockney, with his musical voice and his afflicting accent, whose emotions declared themselves publicly and who yet contrived somehow to remain impenetrable.

Looking off from Harcombe Hill, Keith felt himself severed from the sources of his inspiration; a sense of intellectual dissolution came over him, the corruption and decay of the poetic faculty within him. Suddenly the vision of Lucia Harden rose before him, exposing the real nature of what had seemed to him pleasures—getting drunk and making love to Poppy Grace, of the Jubilee Variety Theater. When the meaning of his depression and his disgust revealed itself, the first exaltation of his dream of love was followed by a clear vision of the comedy and the tragedy of his passion.

When Lucia spoke of the sonnet she had found, he asked whether he might send her the manuscript of his drama. Reading it, she felt herself in the grasp of a new power, and thought of the impertinence of pitying the man that had written it; she found herself defending him against her own criticism as she listened fascinated while his wonderful voice brought out the subtler meanings of his work, covering its own offenses with exquisite resonances and overtones. And he stared in amazement at the young girl who seized on the essential with a genius of intuition, and saw no end to her powers of divination. But her insight had not told her that she was his inspiration. Her attitude to his genius was humbly reverent; her attitude to his manhood was profoundly unconscious.

Himself Keith saw as an abominable object, a thing with a double face and an unclean and aitchless tongue, spying, calculating, appraising, with a view to fraud. So at least would it seem to her if she knew the reason why he was there to catalogue the Harden library; and he had resolved to tell her, when she was called to Cannes by the death of her father.

He wrote to Jewdwine, assuming that he knew of the sale and telling him that Rickman's was negotiating for its purchase from Pilkington, but that he thought it only fair that some member of the family should have an opportunity to buy it. The security was a thousand pounds, the price twelve hundred, the value four or five thousand.

No reply came from Horace, who had just been appointed editor of *The Museion*. He saw that to buy the library—as he could, even with his limited resources—was the beautiful thing to do for Lucia. But as he thought it over he became suspicious of Rickman's as probably anxious to be relieved of a bad bargain. Finally he offered thirteen hundred pounds, to learn that

he was too late. While he persuaded himself that he would
have done the generous thing if more time had been given, he
was yet almost grateful to Rickman's for saving him from an
outlay that would have clouded his future.

Lucia returned to find that nothing in Court House remained
to her except her own personal possessions; Pilkington's bill of
sale included everything; her home must be sold, and her income
would be very small indeed. Keith explained the affair of the
library with great difficulty; to his confusion and distress, she
took for granted the integrity of Rickman's and thought there
would be nothing in the way of an arrangement by which she
should receive something near the value of the library.

He proposed to his father that they should either withdraw
or pay the price at which he valued the property—four thousand
pounds. Isaac refused to do either, believing that if Keith
should carry out his threat to leave the business he would soon
be forced to return by the difficulty of providing for himself
otherwise. Keith had told Lucia's friend, Kitty Palliser, of his
letter to Horace; but Lucia's solicitor threw some doubt upon
the statement, as Horace had not mentioned it to him; and he
pointed out to her the evidence of young Mr. Rickman's dishonesty in regard to the sale.

The question of his honesty was now the burning question
with her; for it involved the ardor or indifference of Horace.
To her inquiry Keith replied that he had written, and, seeing
her anxiety and divining her wish, added that he presumed
it was too late. He knew that he was deliberately suppressing
the one detail that proved his innocence. But as their eyes
met he saw that she knew it too. She could have loved him for
the lie; and when he had confessed his true connection with
the sale, she still declared her belief in his integrity and sincerity.

Lucia wrote to Horace, explaining what Keith had done or
tried to do for her, and asked that her cousin should do something for him. After careful reflection, Horace offered him an
engagement as a regular contributor to *The Museion*, the one
literary journal that openly professed a philosophy of criticism,
and gave him temporarily the post of subeditor, which would
give him about two hundred pounds a year.

Keith's genius throve upon his suffering and his anxiety

about Lucia, of whom he heard nothing, for Horace never spoke of her. The following spring he published a volume of poems, which was enthusiastically praised in four columns of *The Planet*, to which he still contributed. Jewdwine, then, feeling that Keith was no longer his discovery, wrote a review so judicial and impartial that it injured the book, coming as it did from the author's chief, who would presumably say all he could for it. And Horace, having given grounds for bitterness, himself began to grow bitter.

A sequence of *Nine and Twenty Sonnets*, recording nine and twenty moments in Keith's love for Lucia, was written at this time; but these were too intimate and personal for the eye of the public, and he kept them hidden.

In the two following years, during which he heard nothing of Lucia, there were times when he was aware of a distinct cleavage between his soul, still faithful to her, and his senses; and at just those moments Miss Flossie Walker, a fellow-boarder, a plump and rosy young woman, appeared to be lying in wait for him. At first he had pitied Flossie and enjoyed the superior position of benefactor. Then suddenly he ceased to take her about, and grew irritable and rude. It angered him to realize that she had any power over his emotions. Her prettiness tormented him; he hated her and everything connected with her.

Keith was horribly afraid; he dared not stay in the house with her, and went out to Hampstead. Four days later he returned and found Flossie dusting the books in his room. Even as he put his arms about her and kissed her he felt that he was held over the brink of the immeasurable, inexpiable folly. His genius remained alone and apart, unmoved, as if it knew the golden chain still quivered. The game was over, and Flossie had won.

In the following days he found her singularly inscrutable. She often annoyed him by little insistences on his poverty; for, though he had told her they could not marry at once, he would have been better pleased if she had not assumed so ostentatiously the air of preparing to be a poor man's wife. In reality, Flossie considered that she was engaged to a man very well off indeed, and she resented the delay.

After a year and a half had passed, she threatened to leave the Bank of England, where she was employed as a sorter, to take a place in the office of a wine-merchant. There was a terrible storm; and the incident closed with the understanding that Flossie should renounce the wine-merchant and they should be married in the autumn.

Keith was curiously shaken by this interview. He had been working at a tragedy; his mind had been almost intolerably luminous; now he could not recall his inspiration; far away he seemed to catch the light laughter of the fugitive Muse. The approach of the time for his marriage filled him with misgiving and even terror. Flossie left him plenty of time for the everyday work that paid; but the days when he was "as a god watching his creations careering in the intellectual void" were fast vanishing.

Among the boarders at Mrs. Downey's was a Miss Roots, who had been Lucia Harden's governess. About a month before the date fixed for the wedding Miss Harden, having come to pay her a visit, entered the dining-room with her. As Keith saw her swift smile of pleasure at recognizing him, the past years fell away—the long estranging years of bitterness and misery and vain desire, and the years, still more estranging, of his madness and his folly. And Lucia saw that his face had lost the restless look of youth that had helped to make it so irregular and had settled into the other look she had found there more rarely, the look that strengthened and refined the mobile features.

She told him she had been staying with the Jewdwines, and wondered that he had not been to see her; she winced as if a thought had struck her like a blow when she found that Horace had given him none of the messages she had sent. Her attitude toward Flossie indicated, if he could have read it, the height of her trust in him, the depth of her ignorance. She was ready to credit Flossie with some rare and lovely quality of soul. But he was conscious only of the mingled beatitude and torture of the moment.

He could have forgiven Jewdwine anything but the withholding of Lucia's messages. It he had known that he still had her friendship, he thought he could have lived on the memory of her and been saved from this base concession to the folly of the flesh, this marriage, which seemed to him more and more disastrous.

Lucia, during the interval, had been music-mistress in a college for women, and had paid off the debts she had received as a legacy; but her health had broken under the strain. She had waited for Horace's love with serene confidence; now she found that she no longer desired it.

Meanwhile Flossie went on furnishing her future home, approving of Keith's friendship with Lucia as conferring importance upon him. And he grew ever more furious with himself and furious with fate for casting her in his way. Yet it never occurred to him to break the engagement.

One day Keith was trying to make Lucia understand what she had done for him; and when she declared that she would be glad to know she had helped him in any way, he said:

"Then you shall know it," and he brought her his sonnets. He had not intended that she should see them till death had removed from her his embarrassing, preposterous personality; but now, looking forward, it seemed to him that he should never die. He believed that the work would be immortal; but as it concerned her so intimately, it could not be given to the world without her consent.

She found in the sonnets a revelation more sacred, more personal than she expected. That three-weeks' passion—for so she dated it—was laid before her in all its immortal splendor and all its mortal suffering and shame. She believed that he would not have let her know had it not been all over. She felt joy that it was over, pride that it had been, and thankfulness that it had been given her to know. She met him with joyful consent to accept their dedication to her, and was surprised to learn that he purposed to suppress the poems in deference to any scruples of hers.

"It is absurd to talk about my consent. Besides—why should I mind now, when it is all over?"

"You would not consent but for that?"

"Why talk of that now? Isn't it enough to be glad that it is all over, and that this is the end of it?"

"But it isn't all over, and this is not the end."

She handed him back the manuscript with a look of pain

and vague terror, declaring that it was not true; and he saw how terrible to her was the thought of being the cause of disloyalty in him.

The death of Keith's father when the marriage was imminent caused it to be indefinitely postponed. The business had not prospered since Keith's withdrawal; and a mortgage delivered the Strand house to Pilkington, only a small share of the City house falling to Keith; it was mainly owned by his stepmother. The Harden library was mortgaged to Pilkington for three years for four thousand nine hundred pounds. To redeem it Keith regarded as his destiny. Mrs. Rickman bought him out for four thousand pounds, which, with what he had, left seven hundred and fifty to be saved in three years from an income of three hundred and fifty—which would be impossible if he were to marry, barely possible if he were not.

He admitted that it was hard on Flossie, who by a masterly cross-examination possessed herself of all the details of the obligation and thought it too much that she should have to "slave" while he was "throwing away all that money on another woman"; whereupon he offered to release her, but would not take an instant decision, though he knew she was in a mood to decide as he was longing to have her do. Days and weeks passed before she made known her decision, which was to marry Sidney Spinks, an admirer of long standing.

In eighteen months Keith had paid off half of the debt; then he quarreled with Maddox, editor of *The Planet*, over Jewdwine, and gave up his connection with *The Planet*, realizing too late that he had sacrificed a permanent source of income and alienated his best friend for the sake of an idea—his idea of Jewdwine.

Jewdwine was touched by his devotion, and gave him some increase of salary. But after six months, while Jewdwine was at home with illness, Keith wrote a two-page article in praise of the *Poems* of a dying boy from whom no more was to be expected, and a paragraph about the *Poems* of a Cabinet Minister, a man of eminence and influence. But Jewdwine made a few ingenious transpositions, so that the Cabinet Minister had the article and the young poet the paragraph. Keith, in his indignation, resigned, thus depriving himself of another source of income; and the failure of a paper he was next engaged upon left him without any regular salary.

He got an extension of time from Pilkington, moved into an attic, and did what he could. But his exertions and privations brought on an illness that threatened to be fatal. His friends were filled with remorse for their neglect; and when he recovered Maddox paid him enough for what he had still unpublished to enable him to redeem the library, which he was now free to offer to Lucia. But she refused it.

"And what is it that I'm asking you to take?" he said, after other persuasion had failed. "Something that isn't mine and is yours. But if it were mine it would be a little thing compared with what I wished to give you and you wouldn't have."

She looked at him, and saw the sharp lines of his body and face, saw too the evidences of his poverty; and her love, so long hidden, sheltered and protected by her pity, came forth and knew itself as love.

"I will take everything—on one condition: that you will give me—what you said just now I wouldn't have."

Slowly he realized that what he had dreamed and despaired of was being divinely offered to him; but he felt that in his poverty he could not take advantage of a moment's inspired tenderness. Though his passion leaped to his tongue, he held it back so well that she read him wrongly and turned white with terror for what she had said—she had proposed to him and had been rejected.

Jewdwine came down, and was fascinated by her indifference; but from the look in her eyes when they discussed Rickman, whose drama, *The Triumph of Life*, was being played, he saw that his cousin no longer adored him. Did she adore Rickman?

Lucia went to London to see the play, and seeing it felt that something of Keith's genius had passed from her possession, realizing that henceforth he belonged to the world and not to her. At this time her strength, which had been undermined by her exertions after the death of her father, failed, and she left London very ill. Keith heard rumors of her engagement to Jewdwine, then that it was broken, both set afloat by Jewdwine himself; Keith went to him and learned of her illness.

"Kitty," said Lucia, as they were waiting for the visit of the great specialist, Sir Wilfrid Spence, and talking of the presentation of Keith's play in Paris—"Kitty, he is coming. By the terrace. Can't you hear?"

Kitty heard the rain dancing in the courtyard.

When Keith entered Lucia rose and went to him, never swaying till his arms held her.

"Lucia, are you very ill?"

"No; I am very, very well."

He thought she meant that death is well; but she looked smiling into his face, and he was reassured.

"Lucia," he said, "can you stand living with me in a horrid little house in a suburb?"

"I should love it."

"But it isn't a pretty house."

"It will be when I am in it."

"Then we shall not have to wait."

"But, Keith, darling, don't make plans till we know what Sir Wilfrid says."

Sir Wilfrid said: "There isn't anything wrong with her. What fool said there was? She has been made ill by grief."

"Lucia," asked Keith, "can you forgive me for being what I was?"

"It was before I knew you."

"Yes; but after? That was the worst, for I had known you."

"It was my fault. I should have been there."

Then he knew that, after all, she had understood.

FRANCIS HOPKINSON SMITH

(United States, 1838)

COLONEL CARTER OF CARTERSVILLE (1891)

The embodiment of Colonel Carter in book form grew out of a suggestion made by Mr. Richard Watson Gilder, editor of the *Century* magazine, his idea being that Mr. Smith should gather for the *Century* the various after-dinner stories which, told by Mr. Smith, had already made his Colonel Carter a distinct entity among the clubmen of New York, these stories to be published as told around the Colonel's table. As the author continued his work, however, the Colonel's personality took complete possession of him, and Mr. Smith became convinced that the man he portrayed was in reality one of the last remaining types of an old order of things, one whose courtesy, sweetness, impracticability, and generosity were purely Southern—a type driven out of existence with the end of the Civil War. The national recognition that greeted the Colonel's appearance proved how sincerely he was loved by both North and South, and how universally he was respected. The story was dramatized by Augustus Thomas, and was played in most of the large cities of the United States. We present here Mr. Smith's own version, prepared for this work.

HE Colonel had invited me to dinner, in one of his characteristic notes:

"No. 51 BEDFORD PLACE, NEW YORK, Friday.
"Everything is booming—Fitz says the scheme will take like the measles—dinner to-morrow at six—don't be late."

He was living at this time in an old-fashioned, partly furnished, two-story house, which crouches behind a larger dwelling on Bedford Place within a stone's throw of the tall clock-tower of Jefferson Market. He brought with him from his Virginia home his negro servant, Chad—an abbreviation of Nebuchadnezzar—who was chambermaid, cook, butler, body-servant, and boots. The features of the house were the low ceilings and its two fireplaces—an open wood-fire, which laughed from behind andirons, and an old-fashioned English grate—convenient and necessary for the various brews and mixtures for which the Colonel was famous.

He was, perhaps, fifty years of age, tall and slightly built; with iron-gray hair brushed straight back from his forehead, overlapping his collar behind. His moustache drooped over a firm, well-cut mouth, uniting at the ends with a gray goatee. His voice was soft and low, and tempered with a cadence that was delicious.

He wore a black broadcloth coat—a double-breasted garment, with similar colored waistcoat and trousers, a turn-down collar, a shirt of many plaits, which was under-starched and over-wrinkled, but was always clean, large cuffs very much frayed, but which he never forgot to trim as he dressed, a narrow black or white tie, and low shoes with white cotton stockings. He was a Virginian of good birth, fair education, and limited knowledge of the world; proud of his ancestry, proud of his State, and proud of himself; believing in States' rights, slavery, and the Confederacy; and, away down in the bottom of his soul, still clinging to the belief that the poor white trash of the earth included almost everybody outside of Fairfax County.

When he handed you his card it bore this unabridged inscription:

COLONEL GEORGE FAIRFAX CARTER,
OF CARTER HALL,
CARTERSVILLE, VIRGINIA.

He omitted "United States of America" simply because it added nothing to his identity or his dignity.

The scheme to which the Colonel referred in his invitation was a proposed railroad running from Cartersville to the sea. This railroad was the Colonel's only hope for the impoverished acres of Carter Hall, but lately saved from foreclosure by the generosity of his aunt, Miss Nancy Carter, who had redeemed it with almost all her savings, the house and half of the outlying lands being thereupon deeded to her. The other half reverted to the Colonel.

On the arrival of Fitzpatrick—a Wall Street bond-broker, who had undertaken to help the Colonel in his enterprise—dinner was announced.

I explained to Fitz that I was a humble landscape-painter,

but that the Colonel always insisted upon surrounding himself with a staff.

The Colonel seized the poker and rapped three times on the floor. A voice from the kitchen rumbled up:

"Comin', sah!"

It was Chad "dishin' the dinner" below; and in a moment more, brilliant in white jacket and apron, he had ranged himself behind the Colonel's chair, announcing with dignity that dinner was served.

"Come, Major! Fitz, sit where you can warm yo' back—I was worried about you when you came in—you are not thawed out yet. Fact is—" the Colonel had turned to me—"Fitz is a little overworked. Enormous strain, suh, on a man solvin' the vast commercial problems that he is called upon to do every day. One minute, gentlemen—an old custom of my ancestors, which I never omit."

The blessing was asked with becoming reverence; there was a slight pause, and then the Colonel lifted the cover of the tureen and sent a savory cloud of incense to the ceiling. The soup was a cream of something with baby crabs. There was also a fish, then a ham, brown and crisp, and bristling all over with cloves. Then the ducks!

It was beautiful to see the Colonel's face:

"Lay 'em here, Chad—right under my nose. Now hand me that pile of plates sizzlin' hot, and give that caarvin'-knife a turn or two across the hearth. Major, dip a bit of celery in the salt and follow it with a mou'ful of claret. It will prepare yo' palate for the kind of food we raise gentlemen on down my way. See that red blood followin' the knife, suh?"

"Suit you, marsa?"

"To a turn, Chad—I wouldn't take a thousand dollars for you," replied the Colonel, relapsing unconsciously into an old habit.

The Colonel loved a good dinner. To dine well was with him an inherited instinct; to share with you his last crust was a part of his religion. In fact, the head of the Colonel's table was his throne. Nowhere else was he so charming, and nowhere else did the many sides to his delightful nature give out such varied hues.

"There, Major," said the Colonel, as Chad laid the smoking plate before me, "is the breast of a bird that fo' days ago was divin' for wild celery within fo'ty miles of Caarter Hall. My dear old Aunt Nancy sends me a pair every week, bless her sweet soul! Fill yo' glasses, and let us drink to her health and happiness." Here the Colonel rose from his chair: "Gentlemen, the best thing on this earth—a true Southern lady! Now, Chad, the red pepper."

"No, jelly, Colonel?" said Fitz, with an eye on the sideboard.

"Jelly? No, suh; not a suspicion of it. A pinch of salt, a dust of cayenne, then shut yo' eyes and mouth, and don't open them 'cept for a drop of good red wine. It is the salt marsh in the early mornin' that you are tastin', suh—not molasses candy. You Nawtherners don't really treat a canvasback with any degree of respect. You ought never to come into his presence when he lies in state without takin' off yo' hats. That may be one reason why he skips over the Nawthern States when he takes his annual fall outin'." And he laughed heartily.

"But you use it on venison?" argued Fitz.

"Venison is diff'ent, suh. That game lives on moose-buds, the soft inner bark of the sugar-maple, and the tufts of sweetgrass. There is a propriety and justice in his endin' his days smothered in sweets; but the wild duck, suh, is bawn of the salt ice, braves the storm, and lives a life of peyil and hardship. You don't degrade a' oyster, a soft-shell crab, or a clam with confectionery; why a canvasback duck? Now, Chad, serve coffee."

No business had yet been touched upon, a rule of the Colonel's, never infringed, being that the dinner-hour was to be kept sacred.

"Salt yo' food, suh, with humor," he would say. "Season it with wit, and sprinkle it all over with the charm of good fellowship, but never poison it with the cares of yo' life. It is an insult to yo' digestion, besides bein' a mark of bad breedin'."

The pipes being lighted, the Colonel loosened the string around a package of papers and spread them out like a game of solitaire.

"Draw yo' chair closer, Major. Fitz, hand me the map."

As the map had been left at the office, the Colonel proceeded without it.

"Befo' I touch upon the financial part of this scheme of mine, Major, let me show you where this road runs," said the Colonel, reaching for the casters. "I am sorry I haven't the map, but we can get along very well with this—" and he unloaded the cruets.

"This mustard-pot, here, is Caartersville, the startin'-point of our system. This town, suh, has now a population of mo' than fo' thousand people; in five years it will have fo'ty thousand. From this point the line follows the bank of the Big Tench River —marked by this caarvin'-knife—to this salt-cellar, where it crosses its waters by an iron bridge of two spans, each of them two hundred and fifty feet. Then, suh, it takes a sharp bend to the south'ard and stops at my estate, the road-bed skirtin' within a convenient distance of Caarter Hall. Please move yo' arm, Fitz. I haven't room to lay out the city of Fairfax. Thank you.

"Just here," continued the Colonel, utilizing the remains of the cheese, "is to be the future city of Fairfax, named after my ancestor, suh, General Thomas Wilmot Fairfax, of Somerset, England, who settled here in 1680. From here we take a course due nawth, stopping at Talcottville, eight miles, and thence nawthwesterly to Warrentown and the broad Atlantic—in all, fifty miles."

"Any connecting road at Warrentown?" I asked.

"No, suh, nor anywhere else along the line. It is absolutely virgin country, and this is one of the strong points of the scheme, for there can be no competition."

I preserved my gravity, and then asked whether the Big Tench could not be crossed farther up, and, if so, why it was necessary to build twelve additional miles of road.

"To reach Carter Hall," said Fitz quietly.

"Any advantage?" I asked, in perfect good faith.

The Colonel was on his feet in a moment.

"Any advantage? Major, I am surprised at you! A place settled mo' than one hundred years ago, belongin' to one of the vehy fust fam'lies of Virginia, not to be of any advantage to a new enterprise like this! Why, suh, it will give an air of respectability to the whole thing that nothin' else could ever do. Leave out Caarter Hall, suh, and you pa'alyze the whole scheme. Am I not right, Fitz?"

"Unquestionably, Colonel. It is really all the life it has," replied Fitz, solemn as a graven image, blowing a cloud of smoke through his nose.

"Now, Major," locking his arm in mine, "listen; for I want you both to understand exactly the way in which I propose to forward this enterprise. Chad, bring me three wine-glasses, and put that Madeira on the table—don't disturb that railroad—so."

"My idea, gentlemen," the Colonel continued, filling the glasses himself, "is to start this scheme honestly in the beginnin', and avoid all dissatisfaction on the part of these vehy bondholders thereafter. Now, suh, in my experience I have always discovered that a vehy general dissatisfaction is sure to manifest itself if the coupons on secu'ities of this class are not paid when they become due. As a gen'ral rule, this interest-money is never earned for the fust two years, and the money to pay it with is inva'ably stolen from the principal. All this dishonesty I avoid, suh, by the issue of my Deferred Debenture Bonds."

"How?" I asked, seeing the Colonel pause for a reply.

"By cuttin' off the fust fo' coupons. Then everybody knows exactly where they stand. They don't expect anythin', and they never get it."

Fitz gave one of his characteristic roars and asked whether the fifth would ever be paid.

"I can't at this moment answer, but we hope it will."

"It is immaterial," said Fitz, wiping his eyes.

"No, gentlemen, the plan is not only fair, but reasonable. Two years is not a long period of time in which to foster a great enterprise like the C. and W. A. L. R.R., and it is for this purpose that I issue the Deferred Debentures. Deferred—put off; Debenture—owed. What we owe we put off. Simple, easily understood, and honest.

"Now, suh," turning to Fitz, "if after this frank statement any graspin' banker seeks to trammel this enterprise by any fo'closure clauses, he sha'n't have a bond, suh. I'll take them all myself fust."

Once in the street, Fitz turned to me and said with a tremor

FRANCIS HOPKINSON SMITH

in his voice: "I couldn't raise a dollar in a lunatic asylum full of millionaires on a scheme like the Colonel's, and yet I keep on lying to the dear old fellow day after day, hoping that something will turn up by which I can help him out."

"Then tell him so."

Fitz laid his hand on my shoulder, looked me straight in the face, and said:

"I cannot. It would break his heart."

The Colonel's hospitality naturally involved him in debts, a fact that caused much anxiety to his old servant, Chad.

"Don't tell de Colonel I axed ye," Chad whispered to me one night, "but when is dis yer railroad gwineter fotch in some money? Dese yer gemmans on de avenue is gittin' ugly. When I got dat Madary de udder day, de tall one warn't gwineter gib it to me, pass-book or no pass-book; what he wanted to see, he said, was de color of de Colonel's money. Been mo'n two months, an' not a cent. Ain't no use tellin' de Colonel; on'y worry him. You know, Major, same as me, dat de Colonel nuffin but a chile, an' 'bout his bills he's *wuss*. But I'm yere, an' I'm 'sponsible. 'Chad,' he says, 'go out an' git six mo' bottles of dat ol' Madary'; an' 'Chad, don't forgit de sweet-ile'; an' 'Chad, is we got claret enough to last ober Sunday?'—and not a cent in de house. I ain't slep' none for two nights, wor-ritin'."

The Colonel, untouched by anxiety, came in as the conversation was going on, and seeing the pass-book held it off admiringly, his face lighting up at the goodly number of clean pages still left.

"Vehy beautiful custom, this pass-book system, gentlemen," he said, turning to Fitz and me. "One of the most co'teous attentions I have received since I have taken up my residence Nawth. See how simple it is. I send my servant to the sto' for my supplies. He returns in haalf an hour with everything I need, and brings back this book which I *keep*, a mark of confidence which in this degenerate age is refreshin'. No vulgar bargainin', suh."

"When are the accounts under this system usually paid, Colonel?" asked Fitz, his eyes twinkling.

"I never have inquired, suh, and would not hurt the gentleman's feelin's by doin' so fo' the world," he replied with dignity. "I presume when the book is full."

"De grocerman was yere, Colonel," said the old servant anxiously, "an' lef' word dat he was comin' agin later."

"You don't say so, Chad, and I was out—most unfortunate occurrence! When he calls again show him in at once. It will give me great pleasure to see him."

Then, turning to me, his mind on the pass-book and its empty pages—"I'll lay a wager, Major, that man's father was a gentleman. The fact is, I have not treated him with proper respect. He has shown me every co'tesy since I have been here, and I am ashamed to say that I have not once entered his doors. His calling twice in one evenin' touches me deeply. I did not expect to find yo' tradespeople so polite."

While he was speaking, the grocer came in—a tall, red-headed man with closely trimmed side-whiskers, who ran the gamut of Chad's profound but rather anxious bow, and advanced toward the Colonel, hat in hand.

"Which is Mr. Carter?"

The Colonel rose gracefully. "I am Colonel Caarter, suh, and I presume you are the gentleman to whom I am indebted for so many co'tesies. My servant tells me that you called earlier in the evenin'. I regret, suh, that I was detained so late at my office, and I have to thank you for perseverin' the second time. I assure you, suh, that I esteem it a special honor."

The tall gentleman with the auburn whiskers wiped his face with a handkerchief, which he took from his hat, and said, with some timidity, that he hoped he did not intrude at that late hour. He had sent his pass-book, and—

"I have looked it over, suh, repeatedly, with the greatest pleasure. It is a custom new to us in my country, but it meets with my hearty approval. Give yo' hat to my servant, suh, and take this seat by the fire."

The proprietor of the hat, after some protestations, suffered Chad to bear away that grateful protection to his slightly bald head, retaining his handkerchief, which he finally rolled up into a little wad and kept tightly clenched in the perspiring palm of his left hand, and then threw out the additional hope that everything was satisfactory.

"Delicious, suh; I have not tasted such Madeira since the wah. In my cellar at home, suh, I once had some old Madeira of 'twenty-eight that was given to my father, the late General John Caarter, by old Judge Thornton. You, of course, know that wine, suh. Ah—I see that you do."

And then followed one of the Colonel's delightful monologues descriptive of all the vintages of that year. For the moment the worthy tradesman began to wonder why he had not long before risen from the commonplace level of canned vegetables to the more sublime plane of wines in the wood.

"Now, the Madeira you sent me this mornin', suh, is a trifle too fruity for my taste. Chad, open a fresh bottle."

The owner of the pass-book instantly detected a very decided fruity flavor, but thought he had another wine, which he would send him in the morning, that might suit the Colonel's palate better. The Colonel thanked him, and then drifted into the wider field of domestic delicacies, the future wine-merchant becoming more and more enchanted as the Colonel flowed on.

When he rose to go, the grocer had a mental list of the things he would send the Colonel in the morning, all arranged in his commercial head, and so great was his delight that, after shaking hands with me once and with the Colonel three times, he would also have extended that courtesy to Chad, had not that perfectly trained servant checkmated him by filling his extended palm with the rim of his own hat.

The Colonel's debts continued to increase. From the more pressing of these he was relieved only by the arrival of his aunt, Miss Nancy Carter, the dearest woman in the world, her cheeks as soft as a child's and fragrant with rose-water, who, on the night of her arrival, had collected all the bills, including the highly prized pass-book, and who early next morning had sent Chad on a liquidating tour. The Colonel, surprised, buttoned his coat tightly and with some dignity said to his aunt:

"Nancy, yo' interfe'ence in my household affairs this mornin' was vehy creditable to yo' heart, and deeply touches me; but if I thought you regarded it in any other light except as a short tempo'ary loan, it would offend me keenly. Within a few days, however, I shall receive a vehy large amount of secu'ities from an English syndicate that is investigatin' my railroad."

That very morning he had turned his pockets inside out for the remains of the last dollar of the money she had given him when he left home. When it had all been raked together, and its pitiable insufficiency had become apparent, this dialogue took place:

"Chad, did you find any money on the flo' when you breshed my clothes?"

"No, Colonel."

"Look 'round on the mantelpiece; perhaps I left some bills under the clock."

"Ain't none dar, sah."

Then Chad, with that same anxious look revived on his face, went below into the kitchen, mounted a chair, took down an old broken teacup from the top shelf, and poured out into his wrinkled palm a handful of small silver coin—his entire collection of tips, and all the money he had. This he carried to the Colonel, with a lie in his mouth that the recording angel blotted out the moment it fell from his lips.

"Here's some change, Marsa George, I forgot to gib ye; been lef' ober from de marketin'."

And the Colonel gathered it all in, and went out and spent every penny of it on roses for "dear Nancy."

To further the sale of the bonds that were to build the road, the Colonel had an office down-town—like most of his valuable possessions, the property of somebody else—in which he did not even pay for the stamps, stamps having always been part of the hospitality of Carter Hall. Undiscouraged by difficulties, he went on booming his pet project, mentioning casually one day to an English agent the existence of coal-deposits at Cartersville. The agent became interested at once. And at still another dinner, at which he was present, it was decided that a visit to the coal-fields was necessary; and the result of the expedition proved a solid bed of bituminous coal, for which the agent offered the Colonel one hundred thousand dollars, with a royalty of fifteen cents on every ton. The joyful excitement at Cartersville was intense, until it was discovered that every ton of coal was on Miss Carter's half of the property—not the Colonel's—the half

that he had given his aunt in payment for moneys advanced him
to pay off the mortgage and for his personal expenses. The
Colonel saw the death of his railroad; but again his aunt came
to his aid and gave him back the coal-fields, an act which, while
ending all possibility of the construction of the railroad, created
such enthusiasm among the Colonel's friends that he failed to
grasp the true inwardness of the situation. That night at dinner in the old dining-room at Cartersville, the Colonel, radiant
to the very tip-ends of his cravat, and in a voice that trembled,
rose and addressed his guests:

"Gentlemen, the events of the day have unexpectedly brought
me an influx of wealth far beyond my brightest anticipations.
This is due in great measure to the untirin' brain and vast commercial resources of my dear friend, Mr. Fitzpatrick. They
have also strengthened the tie existin' between me and my old
friend the Major, on my left.

"But, gentlemen, they have done mo'." The Colonel's feet
now barely touched the floor. "They have enabled me to provide for one of the loveliest of her sex—she who graces our boa'd
—and to enrich her declinin' days not only with all the comforts
but with many of the luxuries she was bawn to enjoy. Fill yo'
glasses, gentlemen, and drink to the health of the greatest of all
blessings—a true Southern lady!"

TOBIAS GEORGE SMOLLETT

(Scotland, 1721–1771)

RODERICK RANDOM (1748)

"Of the first three novels of Smollett, *Roderick Random*, *Peregrine Pickle*, and *Ferdinand Count Fathom*," says David Hannay in his *Life of Smollett*, "*Roderick Random* is by far the most important; it is fresher and better reading than the other two, and the method is the same" (*i. e.*, personal relation of a string of adventures lacking the organic unity of plot). "It is a material help," continues Hannay, "that so much of his first book should be founded not on life in general but on his own life. Smollett took the outline of this and painted into it all the selfishness, envy, and base indifference of mankind he needed to produce the desired literary effect. The convenient looseness of construction of these *Adventures* makes it permissible to pick Smollett's seamen and pictures of sea-life out of his work and take them by themselves. What is best remembered in *Roderick Random* is the figure of Lieutenant Thomas Bowling, and the expedition to Carthagena. Probably there is no part which is so nearly literally true. There is some heightening of the color unquestionably. No captain can ever have cleared his sick-bay quite so brutally as Captain Oakum. No surgeon was ever quite such a fool, coward, and ignorant lickspittle as Mackshane. Even if all the incidents which Smollett has introduced were actually founded on fact, it is not likely that they can all have happened in one ship within one short year. But if Smollett had chosen he could have made a key to *Roderick Random* every whit as convincing as was the key to *Uncle Tom's Cabin*.

 WAS born in Scotland, in the house of my grandfather, a gentleman of considerable fortune and influence. My father, his youngest son, had privately espoused a poor woman, who was my grandfather's housekeeper, and I was their firstborn child. Before my birth my mother dreamed she was delivered of a tennis-ball, which strangely typified the manner in which I have been knocked about by Fortune, yet, owing to the elasticity of my temperament, with no damage to my nature.

My mother's condition made further concealment of my parents' marriage impossible, and they were driven by my stern grandfather from his house. About the time I was to be born my mother visited my grandfather to plead for my father's forgiveness. He received her so harshly that she was seized in his presence with the pangs of childbirth. A friendly servant conveyed her to the garret, where I was born. Learning of this three days after the event, my grandfather ordered her out of the house and dismissed the servant who had preserved her life. My father in a wild rage sought out his inhuman parent and cursed him with the most dreadful imprecations, swearing never to forget or forgive his barbarity.

My mother died from exposure and my father disappeared from the neighborhood, it being supposed that he had made way with himself. His hard-hearted sire then relented so far as to receive me in his home. To get me out of his sight, he sent me to school at an early age, but made such scant provision for my support that the schoolmaster, Mr. Syntax, treated me worse than if I were a charity scholar. Nevertheless I made progress in my studies, especially Latin, and soon became the leader of my mates—in mischief, I must confess, as well as in my books. I particularly attached to myself Hugh Strap, a shoemaker's son, who, though an even better Latinist than I, regarded me with doglike devotion, as of a higher social order than himself.

When I had grown to be a considerable lad my grandfather designed to apprentice me to a mechanic trade, which purpose, however, was thwarted by the advent of my mother's brother, Tom Bowling, a lieutenant of a man-of-war. As he approached my grandfather's house, dressed in full uniform, with a good oak-plant under his arm, my cousin, the heir, who hated me, turned loose the two watch-dogs on him. Bowling killed them with his sword and cudgel, and, making his way to my grandfather's presence, cursed him roundly for his inhuman treatment of me and convoyed me away from the house. He then went with me to the school, and in the presence of the scholars, with the assistance of Strap and myself, bound Syntax to his desk, and, baring the schoolmaster's back, applied his rod so vigorously that Syntax roared like a mad bull. At last, loosing the schoolmaster, my uncle said: "I have given you a sailor's lesson in flogging, to teach you to have more sympathy in the future." Then he addressed the delighted schoolboys: "Shout, lads, shout!" This ceremony being over, he invited the school, including the master, to a treat at the public house. Mr. Syntax refused the offer in great disdain. "Well, well, old surly," replied my uncle, shaking his unwilling hand, "thou art an honest fellow notwithstanding; and if ever I command a ship, thou shalt be our schoolmaster, i' faith!" So saying, he led the boys out in a tumultuous troop to the public house.

Before sailing my uncle placed me in the house of Mr. Potion, one of my mother's relatives by marriage, who was an apothecary in a neighboring town, and made provision for my support until he should return from his voyage.

Here I not only learned the business by acting as my relative's assistant, but I also applied myself to my studies, becoming an accomplished classical scholar. It had been better for my immediate needs if I had learned a handicraft, for my uncle lost his place in the navy, owing to his killing his captain in a duel, and so was unable to send the apothecary money for my support; and Mr. Potion, having in view a new apprentice whom he could pluck, sent me packing. Thereupon I engaged myself as assistant to a drunken surgeon, Crab by name. Crab was a bully, who browbeat his family, and therefore despised them. Observing this, I resented his insolence with spirit, and so won his respect. Although I made myself indispensable to him, he came one day and told me that a bright young man like myself was wasting his talents in a small country town, and that I should go to London. For this purpose he supplied me with ten guineas. It was not until after I had gone that I learned his real purpose in this seeming generosity, which was to father on me one of his own bastards that was born to his servant-maid shortly after my departure.

My faithful admirer, Strap, who was applying blade to leather, not in the hereditary Strap employment as cobbler, but as a barber's apprentice, insisted on going to London with me. To save our money we decided to walk much of the way. So, with ten guineas, a change of linen, a pocket Horace, Wiseman's *Surgery*, and a letter from Crab to our member of Parliament recommending me to government preferment, I set off on the tramp with Strap, who was even more meagerly equipped than I, having only his shaving utensils, with as many crowns as I had guineas.

We had many stirring adventures on the road, and fell in with a variety of strange characters, such as a craven highwayman, a publican who talked to us in Latin, and thereby gulled us into unwise extravagance, and a blackleg gambling curate, who soothed his victims' wrath by fiddling to them and singing loose songs.

Arrived in London, I began dancing attendance upon Mr. Cringer, the member of Parliament to whom I had the letter of introduction, but all to no purpose. Mr. Cringer made many promises, none of which was fulfilled. Our money became exhausted and poor Strap was forced to accept a situation as valet to a gentleman who was going abroad, while I became assistant to a French apothecary. Monsieur Lavement did a good deal of business, but as it was mostly among his fellow-refugees his profits were small. However, his expense for medicine was not great, for he was the most expert man at a *succedaneum* of any apothecary in London. I have seen him make up a physician's prescription though he had not in his shop one ingredient mentioned in it. Thames water he could invent into *aqua cinnamoni*; turpentine, into *capivi*, disguising the fraud in color and taste with cochineal and oil of cloves.

I gave great satisfaction to my employer, but soon had his wife and daughter about my ears for refusing to aid either of them in their rival amours with a certain Colonel O'Donnell. They succeeded by an artful conspiracy in having me dismissed for theft. I was thus forced, because of my poverty and blasted reputation, to live with the vilest people in London. But I had the good fortune to cure of a loathsome disease a woman of good family, Miss Williams by name, who had been dragged into an evil life by a scoundrel in whom she had trusted. We lived together apparently as lover and mistress, though we were really nothing more to each other than comrades in misfortune. Indeed, it was she who encouraged me to rescue myself from my deplorable situation by marrying an honest and well-to-do woman. She resolved for herself, as soon as she recovered her health, to go out of town and return to it in the homely garb of a country wench, and so secure employment as a girl new to service.

Fate now stepped in and did what it seemed the Admiralty

was not able to do, viz., send me to sea. I went one day to Wapping to learn perchance from the sailors on returning vessels news of my uncle, Tom Bowling. There I was set upon by a press-gang, who put me by force on a tender, which delivered me to the man-of-war *Thunder*. Here I found friends in Mr. Thomson, the steward, and Mr. Morgan, a Welshman, the first mate. They secured for me the post of assistant to the surgeon, Dr. Atkins.

When I followed the doctor with medicines into the "hospital," I was much less surprised that people should die on board than that any sick person should recover. Here I saw about sixty miserable, distempered wretches, suspended in rows, so huddled one upon another that not more than fourteen inches of space was allotted for each with his bed and bedding, and deprived of the light of the day, as well as of fresh air; breathing nothing but a noisome atmosphere of the morbid steams exhaling from their own diseased bodies, devoured with vermin hatched in the filth that surrounded them, and destitute of every convenience necessary for persons in that helpless condition.

Dr. Atkins was an indolent man, yet so kindly that we were grieved when Captain Oakum came on board with sailing orders, accompanied by a new surgeon, Dr. Mackshane, a crony of his, and an utterly incompetent man, who was to supplant the old doctor. Morgan, our first mate, according to custom, waited on the Captain with the sick-list, which, when he had perused, he exclaimed: "Blood and oons! sixty-one sick people on board of my ship! Harkee, you sir, I'll have no sick in my ship, by God!"

The warm-hearted Welsh mate could hardly restrain his indignation at this inhuman treatment in the Captain's presence. Hurrying back to the steward and myself, who were busy preparing medicines, he bade us leave off our labor and go to play, "for the Captain, look you," said he, "by his sole word, and power, and command, has driven sickness a-pegging to the tevil, and there is no more malady on board." So saying, he drank off a gill of brandy, sighed grievously three times, ejaculated "God pless my heart, liver, and lungs!" and then began to sing a Welsh song—which, I afterward learned, was his method of relieving anger.

Soon after this we received an order from the new surgeon to bring all the sick men on the quarter-deck to be reviewed by the Captain. As we knew that protest would be useless, we quietly obeyed the order. Many of the poor fellows were brought up in the height of fevers and rendered delirious by the injuries received on the way. Some gave up the ghost in the presence of their inspectors; and others, who were ordered to do their duty, languished a few days at work with their fellows, and then departed without any ceremony. The number of the sick was soon reduced to less than a dozen.

When the Captain inquired whether all the sick had been brought on deck, he was informed that a maniac was confined below. He ordered that this man be produced. The madman very earnestly assured the Captain that he was perfectly sane, but was kept in bonds by the mate, who had a grudge against him because he knew that the mate's wife kept a gin-shop in Rag-Fair. This statement produced a laugh at the expense of the Welshman, who, indignant at the laughter, though pitying the man who had instigated it, declared with heat that the story was a falsehood. Captain Oakum, however, accepted it as true, and ordered the sailor to be unfettered, at the same time threatening to make Morgan exchange places with him. But the Welshman, hearing the decision in favor of the madman, sprang up the mizzen shrouds, crying to Thomson and me to get out of reach of the lunatic, for we would see him play the devil with a vengeance. Accordingly we got up on the poop, whence we beheld the maniac, as soon as he was released, fly at the Captain like a fury, crying, "I'll let you know, you scoundrel, that I am commander of this vessel," and pommel him without mercy. Dr. Mackshane, who went to the assistance of his patron, suffered the same fate, and it was not without damage to all who laid hands on the maniac that he was at last mastered. The Captain was hardly restrained from pistoling him, and, indeed, swore vengeance on him, which the poor fellow evaded by breaking loose from his captors and leaping overboard.

Taking on provisions for six months, we sailed in the grand fleet bound for the West Indies on the ever-memorable expedition of Carthagena. Fifty leagues to the west of the Lizard a terrific hurricane smote us, which scattered the fleet so that of a hundred and fifty sail but twelve were in our sight. Our officers and sailors ran to and fro, with distraction in their looks, hallooing to one another, and undetermined what they should attend to first. Some clung to the yards, endeavoring to unbind the sails that were split into a thousand pieces flapping in the wind; others tried to furl those that were still whole, while the masts, at every pitch, bent and quivered like twigs, as if they would have shivered into innumerable splinters. While I considered this scene with equal terror and astonishment, one of the main braces broke, by the shock whereof two sailors were flung from the yard's arm into the sea, where they perished; and one, Jack Rattlin, was thrown down upon the deck at the expense of a broken leg.

Morgan and I rushed forward and bore him down to the cockpit, where Dr. Mackshane examined him and ordered that the broken limb be amputated. This was a dreadful sentence to the patient, who, recruiting himself with a quid of tobacco, asked ruefully: "What, must I be docked?—Can't you splice it?" He was enforced by Morgan, who said: "Assuredly, Dr. Mackshane, with submission, and deference, and veneration to your superior abilities, and opportunities, and stations, look you, I do apprehend and conjecture, and aver, that there is no occasion nor necessity to smite off this poor man's leg."

"God Almighty bless you, dear Welshman!" cried Rattlin, "may you have fair wind and weather wheresoever you are bound, and come to anchor in the Road of Heaven at last."

Mackshane, incensed at Morgan's opposition, peremptorily ordered him to apply the tourniquet, whereupon Jack cried:

"Avast, avast! damn my heart if you shall clap your nippers on me! Mr. Random, won't you lend a hand toward saving my precious limb? Odds heart! if Lieutenant Bowling was here he would not suffer Jack Rattlin's leg to be chopped off like a piece of old junk."

I supported so earnestly the mate's opinion that the leg could be saved that the surgeon, either not daring to oppose me, or seeing an opportunity for discrediting me and exalting his own ability in case of my failure, gave me leave to attempt to preserve the limb if I would be answerable for the consequence.

To this I agreed, and effected a complete cure in six weeks, thereby earning the undying devotion of Rattlin and the implacable enmity of Mackshane.

To revenge himself the surgeon had me put in irons on the charge of instigating a mutiny against the Captain. While I was in duress we met a French ship-of-war, with which we hotly engaged, and which we finally put to flight. During the entire battle I remained fettered to the poop, exposed to the enemy's shot. Thomson, the steward, who had all my work to do in the dreadful task of attending the wounded—for Dr. Mackshane had hidden himself in his cabin—became so despondent and desperate that he leaped overboard.

My trial was held after the battle. The chief evidence against me was my journal, which I wrote in Greek characters. Dr. Mackshane, pretending to be a Greek scholar, declared that the writing revealed a treasonable plot. To this I replied that if he could speak Greek with one of the sailors on board who came from the Levant, I would resign myself to any punishment they might choose to inflict. Thereupon the wily surgeon selected one of the Greeks who had picked up a smattering of Erse in knocking about the Irish coast, and carried on a conversation with him in the ancient Irish language, on the pretense that they were talking Greek. However, fearing that the fraud would be discovered, and needing my services as assistant, he interceded with the Captain and obtained my release.

Soon after this we arrived at Jamaica, where we remained a month. We then sailed for Carthagena, where, after a disastrous delay, which gave the enemy time to prepare for our attack, we landed our marines, all newly taken from the plow-tail, and made them encamp under the very guns of the enemy's fortifications—which, I believe, never was done before in the history of war. The ministry has been censured for sending raw recruits and ignorant commanders on such desperate service, but surely our wise governors had their reasons for so doing, which possibly may be disclosed with other secrets of the deep.

Our diet also must have been ordered with the same inscrutable wisdom. There was a quart of water *per diem* to each man, when a gallon would hardly supply the bodily waste in that torrid climate, especially when the nature of our provision is considered. This consisted of putrid salt beef, called by the sailors "Irish horse"; salt pork of New England, which, though neither fish nor flesh, savored of both; biscuits, each of which, like a piece of clockwork, moved by its own internal impulse, owing to the myriads of insects within; and butter served out by the gill, that tasted like salted train-oil. Our liquor was fiery rum, without sugar or fruit to render it palatable, and with no extra allowance of water for diluting it, for which reasons it was known as *Necessity*. Nor was this limitation of simple element owing to its scarcity on board, for there was a supply of a half gallon per day to each man for six months. Perhaps this fast was intended to mortify the marines into a contempt for life, and so render them in battle more resolute and regardless of danger. How simple, then, are those people who argue and affirm that many valuable lives would have been saved if the useless transports had been employed in fetching fresh water, turtle, fruit, and other refreshments from Jamaica and other adjacent islands!—seeing, it is to be hoped, that those who died went to a better place, and those who survived were the more easily maintained. After all, a sufficient number remained to fall before the fortifications, where they behaved like their own country mastiffs, which shut their eyes, run into the jaws of a bear, and have their heads crushed for their valor.

The wet season found us with only the outer works of the enemy taken. The incessant rains, the heat of the climate, and our bad and inadequate provisions, combined with despair at our ill success to introduce bilious fever among us. Three fourths of those infected died, their skins turning black as soot.

Accordingly we returned to Jamaica, after blowing up the forts we had captured.

Here, to my astonishment and delight I met Thomson, the steward, who had thrown himself overboard after the fight with the Frenchman. He had been picked up by a New England trading-sloop and taken to Jamaica, where, becoming overseer of a plantation, he had married the planter's daughter, and on his death had succeeded to the estate. He fitted me out with clothing as a gentleman, and forced money upon me. My appearance easily procured me the appointment of surgeon on a vessel, the *Lizard*, which was returning with despatches to England. Our captain, however, was inefficient, and, owing to his perversity in not taking soundings, we were wrecked on the coast of Sussex.

I swam ashore, the only one of the crew that was saved, landing on the coast of England even poorer than I had left it, for I had stripped to my drawers. It was a cold winter's night, and, coming to a barn, I slept in the hay. I was found half dead next morning by the farmer, and carried by him to the door of a neighbor whom he thought better able than himself to bear the expense of my care. This man, discovering me, bore me to the vicar, and in turn, I was taken to house after house in the neighborhood, till an old woman, Mrs. Sagely by name, who was regarded as a witch, received me and nursed me back to health and strength. I found her to be a woman of superior mind and breeding, and learned to love her as a mother, and she loved me as a son. When I had fully recovered I removed the burden of my support from her by assuming the name of John Brown and taking the situation of footman to an eccentric lady in the neighborhood.

My mistress I found to be a maiden lady who was so absorbed in intellectual pursuits, especially the wooing of the Muse, that she had risen above all consideration of sex, and employed me chiefly as her lady's maid. However, my duties were very light, as she rarely changed her linen—which, to all appearance, never was washed but in Castalian streams.

I bore willingly my degrading servitude because of the presence in the house of my mistress's niece, who had not the innocence of abstraction and artifice but that of natural sweetness, beauty, and purity. This nymph was pursued by the attentions of a satyr, a young, drunken, fox-hunting squire, from whose violence I one day rescued her. The squire vowed vengeance upon me, and Narcissa, for such was the name of my adored one, implored me to flee. That I might return and wed her in my proper character, I yielded.

As I wandered on the beach ruminating on my next excursion, the question was determined by the appearance of a company of smugglers, who, taking me for a customhouse spy, kidnaped me, and, transporting me to the French coast, there released me.

I strolled into a cabaret, where I found a man as forlorn as myself. Misery loving company, I approached him. Good Heaven, it was my uncle, Tom Bowling! With difficulty I persuaded him that I was his nephew, Roderick Random. Observing my servant's garb he said: "I am sorry to see you, my lad, under such colors, for it is not in my power to change them; it has been banyan day [days when no meat is served to sailors] with me a great while. After I ran the Captain through at Cape Tiberoon, and was marooned there, to get away I was obliged to ship as a common foremast man on a French vessel. Since then I have been knocking about in French and Spanish bottoms. Owing to the war, I have never been able to get nearer to England than this. If I could get to Wapping, Dan Whipcord, the ship-chandler, I know would not refuse me credit. But if he's dead I wouldn't know where to turn."

Sad at heart to see so worthy a man so destitute of friends, I resolved that he should at least go to the one that remained. The little money I had with me sufficed to pay the passage of one man to England. This I pressed upon my uncle, assuring him that it was all one to me where I sought my fortune.

I found it utterly impossible to secure even a footman's position in France, and, to keep from starving, enlisted in the army. I fought under the Duc de Grammont at Dettingen, where we were defeated, much to my patriotic pleasure, but not to my personal profit, for thereafter the pay of a common soldier, such as I was, was reduced to five sols a day, which could scarce keep soul and body together.

Fortunately, at this juncture, whom should I meet but my old comrade Strap! The English gentleman with whom he had gone abroad had died, and had left him a tidy sum of money as a reward for his fidelity; and under the name of Monsieur d'Estrapes he had won the regard of all about him as a modest, melancholy gentleman of scholarly attainments, especially in the classics.

Strap at once put his money and his services at my disposal to enable me to return to England, marry a lady of fortune, and take my proper station in life. He was so overjoyed at the prospect of getting into service again (for acting the gentleman had preyed upon his disposition) that I could not refuse him, and back we went to London, I as master and he as servant.

Stopping at Wapping, I found that my uncle had gone to sea again. Proceeding in somewhat lonely mood to London, I passed a smart millinery store kept by a "Miss Williams." Thinking the proprietor might be my old she-comrade risen to prosperity, I stepped within, followed by Strap, and found this to be the case. Miss Williams was overjoyed to see me. I told her my sorrowful history, down to the turn of the tide in my meeting Strap. She overwhelmed the modest fellow with praise for his generosity, and, declaring that she would not be outdone in loyalty to me, entered into the conspiracy to restore my fortunes. I confessed to her my love for Narcissa, and she set about arranging her affairs to go to Sussex, find the object of my affections, report to me the situation of affairs, and, in general, act as my intermediary.

Going out of the shop I was accosted by a ragged woman who begged alms of me for a "poor soldier's wife." To my astonishment I recognized in her the apothecary's daughter who had ruined me by falsely charging me with theft. Having won the affections of the Colonel away from her mother, she had been disowned by her parents, and, her husband going to the wars and never having been heard of since, she was reduced to beggary. I gave her of Strap's money probably more than I had a right to spare, and, with tears in her eyes, she begged my pardon for the wrong she had done me, promising to inform her father of my innocence. So we went together to the apothecary's, where we found M. Lavement in mourning for his wife. The old Frenchman, on hearing his daughter's story, took her to his heart and also embraced me in reconciliation.

While I was waiting in London to hear from Miss Williams in Sussex, my uncle returned from a successful cruise, having a large sum of prize-money. The owners of the vessel gave him command of another of their ships, and he proposed to take me with him as surgeon.

The expected letter from Miss Williams came, bearing tokens of love from Narcissa and good Mrs. Sagely, whom my sweetheart had taken to her bosom as if she were my mother. Fortified by Mrs. Sagely's confidence in my return, Narcissa had fought off the odious attentions of the neighboring squire, and now was waiting with languishing impatience to see me again and exchange reciprocal vows. I hurried down to Sussex and met her by night at Mrs. Sagely's. Not only she and I within the cottage, but Strap and Miss Williams on guard without, pledged mutual faith, and my good servant and I rode back to London the happiest men in England.

Our ship was a slaver, which ran from Guinea to Buenos Ayres, transporting negroes to the plantations of Paraguay. I discovered that one of these planters was an Englishman, although he was known as Don Rodrigo. When I informed him that this, in the English form, was my name also, he was greatly interested. "And what may your full name be?" he inquired. On my replying "Roderick Random" he embraced me with tears of joy, saying: "My son, my dear Charlotte's baby boy!"

Selling his plantation, my father returned with us to England. Finding that the heir to the home estate in Scotland had become bankrupt and was offering it for sale, my father bought it, and so at last came into his own. Here I brought Narcissa as my dear wife, and here, attended by my old comrades and devoted retainers, Mr. and Mrs. Strap, I expect to end my days.

PEREGRINE PICKLE (1751)

England and adjacent parts of the Continent provide the scenes for the numerous adventures of *Peregrine Pickle,* which cover a period of about twenty-five years contemporaneous with the author's life. Aside from the story itself, which is a complete biography of its hero from his birth to his marriage, the book is remarkable for a brilliant but unrestrained satire on Mark Akenside, one of the most learned writers of the time, and the interpolation of a story of considerable length by another author. Akenside was satirized in the personage called "the doctor" in the story. It is believed that the interpolated narrative called *Memoirs of a Lady of Quality* was written by Lady Vane (Frances Hawes). Presumably Smollett gave her manuscript some editorial attention, but there is no doubt that he did not write the whole of these memoirs. Furthermore, it is well established that Lady Vane paid him liberally to incorporate the story of her shame in his novel. Her *Memoirs* have no bearing whatever on the fortunes of Peregrine, and therefore are not referred to in this record of his adventures.

PEREGRINE PICKLE was the eldest son of a retired London tradesman whose wife took an unnatural but unmitigable dislike to her first-born. When the child was no more than six years old, such slight affection as the mother had had for him had been supplanted by a daughter, and more by another son, and at that tender age Peregrine was sent away to school. Fortunately for him, his early tutors were men of sense, and he was well advanced on the road to learning before the evil influence of charlatan teachers in other schools turned his boyish spirits to mischief rather than to books. It should be said, however, though not in exculpation of his later teachers, who were, indeed, utterly inefficient—that the lad's spirits, long before a beard roughened his chin, manifested the beginnings of what became for years afterward the dominating impulse of his life. This impulse appeared to take root in a profound contempt for the world which led him, times without number, to expose some part of it to ridicule. In this he spared neither friends nor foes, schoolmasters nor playfellows, not even his most loving benefactors. The result was a succession of boyish pranks, followed pretty often by scrapes that gave anguish to the heart of his maternal parent to such a degree that she repined bitterly that she had given him birth.

The boy was not half grown before his mother had developed such hatred of him that she could by no means endure his presence in her house, and he could get no compensation from his father for the lack of motherly affection. Pickle the elder was not hard-hearted; he was simply weak-willed. He had retired from business because he had not character enough to retain what property he inherited, and had settled in the country because he could live there without effort on the remnant of his fortune, which was really considerable. His wife dominated him absolutely, and he uttered no protest against the reviling which she heaped upon their elder son. In these ungenerous circumstances it was lucky for the lad that his uncle, Hawser Trunnion, took a fancy to him. Trunnion had been a commander in the Royal Navy. Retired from service, and compelled to live ashore, he clung to his old habits and conformed his life as far as possible after the manner of the sea. His house was manned, as he called it—for he could not converse or write without expressing himself in nautical terms—by sailors, and he named his establishment "The Garrison." Lieutenant Hatchway, a one-legged veteran, was his constant companion, and his favorite servant was an able seaman named Pipes.

Nothing can better suggest the never-failing oddity of Trunnion's life ashore than a circumstance attending his marriage to Peregrine's aunt. The ceremony was to be performed at the village church, some miles from The Garrison, and Trunnion bought horses, for which he had had no use theretofore, for the express purpose of conveying himself and crew to it in a manner befitting the occasion and his dignity as a landlord. The hour arrived, the bride was in her place, the church crowded, but there was no sign of the bridegroom. After some time had elapsed natural anxiety caused the sending of a servant in the direction of The Garrison to discover what might be amiss. The courier had not gone a mile from the church before he saw Trunnion, at the head of his whole company of servants, riding obliquely across a field. Arrived at a hedge, which blocked their farther progress in that direction, Hatchway fired a pistol, whereupon Trunnion gravely turned about and set out across the field at an obtuse angle to his former course, the rest trailing out behind him like a flock of geese, or like the bobs tied to the tail of a kite. The messenger, astounded at this strange proceeding, managed to deliver his message, to which Trunnion replied:

"Hark ye, brother, don't you see we make all possible speed? Go back and tell those who sent you that the wind has shifted since we weighed anchor, and that we are obliged to make very short trips in tacking by reason of the narrowness of the channel."

"Lord, sir!" said the valet, "do but clap spurs to your horse and ride straight forward, and I'll engage that you shall be at the church in less than a quarter of an hour."

"What! right in the wind's eye?" answered the commander; "where did you learn your navigation?" and he stormed on that he would proceed as he had been taught. Indeed, he continued to zigzag, that is, tack, across the road until his horses took notice of a pack of hounds and bolted away with him to such purpose that he never arrived at the church at all, but, when he had recovered from his injuries, was married in his own house by special dispensation.

Trunnion, having taken pity on Peregrine's unhappy situation, undertook to provide for his education, a matter that Mrs. Pickle had compelled her husband to renounce. He sent the lad to Winchester school, with Pipes as his servant, a post that Lieutenant Hatchway would have taken gladly, for all the hardy mariners in The Garrison were devoted to the boy. Sensible of his uncle's kindness, Peregrine devoted himself assiduously to study for a time. Indeed, his pranks were but as intermissions in his graver pursuits, and he made such progress as served him well in after life, even if it did not satisfy his masters.

The important episode of his Winchester days was his meeting with Miss Emilia Gauntlett, the beautiful young daughter of an army officer's widow. Mrs. Gauntlett lived in humble but respectable circumstances in a village about sixteen miles from Winchester; and Peregrine saw Emilia first when she chanced to be on a visit to the school town.

He fell deeply and honestly in love with her at sight, and he paid his attentions to her with all frankness and to the exclusion for the time of every other pursuit. Emilia liked him, and her mother was pleased that her daughter should have found favor in the eyes of a young man of such good social standing. But Emilia was a wise child. Native prudence forbade her to make unequivocal confession of her love until her lover should specify marriage as the end of his desires. As to that matter, Peregrine was then too young, and his passion too pure, to think of marriage. He was simply in love, and reveled in the joy the presence of his sweetheart gave him. Soon after she returned to her home he ran away from school, walked the entire distance across fields, so as to balk pursuit, and took lodgings near Emilia, whom he visited daily. The school authorities searched for the lad in vain, and at last, Trunnion having been informed of his disappearance, Hatchway was commissioned to find him. By the merest accident Hatchway succeeded after a long time, and by dint of arguments, persuasion, affectionate remonstrance, and every appeal that can be made to a spirited boy's nature, conveyed him back to school.

Arrived there he wrote a letter to Emilia, enclosing a copy of some original verses, which, if not the most exalted poetry, were at least dignified in style and a worthy expression of serious love. This precious missive he entrusted to Pipes to deliver into Emilia's hands. Pipes, solemnly conscious of the importance of his errand, bethought himself shrewdly how best he could convey the document with the least danger of losing it or being robbed of it. The result of his cogitation was that he put the manuscript between his stocking and the sole of his foot. When he removed it at the end of his journey he was dismayed to discover the missive not only crumpled and soiled, but in a hundred moist pieces! What should the faithful Pipes do then but seek to repair the damage by hiring the village clerk to compose a love-letter for him, addressed to Miss Gauntlett and signed with the name of Peregrine Pickle! The scribe concocted a most bombastic bit of rhetoric that might have done for a milkmaid who could not read, but which impressed Miss Emilia as an insult. Having read it with the utmost care several times over, she conceived it to be young Mr. Pickle's delicate way of informing her that he had not been serious in his advances, and she accordingly told Pipes that the letter required no answer.

Peregrine could not understand it. When the post brought no word from her, he tried to see her but was rebuffed disdainfully; and this misunderstanding endured for years. Not until he was a student at Oxford did circumstances again bring them together in such a way that they could compare notes, so to speak. Emilia had kept the extravagant essay of the village scribe, and when Peregrine saw it he quickly summoned the well-meaning Pipes and extracted a confession of the facts from him. Love then flourished anew, but at this juncture Uncle Trunnion took a hand in the matter. He knew only as much as this: that his nephew was deeply interested in a penniless girl, and he feared the young man's impetuosity might entangle him in a match much less brilliant than one to which the heir of Hawser Trunnion might aspire. Accordingly, after the manner of wise parents and guardians, he decided to attempt a cure of his nephew's malady by giving him a social course in Paris! Peregrine was not averse to the treatment, though he was not aware of its intent. He visited Emilia before his departure and left her with vows of eternal constancy.

Pipes attended him on his travels, and also one Joulter, who was nominally the youth's governor, but who in reality had not the slightest influence on his disposition or behavior. In truth, the young man was much set up by the circumstances of his journey. He was provided with money in plenty, and his vanity was quickly aroused to pose as a man of the world and take all its pleasure with unstinting hand. So he began a career of prodigality that would speedily have reduced him to need if, like most prodigals, he had been addicted to gaming; but in that one respect Peregrine Pickle might almost be held up as a model, for he despised gambling in all forms and only indulged in it mildly when circumstances made it impossible to avoid play. He had hardly set foot on French soil when he made amorous advances to the wife of a traveling Englishman. The husband, suspecting him, and his wife no less, managed to elude him for a time, but not long after their arrival in Paris Peregrine discovered where she lodged and eloped with her. He established her in a hotel outside the city walls, and was induced to give her up only by the intervention of the British ambassador, whose good offices had been sought by the distracted husband. The ambassador proved a good friend to Peregrine. He gave him not only sensible advice but introductions to personages of high rank whom he could hardly have hoped to meet without credentials of such commanding influence.

He disported himself in high society with as much assurance and energy as he had in that of his own level, and was not long in coming to believe that the upper level was his rightful place. Altogether his vanity was immensely puffed up, but he continued, nevertheless, to vary his numerous amours and his appearances in high life with those spicy adventures which arose from his insatiable love of the ludicrous. It was such an adventure that, after a year and a half of intense activity, led to his enforced departure from the French capital. Among the acquaintances he had made there was an English painter, named Pallet, whose taste and accomplishments were in inverse ratio to his pretensions. Pickle never lost an opportunity to play upon and expose Pallet's ignorance, and when no opportunity lay to hand he invented one. In this instance he suggested to Pallet that they should attend a masked ball, and that Pallet should go disguised as a woman. The silly painter consented, and, although his figure was huge and ungainly, he managed to borrow garments from his landlady that gave him a sufficiently feminine appearance for the occasion.

It may readily be understood that Pickle and his companion attracted a great deal of attention at the ball, and as soon as he was sure that all eyes were upon the preposterous female the unconscionable joker gave Pallet the slip and entertained himself at a distance. Matters became most embarrassing for Pallet, because he had neither ready wit nor knowledge of French, and his clumsy efforts to avoid the attentions of the boisterous dancers were highly diverting to his observing escort. Just when there was manifest danger that Pallet would get into serious trouble, Pickle appeared and took him under a protecting arm, vastly to the painter's relief; but at that moment a certain nobleman desired some fun at the strange female's expense, and tried to thrust himself between "her" and Pickle. Thereupon Pickle struck the nobleman and stalked out of the place to his carriage, into which he handed the trembling Pallet. The nobleman promptly exerted his authority and commanded soldiers to throw both Pickle and his companion into the Bastile. This was done, and there both men bade fair to languish indefinitely, for Pickle was too proud to ask for relief.

The faithful Pipes discovered where his master was confined, and informed Joulter, who laid the matter before the British ambassador. This official was more amused than exasperated at the new escapade of his young countryman, and quickly effected an understanding whereby Pickle might be released if he would apologize to the offended nobleman; but this Pickle grandly refused to do. To arguments and pleadings that he be sensible he responded by drawing scurrilous caricatures of the nobleman and the French authorities on the walls of his cell. At last, so stubborn was the prisoner, the ambassador had to resort to peremptory demands, and the Government yielded on consideration that Pickle and Pallet should leave France within three days.

On his return to England Pickle disported himself in London and Bath much as he had in Paris, until the final illness of his uncle called him for a time to The Garrison. The old mariner had retained his affection for his wild nephew and left him all his property, which amounted to more than thirty thousand pounds. Pickle, after an unsuccessful effort to come to an amicable understanding with his parents, gave Hatchway the free use of The Garrison and contingent property for life, and returned to London. There he indulged in every sort of extravagance. He gave such expensive entertainments that magnified reports of his wealth went abroad, and he soon found himself not only welcomed in great houses but the subject of matrimonial snares by managing mammas of the nobility. The snares were readily enough avoided, because Pickle's conceit had come to be so boundless that every opportunity to marry seemed to him unworthy of his brilliant gifts.

Emilia had not been forgotten, but remembrance of her had no influence in determining his course to further dallying with the pleasures of bachelorhood. Quite the contrary, for, so well had he learned the lessons of Paris and the greater world, that he had come to look forward to the conquest of Emilia on the same terms as practised in his ordinary amours. It was out of the question that he should marry her, for she was still a penniless girl, and he gave no thought to such a possibility. He made no attempt to deceive her, however, until she had occasion to visit London. Then he sought her out and undertook to atone for his long neglect by the most violent protestations of love. In this campaign he employed all the artifices of which he had become a master, and proceeded with the utmost confidence, the only difference being that he was conscious of actually loving the young lady very dearly.

She was still as prudent as she had been in the Winchester school-days. It was painfully clear to her that Peregrine had undergone great changes, and she was more than ever chary of avowing frankly the emotions that stirred within her; but she could not conceal the fact that her love was the same as before, and Pickle fatuously believed that the shameful battle was won. He invited her to an entertainment, to which she consented to go on condition that another lady accompany them. Pickle agreed readily, though he raged inwardly, and in the end contrived by a wicked subterfuge to get her separated from her companion. Then he tried to undermine her judgment with wine, and when she drank sparingly, he resorted to drugging the beverage. It was all to no avail. When he handed her into a strange house instead of her uncle's, where she was visiting, she understood his purpose and turned upon him indignantly. Then his passion broke from such restraint as had hitherto been put upon it, and he tried to overcome her by force. Emilia tore herself away, went out to the street and had a watchman get her a sedan-chair, in which she returned alone to her uncle's house. Next day she refused to see the penitent Pickle, who now would have married her out of hand, and returned to him all the costly presents which he had heaped upon her during the preceding days.

Pickle was not easily defeated. He tried every possible means of regaining Emilia's favor, going so far as to pursue her across country when she journeyed to her home. In this episode, by reason of falling upon a false clue, he chased from town to town an apprentice eloping with his employer's daughter, so that Emilia reached her home unimpeded; and when at last he had to conclude that he was utterly disdained his spite led him to determine to take up with the first marriageable woman he met.   This led to the most outrageous escapade with which he starred his career in London, for the first woman he met was the daughter of a beggar.   The girl was about sixteen, ignorant, and given to the most offensive vulgarities of speech.   Pickle bought her from her mother and took her to The Garrison for a few weeks.   There he provided her with elegant clothes, and trained her in manners, teaching her a number of French phrases and quotations from the classic poets, and exercising her in using them in the course of conversation.   When he thought she would serve the brilliant purpose that had not entered his head until after he first saw her, he took her to London and introduced her, as a relative, to all his friends in high society.   Of course she was received with favor, and her occasional slips in deportment were forgiven on the wealthy Mr. Pickle's account, and explained on the ground of her diffidence, in which characteristic, to say the truth, she was wholly lacking.   The imposition flourished, to Pickle's infinite amusement, until one evening when the girl detected a haughty dame in the act of cheating at cards.   Then nature asserted itself, and previous conditions overwhelmed the slender restraints of recently acquired manners.   From the girl's lips poured such a flood of opprobrious billingsgate that the party was broken up in scandalous confusion.   Pickle's contemptuous joke was exposed, and he found many doors closed to him in consequence.

About this time a lord who pretended to a friendly interest in him advised him to seek election to Parliament, promising to bring the interest of a powerful minister in his behalf.   The suggestion inflamed Pickle's vanity and led him to lend respectful ear to the lord's advice that he curtail his expenses and conserve what might be left of his property.   The young man took an account and found himself possessed of less than fifteen thousand pounds.   He invested two thirds of this in a mortgage on the friendly lord's property, put a part of the balance into marine ventures, indorsed a friend's note for a thousand, and with his modest balance set forth to a rural constituency to contest the election.   His opponent had such a long purse that before the campaign was half over Pickle was forced to borrow.

The friendly minister loaned him twelve hundred pounds, but on the day before the polling decided that it would be the best political tactics to abandon the constituency. He therefore sent word to Pickle to withdraw, promising to give him another chance later. Pickle's rage was unbounded. He refused to withdraw, whereupon the minister, having foreseen the possibility of such obstreperousness, had him arrested for debt. The young candidate was locked up during polling day so that his adversary was returned unopposed.

After that matters went rapidly from bad to worse. The lord to whom Pickle had loaned most of his money died, and it was discovered that the mortgage was worthless in law. The friend whose note he had indorsed defaulted. His maritime ventures were still in abeyance, and Pickle was penniless. There was nothing for it but to turn to literature, that last resort of persons who are good for nothing else, and his first effort was a bitter but brilliant satire against the minister who had been false to him. The article was published and caused a deal of comment. The minister had no difficulty in discovering who was the author, and, this done, he clapped Pickle in jail again for the money owed on account of election advances.

A few friends were faithful to Pickle in his adversity, among them Pipes and Hatchway. Each of these worthies had saved money and each brought his savings to the Fleet, where Pickle was confined, but he obstinately refused to touch a penny. It was his intention to earn his way out by literary work or die in the effort. After some months it began to look as if death by starvation would be the outcome, for, what with his generosity to his fellow-prisoners and his inability to endure an inactive life, he was gradually wasting away and earning insufficient to keep himself fed in spite of the dogged persistence with which he tried to work. Emilia heard of his misfortunes, and, through her brother, who visited Pickle, how disaster had modified his former temper. There was now no question that Pickle was sincerely penitent for his former wicked designs against Emilia, and that his love for her was the one lingering sweetness of his wretched existence. At this time Emilia fell heir unexpectedly to ten thousand pounds, and this she placed at her lover's disposal, with herself if he would take the gifts. Pickle was overwhelmed with sadness and joy at once; joy, because his sweetheart had relented and forgiven; sadness, because his stubborn pride would not let him be beholden to her. He conceived it necessary that he should pay the full penalty for his follies and wickedness.

Thus affairs stood when Peregrine's father died. For some unknown reason, perhaps lurking regard for his neglected son, he had not made a will. Peregrine, therefore, was heir to all he possessed, a comfortable matter of more than eighty thousand pounds. There was no pride to prevent him from taking advantage of this good fortune. He went straight from the Fleet to his home, which his mother deserted forthwith, and assumed control of the estate. Having provided generously for his mother, he sought Emilia, made a proposal of marriage in due form, and, with characteristic impetuosity, insisted that she marry him on that very day. After so long and varied a courtship she could not refuse, and with her at his side Peregrine gladly took up the unadventurous duties of a country landlord.

THE ADVENTURES OF FERDINAND, COUNT FATHOM (1753)

Smollett was a physician as well as an author, and in his stories he frequently drew upon the observations and experiences of his practise for color and episodes. This is especially the case in *Count Fathom*, which was written immediately after the author had spent two years at his profession in Bristol. Fathom is an unmitigated scoundrel, and the devices to which he resorts for money are as various as Smollett could invent. His trial of doctoring was so conducted as to have but slight bearing on the development of the main story of his life; but the chapters devoted to that episode are highly entertaining in their satire on the author's profession, as well as in the picture of the times they present. The action of the tale, which is contemporaneous with the period of the writing, covers a great part of Europe—Germany, Austria, the Netherlands, Spain, and France—but the tendency of events is ever toward England, where the villainous hero comes to the climax of his career.

OUR hero never had an opportunity for manifesting regard for his father. Not that his father died early in the lad's career, but that he was acknowledged by no mortal sire proceeded solely from the uncertainty of his mother, whose affections were so dissipated among several admirers that she never could pitch upon the person from whose loins our hero sprang. Certain it is that his mother was an Englishwoman who followed the armies in various campaigns on the Continent, furnishing gin and other comforts to the soldiery. Her son was born a little time before her marriage to her sixth husband, a German trooper named Ferdinand Fadom. As soon as the lady had taken possession of her new name, she bestowed it upon her offspring, with a slight euphonic modification, to which act her happy spouse offered no objection. Hence our hero's title, Ferdinand de Fathom, to which, in after years, he added the further title, Count, for reasons that may be readily inferred when his methods of combating the necessities that beset him are understood.

Ferdinand was still of tender years, but a most promising

334

boy, when his mother, prowling over a battle-field to find what might be of value on the bodies of the dead, and to bring a merciful end, if need be, to the agonies of the wounded, discovered an unconscious man whose uniform betokened his high rank. With a shrewd eye that saw farther than her immediate advantage, Mrs. Fadom decided not to give this man the *coup de grâce*, nor even to despoil him without bodily injury. Her compassion having been aroused to contemplation of higher things, she summoned assistance and had the officer conveyed to a tent, where surgical skill presently restored him to consciousness and eventually to health. The officer was the Count Melvil, a man of great wealth and generous character. He was eager to reward her who had saved him, and his principal benefaction consisted in taking Ferdinand into his service, not as an ordinary menial, but in a position somewhat between servant and companion to his son Renaldo, a youth of about the same age as Ferdinand.

These two boys grew up together, with the same educational advantages and the same pastimes. So it came about that Fathom was able to converse in several languages, having learned English from his mother, and other languages from the various countries in which he spent portions of his youth. He was also accomplished in music. While still a prattling youngster he manifested those singular qualities that made him famous: a disposition to study his own advantage without regard to the rights and feelings of others; a genius for throwing the fault of misconduct upon his best friends; a fertility of resource in extricating himself from unpleasant situations; a sublime disregard of property rights, which enabled him without repugnance to convey articles belonging to others to his own uses. And no sooner had his voice taken on the deep timber of manhood than he also betrayed an excessive fondness for the fair sex, which time and again brought him to emergencies fraught with peril.

Renaldo, on the contrary, was the soul of generosity and honor. His virtues were so pronounced that he never could suspect wrong in others; and when outrageous delinquency was plainly proved, as, for example, on the part of Fathom, he was ever ready to forgive. So loyal was he as a friend that he was absolutely blinded to Fathom's faults, and not until years after he came to maturity were his eyes opened to his companion's rascality.

Fathom was still in his 'teens when he conceived the mighty project of cementing the good fortune he enjoyed at the hands of Count Melvil by winning the love of Renaldo's sister. As his undertaking to this end failed to meet with success, he saw fit to make an alliance with a maid servant, through whom he hoped to have his praises sounded to the sister's ears; and this alliance speedily degenerated into a filching partnership, the servant stealing articles of value from various rooms in the castle and conveying them to Fathom, who disposed of them and invented plots whereby Teresa, the thieving servant, was enabled to avoid detection. It was absolutely essential to the alliance that Fathom should vow eternal love to Teresa, and he pursued that policy until the predicament in which he found himself was so difficult that he might never have escaped had it not been that the Count decided to send both young men to Vienna.

In the new field Fathom carried on similar intrigues, that is, he pursued amours not only for their own sake, but as a means to theft, until Vienna also became a most uncomfortable neighborhood; for he was then young, and his genius needed the lessons of experience to conduct his operations so as to avoid detection. That his ripened genius eventually left him a prey to failures may be accounted for by the fact that as he grew in years his operations grew in magnitude. Luck again served him when he fell into troublous circumstances in the Austrian capital; for a war broke out, which induced Count Melvil to take the field and send both Renaldo and Fathom to the front. Renaldo gloried at the opportunity; but Fathom, who always had a deep appreciation of safety, was indisposed to battle, so much so that he malingered successfully whenever an engagement was pending, and spent his time in the hospitals.

In the army Fathom became acquainted with a Swiss soldier named Ratchcali, who proved to be a gentleman after his own heart. They were equally averse to military life, equally inclined to profit by the carelessness of others who left their belongings unguarded. These two, then, decided to dispense with the army at the first convenient opportunity. Meantime Fathom discovered a cheap rogue of a servant rifling Renaldo's baggage, and drove him away before the fellow had abstracted a single article, or piece of money. This done, he carefully searched the baggage and appropriated to himself everything portable of value. Then he raised a hue and cry and appeared well-nigh distracted with excitement when Renaldo and others rushed in. Not only was Fathom not suspected of the robbery, but Renaldo praised him for the feeling he showed over the losses. While the capital thus gained was still unimpaired Fathom and Ratchcali, being on a foraging expedition, managed to elude their comrades and disappear in a forest. By an accident they rode straight into the lines of the enemy, where it was necessary to pose as deserters, a dire expedient, for it compelled them to renew military service in the ranks of the French; but shortly afterward peace was declared and they were free to proceed, as had been their first intention, to Paris.

They traveled a part of the distance together, winning not a little fresh capital by clever handling of cards and dice; but Fathom acquired a considerable distrust of his companion and thought it prudent to part from him. This he did by taking advantage of Ratchcali's absence from their stopping-place one night, and riding hard till dawn in a direction different from the route they had chosen. At the end of his ride Fathom was well content, fully convinced that Ratchcali could not overtake him. It occurred to him then to feast his eyes on the jewels and money that represented the profits of his various undertakings, including his robbery of Renaldo. What was his dismay to discover that the leathern bag in which he kept his valuables contained only a few handfuls of rusty nails! He was not slow in inferring correctly the explanation of this bewildering circumstance: Ratchcali had outgeneraled him.

There was nothing for it but to proceed upon his journey alone, although his funds were so reduced that there was no possibility of reaching Paris unless opportunity should be found to replenish his purse. He set forth with a guide, who abandoned him at a point where the road was in the thick of a forest, and Fathom, fearing an ambuscade, forced his horse among the trees, pursuing a haphazard course in the hope of eluding pursuit and coming eventually to a village. At last he saw a light and made toward it, finding a lonely cabin where dwelt an old woman, who received him with cheerful hospitality when she understood his plight. After he had supped on plain but bountiful fare, she gave him a candle and indicated his sleeping-place in the garret under the roof. Fathom found a bed there, but there was also a heap of straw, which induced him to examine the place carefully. He was well-nigh prostrated with terror when he discovered under the straw the dead body of a well-dressed man. The wounds upon it, and their condition, showed that the man had been murdered recently.

The wayfarer knew then beyond peradventure that his own turn would come ere the night should be past, and so horrified was he at the prospect that he could hardly breathe. It was madness to think of going below and trying to escape from the house, for the old woman's confederates were doubtless at hand. Shrewdness and duplicity must win where courage and strength could not. So Fathom undressed the corpse and laid it beneath the covers of the bed. Having, with characteristic forethought, conveyed all the money and other valuables from the pockets of the dead man to his own, he hid himself under the straw and waited. It was no long vigil that he had to endure, but it was fraught with terror at the last moment; for two villains crept up the stairs, cautiously surveyed the silent form in the bed, and stabbed it twice to the heart. Satisfied that they had done their work thoroughly, they returned below, and Fathom heard them speak of another undertaking at a distance that they must be off to accomplish before daybreak.

Shortly after the sound of their departing steps had ceased, Fathom went down and confronted the old woman, who was instantly terrified into helplessness by the conviction that he was a ghost. Before she had retrieved the ordinary use of her wits he had placed her before him on his horse. Then he compelled her, under pain of instant death, to direct his course to the nearest village. When he came near to one, he let the woman go rather than risk losing his loot from the dead man's clothes by informing against her; for if he had done so, he might have had to endure some annoying questions by the authorities, and it was quite possible that he could not have accounted satisfactorily for the goods in his possession. By this happy issue of an alarming adventure he was not only enabled to reach Paris with-

out further sacrifice of comfort, but to begin life in that capital
in a manner befitting his ambition.

His elegant manners and numerous accomplishments readily won him acquaintances, and his skill at cards and other
games of ostensible chance won him abundance of money to
maintain a rapid pace.   It was in Paris that he first styled himself Count, representing himself as a Polish nobleman traveling
incognito.   His success was highly gratifying; but he had the
misfortune to attract the envious attention of a pair of British
sharpers who were as much cleverer at gaming than he as he
excelled his ordinary victims.   They led him on from loss to loss
until he was penniless.   Chagrined, but with a deeper veneration
for England than he had ever entertained, he disappeared from
polite society altogether, and for nearly a year eked out a precarious living by playing the violin in theater orchestras.   He
economized with all possible care that he might some day have
funds sufficient to take him to England, where he believed he
would find an adequate field for his talents.

While living in this modest way he became acquainted with
a Castilian, Don Diego de Zelos, who had been compelled by the
basest treachery to leave his native land.   The noble Castilian
lived only in the hope that he might ultimately recover his property and be reunited to his wife and daughter.   To this end he
lived sparingly, but he had retained possession of valuable jewels, to be used only when the means to the accomplishment of his
just desires appeared to be at hand.   Fathom persuaded Don
Diego not only that he could institute measures that would re-
dound to his relief, but that he could find a customer for the jewels who would pay an extravagant price for them.   It took much
time and infinite finesse to win the Castilian's confidence, but
Count Fathom succeeded at last, and, as soon as he had possession of the jewels he traveled post-haste to the seacoast and
embarked for England, which country he gained without important adventure en route.

Fathom's career in England was extraordinarily brilliant for
a considerable period.   He had not been long in that country
when he encountered his former companion, Ratchcali, who
greeted him with such effusive apologies for the scurrilous way
he had behaved in France that Fathom thought it best to for-

give him. Accordingly they entered into an alliance that proved highly profitable to both. A house was taken, in which the Count lived in magnificent style. He soon found entrance to the houses of the wealthy, before whom he was ever at pains to display costly jewels, each with a romantic history invented by his own fertile brain; the truth being that the jewels were the results of various conveyances effected by himself and Ratchcali, who was an excellent lapidary and who reset the gems in such style that the owners could not have recognized them. It became quite the fashion to persuade Count Fathom to dispose of his rare possessions at exorbitant prices, whereby the scoundrels profited hugely.

They might have continued their game indefinitely, for Fathom continued in high favor, but for the greed of Ratchcali and the excessive amorousness of the Count. Ratchcali one day foisted a worthless pebble upon a customer in lieu of a genuine stone, and when the fraud was discovered Fathom was hard put to it to maintain his reputation. By promptly buying the pebble back and protesting infinite mortification, he succeeded in holding up his head; but about the same time he was victimized by a handsome dame who, by the connivance of her husband, made an assignation with the Count for the sole purpose of being discovered, it being the design of the precious pair to blackmail Fathom heavily. The husband instituted a lawsuit, in the preparation of which Fathom's lawyers bled him unmercifully. The publicity attaching to the affair reacted upon his popularity among fashionable folk, and his income was correspondingly reduced; so that, when the case came to trial, and the Count was mulcted in two thousand pounds damages, he had not sufficient funds at command to meet the bill. He was indisposed to pay it in any event, and willingly went to prison with the thought that confinement for a space would give him opportunity to retrieve his fortunes by shrewd thought upon the best method to be employed. As none of his former friends would come to his relief, he felt reduced to the necessity of appealing to the generosity of his old-time companion, Renaldo. Accordingly, he gave Ratchcali substantially all the money that remained in his possession, that Ratchcali might travel to Germany and intercede with Renaldo; and Ratchcali prudently betook himself away from England with no idea of returning, or of going as far as Germany.

Count Fathom, therefore, was in a deplorable plight when he discovered that his confederate had again played him false. What way to turn he knew not, when one day Renaldo appeared in the prison. He had come, it appeared, to succor a supposed relative detained there, his generosity having been imposed on by a petty swindler; but when he saw Fathom all the affection of his boyhood arose and stirred him to the most extraordinary benevolence. He bought Fathom's freedom, thereby reducing his own resources almost to nothing; for it seemed that Count Melvil was dead, and that the property, which rightfully belonged to Renaldo, was held by a rascally nobleman who had married the Count's widow. It was now Renaldo's chief aim in life to effect the recovery of his estates, which he believed could be accomplished if he could go to Vienna and lay the case before the Emperor. That he was not now on his way there was due to the interesting fact that he had fallen deeply in love with an orphan, who was an exile in England, and who was dependent solely on such provision as Renaldo could make for her welfare. This young lady was known as Monimia. Renaldo, having released Fathom from prison, introduced him to the lady with many ingenuous expressions of regard, so that Monimia had a very favorable impression of him. It would exhaust the capacity of language to describe the impression that Monimia made upon Fathom. Suffice it that her beauty inflamed him to a degree that such gratitude as he may have felt toward Renaldo was instantly banished from his breast, and in place of it came a peremptory desire to possess the lady, toward the accomplishment of which he thenceforward devoted all his finesse with the most remarkable assiduity. So, while Renaldo was doing his utmost to get together money enough for his necessary journey to the Continent, and meantime paying for the support of both Monimia and Fathom, the latter was delicately exalting himself in the presence of the lady and undertaking with the most diabolical subtlety to undermine her confidence in Renaldo.

Then ensued a period of the keenest distress for Renaldo. Not only was he unable to borrow from friends sufficient for his journey, but there were days when he was hard pressed to obtain sufficient food for himself and Monimia. Meantime, Fathom, by every trick at his command, prevented him from obtaining money, and gave Monimia to understand that the young nobleman's failure was due to his bad character. The lady was rendered very unhappy by these devices, but as yet she showed no disposition to displace Renaldo in favor of Fathom. At last, after incredible failures and suffering, Renaldo at Fathom's suggestion applied to a wealthy Jew for a loan. He took this course in ironical desperation, having no hope whatever of success; but to his amazement the Jew advanced him five hundred pounds without security. Renaldo entrusted half this amount to Fathom for the care of Monimia, and set forth hopefully for Vienna.

Fathom not only kept the money for himself, but persuaded Monimia that Renaldo had fled the country with a woman of the lowest character as his companion. Having convinced her of this by means of forged letters, he made offer of his own love, only to be spurned by the hapless lady with every manifestation of deep repugnance. He was discomfited but not defeated, and he pursued his campaign with such violence that Monimia was constrained to accept the protection of a warm-hearted Frenchwoman, in whose house she fell seriously ill. Fathom discovered her retreat and sought even there to assume command of her affairs; but Monimia was so ill, and her benefactor so distrustful of Fathom, that he was not permitted to enter the room where Monimia lay; and one day when he called as usual to inquire for her, he was informed that she had breathed her last. He was himself so distrustful of all human kind that he did not then give over his quest until he had seen the funeral train go from the Frenchwoman's house to a cemetery, and the unhappy Monimia's coffin conveyed from the hearse to the chapel. This espionage upon the dead he conducted secretly, for fear that if he attended the funeral openly his numerous claims to a certain proprietorship over Monimia would be taken literally, and the expenses of her burial be therefore charged to him.

Convinced that death had robbed him of his prey, he conferred with himself as to the best method of attaining again that affluence of resources without which life was to him a dreary waste; and after some cogitation he undertook the practise of medicine. In this profession he met with a variety of experiences, and, after many discouragements enjoyed one period of popularity and prosperity, which came about, singularly enough, from one of his failures. A certain man whose wife was ill desired that she might be freed from mortal distress and forthwith enter upon such felicities as might be in store for her beyond the veil: and he had resort to Fathom, requesting that he administer such treatment as would assure the dissolution of those ties that kept soul and body together. Fathom cheerfully undertook the case, but he administered a dose so violent that the woman's body rejected it and her disease together, and she recovered her health with amazing celerity. She was lavish of praise for the doctor who had cured her, and Fathom was not slow to claim the merit of a cure, so that his fame spread and for a time his income was eminently satisfactory.

But success founded on such precarious and adventitious circumstances cannot endure the trials that normally attend practise; and eventually Fathom found himself reduced to indigence, when, in endeavoring to extricate himself by fresh devices, he committed certain blunders, including marriage with a widow who proved to be anything but as rich as he had supposed; and, as it never rains but it pours, he was pressed by creditors and cast again into prison, with no hope whatever of finding his way out.

Meantime Renaldo had been wholly successful in his efforts to gain possession of his father's estates, and when that affair was concluded he set forth for England with the liveliest hope of a speedy union with the fair Monimia. On the way he had an adventure in the course of which he saved the life of Don Diego, that unlucky Castilian whom Fathom had cruelly robbed; and thenceforth Renaldo and the Spaniard traveled together. The anguish of the young man on learning that Monimia was no more may be imagined. He had become acquainted with Fathom's scoundrelism in many matters while he was in Vienna, and he had heard Don Diego's story; so it was with entire credibility that he listened to the Frenchwoman who had harbored Monimia, when that excellent lady informed him of Fathom's persecution of the unhappy orphan. His grief was so sincere that any doubts the Frenchwoman may have had concerning his loyalty were removed. He begged to be taken to Monimia's grave, and he was conducted to the chapel into which Fathom had seen her coffin conveyed. There Renaldo determined to keep vigil every night; but on the second night Monimia came to him, a living, loving woman, whose faith in his constancy was as completely restored as was her physical health.

It proved that, in order to evade Fathom's limitless devices to harass her, Monimia and her benefactress had contrived with the physician in attendance upon her and with a parish priest to have her accounted as dead, and the funeral had been a sham devised for the purpose that it served, namely; of throwing Fathom off the track. It proved also that Monimia was the daughter of Don Diego, who, through the aid Renaldo was able to give him, speedily righted his affairs in his native country.

There was no unnecessary delay in bringing about the union of Renaldo and Monimia. Before they left England they came upon Fathom, desperately ill in a shabby hut, attended by one of the hapless women who had been victims of his amorous propensities. She was faithful to him, but in sore distress for their sustenance. Fathom had been liberated by an Act of Parliament for the relief of imprisoned debtors, but his freedom was now of no use to him. The generous nature of Renaldo was then displayed to its utmost. He not only forgave the traitor, with the full consent of Monimia, but provided him with means to retire to a village in the north of England, where he passed the rest of his life in reputable pursuits.

THE ADVENTURES OF SIR LAUNCELOT GREAVES
(1761)

For some years after the publication of *Ferdinand, Count Fathom*, Smollett was occupied with literary hack work, in the course of which he translated *Don Quixote*. He was evidently under the influence of Cervantes when he resumed novel-writing, for his *Launcelot Greaves* is a frank attempt to transplant the Spanish knight errant to English soil. At the time of writing, which is the period of the story's action, knights in armor were a century or more in ancient history, and, in order to establish any sort of credibility for the tale, the author had to suggest that Sir Launcelot was afflicted with temporary insanity. The story has a singular distinction in history in that it was the first English novel to be published serially (in the *British Magazine*) before its appearance in book form. It is also one of the earliest examples in English literature of novels in which the author did not begin with a bombastic address to the Muses or with some other manifestation of false modesty, by way of leading up to the matters in which he purposed to interest the reader. In *Sir Launcelot* Smollett plunges into the story in the very first sentence.

N the great northern road from London to York, at about the hour of eight in the evening, four travelers were, by a violent shower of rain, driven for shelter into a little public house on the side of the highway. The quartette was composed of Mr. Fillet, a country practitioner in surgery; Captain Crowe, a retired mariner; his nephew, Thomas Clarke, an attorney; and a sour-visaged individual whose name was Ferret. With these gentlemen in the kitchen were the landlady and her daughter, Dolly Cowslip. They had not been long sitting and discoursing, as travelers will when circumstances have contrived to bring them together, when they were startled by a summons to open the door, so violent that none durst obey. The summons was repeated, and presently the door was burst open to give entrance to a figure so extraordinary and appalling that the company exercised the utmost expedition to withdraw into the cellar or into adjoining rooms.

This was nothing less than a knight in full armor, bearing a burden that proved to be the body of a man dressed as a squire, both seeming to be apparitions from some forgotten page of ancient history. The knight addressed the disappearing persons in courteous terms, desiring assistance for his man, who had been swept from his horse and nearly drowned in fording a stream in the neighborhood. Mr. Fillet, perceiving the human quality of the visitors, overcame his trepidation and gave his professional attention to the squire with such skill that presently he was revived; and the landlady, having ventured to return to the kitchen, made ready a bed for him and another for the knight, for both were soaked and must needs retire while their clothes were in the process of drying. The kitchen being again at the uninterrupted service of the travelers, all returned, when it proved that Thomas Clarke had recognized the knight as Sir Launcelot Greaves, and he straightway entertained the company with the history of that remarkable individual.

It appeared that he was the only son of a worthy knight who was beloved by all the country roundabout except one Squire Darnel. Indeed, there was traditional enmity between the Greaves and Darnel families, although it was only the head of the latter house who seemed to take the matter seriously enough to keep the feud alive. At one time the feud was in a fair way of terminating in the most agreeable manner, for young Launcelot fell in love with Aurelia Darnel, daughter of the rival house, and there were not wanting indications that his passion was reciprocated in that quarter where properly it most required sympathetic support, which is to say that if all had depended on Miss Aurelia the match might have gone forward; but the Squire was to be reckoned with, which was a matter of difficult obstinacy, and when the Squire died, and his brother Anthony came to be the head of the house, the obstinacy became virulent, and the difficulties of association between the families insurmountable. Nevertheless, Fortune favored young Launcelot in that it fell to him to save the lives of both the young lady and her mother at the imminent peril of his own, whereby he not only lost nothing in the esteem of the beauteous Aurelia, but won an ardent ally in the person of her mother. He retired from this adventure with lively hope, nay, conviction, that his suit would be favored, in spite of Anthony Darnel's opposition, whenever it should be the proper time to press it to an issue; for Aurelia's mother had told him, in language admitting of no misinterpretation, that it was her dearest hope to see the two families allied.

The general circumstances being as stated, the amazement of Launcelot Greaves may readily be imagined when he received a letter from Aurelia conveying a plain dismissal of his pretensions to her hand. There was no shadow of doubt that the missive was written by her, and its terms were unequivocal; but Launcelot could not accept dismissal without at least an effort to come to an explanation, and he used his utmost honorable endeavors to see the fair Aurelia. But she was from home, and the answers vouchsafed to him by the servants of whom he inquired left little room for doubt that she had absented herself purposely in order to avoid the interview which she must have known he would seek.

Deeply cast down, Launcelot journeyed to foreign lands, seeking vainly to overcome his sorrow, and while he was absent his father died. He returned to England and concerned himself with the affairs of his estate, putting everything in order upon a scale of extraordinary generosity. The attorney who regaled the little company at the inn with this history related many astonishing instances of Sir Launcelot's benevolence, but, what was more to the point, he indicated how the young nobleman had made much study of chivalry, and become so infatuated with its ideals that all who knew him believed that his mind had become affected. Be that as it might, he had at last put his knowledge to eccentric use by donning a complete suit of armor, furnishing himself with a lance and other ancient implements of war, and, thus arrayed, had taken to the road in pursuit of wrongs that required redress.

This singular ambition, especially remarkable in an age when chivalry was no better than a little understood name for something long since forgotten, was vouched for by Sir Launcelot himself when he rejoined the company at a later hour.

"Yes, gentlemen," said he, "in the thorny and painful path of knight-errantry I have begun my career, a candidate for honest fame; determined, so far as in me lies, to honor and assert the efforts of virtue; to combat vice in all her forms, redress injuries, chastise oppression, protect the helpless and forlorn, relieve the indigent, exert my best endeavors in the cause of innocence and beauty, and dedicate my talents, such as they are, to the service of my country."

All this made the most profound impression on Captain Crowe, who forthwith announced his determination to become a knight errant also, and to follow Sir Launcelot's lead. His nephew, the attorney, besought him to have resort to reason, advancing many legal arguments against the proposed course, pointing out in specific terms that the career of a knight errant might well be regarded as a disturbance of the King's peace and a contravention of the present laws of the realm; to all of which the old sailor replied in nautical terms of contempt, and was not to be dissuaded even when Sir Launcelot advised him that, prior to becoming a knight errant, he should devote much time to study and eventually gain admittance to the order of chivalry by a proper ceremony. The plain truth was, that the mariner had been completely won by the generous ideals of the order as exemplified in the conduct of Sir Launcelot; and, if the latter knight was really mad, the mariner had caught the contagion. However, matters were not ripe for the immediate transformation of the Captain into a knight errant, there being, for example, no armor at command, and Sir Launcelot departed with his squire, Crabshaw, in quest of adventure.

They had not far to seek, for shortly after daybreak they came upon a coach held at the mercy of robbers. Sir Launcelot charged upon the ruffians, who speedily took to flight, appalled doubtless by the extraordinary appearance of the attacking party. The knight pursued one for a long distance, the fellow escaping at last because he had the fleeter horse. When Sir Launcelot returned to the place where the encounter began the coach had gone on, and it was not until he had paused to rest in a town that information reached him tending to make him suspect that the passengers in the coach had included none other than Miss Aurelia Darnel.

His spirit was mightily wrought upon by this belief, but for the present it could not affect the course of his adventures, which brought him in rapid succession into divers situations of interest. In one town he visited an election was in progress, and the knight rode into the thick of the crowd to listen to the rival candidates for Parliament. When he had heard them utter their pretensions, he was so convinced that neither was worthy of the honor sought that he harangued the crowd most eloquently, condemning first one candidate and then the other, and advising the electors to throw both over and choose a man of genuine patriotism and ability. By this manner of discourse he inflamed the friendly sentiments first of one party, and then of the other, but their hostile sentiments also, and at the end the contending factions made common cause against him, so that he was fain to ride from the town in disgust that his wise advice should be so lightly esteemed.

Just without the town he came upon a quack recommending and selling a nostrum for the prolongation of life. The knight was interested in the fellow's eloquence, and listened until a constable apprehended him for transgressing the law bearing on sales in the highways. The quack pleaded with the knight to rescue him, asserting that it was a case worthy the endeavors of a knight errant; and Sir Launcelot, in doubt on the matter, followed the constable and his prisoner, determined to see the end of the adventure.

Presently his attention was attracted by a familiar voice calling to him from the window of the parish jail, and he beheld Tom Clarke, the attorney, who besought his assistance. Sir Launcelot immediately went within and found not only Clarke, but Captain Crowe, both prisoners. The Captain, obstinately bent upon the practise of chivalry, had hired a traveling tinker to make him what passed for a suit of armor; arrayed in this, he had committed an assault that brought him and Tom, who had perforce to act as his squire, within the toils of the law. Sir Launcelot perceived that the mariner had erred through imperfect comprehension of the requirements of chivalry, and not from any moral obliquity; and he made no doubt that he should be able to bring sufficient influence to bear upon the local magistrate to release both men; but before he could take action accordingly, he discovered that he was himself a prisoner.

It appeared that the quack, incensed that the knight had not defended him against the constable, had laid information against Sir Launcelot, by virtue of which his own offense was compounded. There ensued, in consequence, an experience well

worthy of knight-errantry; for imprisonment enabled Sir Launcelot to perceive not only the misery of many of the prisoners, but
the crass ignorance and cruel injustice of the magistrate.   In the
course of the proceedings it developed that the quack was none
other than the ill-visaged fellow, Ferret, who had been one of the
party disturbed by the knight on the occasion when his squire
was nearly drowned, but that was of less interest than the fact
that the fellow had fled from the vicinity without signing his
name to the information against Sir Launcelot; whereby the
document was invalid and the knight's detention contrary to
law.   This gave Sir Launcelot such a hold upon the wicked
magistrate that, before the affair was finished, he had compelled
the man who so dishonored the bench to free all prisoners unjustly detained, to give a liberal sum to the poor whom he had
oppressed, and to resign his commission.

This triumph of chivalry having been accomplished, Sir
Launcelot went on his way, attended now by the irrepressible
Crowe; and not long thereafter an adventure brought him to an
inn where was put into his hands a purse that had been dropped
by a lady who had left but a short time previously.   Transported with excitement, the knight recognized the purse as the
property of Miss Aurelia Darnel.   Having learned which way
she went, he set forth in a post-chaise after her, bidding Crabshaw, his squire, follow with the horses and accouterments.   In
due time Sir Launcelot arrived at an inn, where inquiry assured
him that the lovely Aurelia was a guest.

At this time Aurelia was upon a journey the purpose of which,
if known to Sir Launcelot, would have aroused his chivalrous
nature in her behalf, even if his soul were not already bound to
her by ties of love.   Sir Anthony Darnel, her guardian, had long
endeavored to win her consent to a match with Sir Philip Sycamore, and to this end he had not scrupled to tell her many
atrocious lies relative to the character and inconstancy of Sir
Launcelot Greaves.   It matters not whether Aurelia believed
any jot of her uncle's fiction; nothing could persuade her to look
with kindly eyes upon Sir Philip.   Despairing at last of accom-
plishing this design, Sir Anthony decided to take such measures
as would put him in control of her property.   To this end, he
proclaimed that she was insane and had her locked up in a

private retreat.   Sir Philip learned of this and planned to rescue her, hoping that her gratitude would cause her to yield to his
love; but he was a man of the least discretion, and he talked
of his plan so openly that noise of it came to Sir Anthony's ear,
wherefore Aurelia was suddenly removed with great secrecy to
another house.   She was on this enforced journey when her
coach was attacked by robbers who were driven away by Sir
Launcelot, whom she recognized at the time; and shortly afterward, when she paused at an inn for refreshment, she managed
to make her grievous estate known to the landlady's daughter,
who was Dolly Cowslip, whose acquaintance we made in the beginning of this history.   Dolly was all sympathy.   She put her
wits to work and contrived a means for Aurelia's escape, and
that young lady, accompanied by Dolly as her maid, was now
hastening to London, where she hoped to find refuge with a
relative against the importunities of Sycamore and the tyranny
of Sir Anthony.

In ignorance of all this, Sir Launcelot, having still in mind
the letter of dismissal that he had received from Aurelia, was
under necessity of constrained behavior when he was admitted to
her presence for the purpose of restoring her purse to her.   He
could not wholly avoid some slight expression of his regard, but
Aurelia, remembering, perhaps, the false tales of his inconstancy,
was at first reserved, and they might have parted with no more
comfort than could be had from her courteous words of gratitude
for his trouble in bringing the purse, if it had not been that Sir
Launcelot let slip some allusion to her letter of dismissal, whereupon she opened her eyes in a way that immediately caused his
heart to leap with anticipation of some manner of statement that
would reveal that fatal document in a new light.   Indeed, they
were at the very verge of an understanding when, unhappily for
their peace, Sir Launcelot was disturbed by a cry of distress
from somewhere without the inn.   This was something that, as
a knight errant, he was bound to regard as of first importance,
and that he recognized the voice of his squire, Crabshaw, in
nowise lessened his interest in the matter.   So, leaving the conversation in mid air, he parted abruptly from Aurelia and went
forth into the night on his errand of succor.   Again he heard
Crabshaw's voice, but it was too dark to see where the man lay,

and Sir Launcelot followed the sound as best he could. It led him a long and circuitous chase, for no sooner did he seem to be near his squire than the voice sounded in another direction. In brief, it was not until near morning that he came upon Crabshaw and the horses, and they were then far from the inn where he had left Aurelia.

It proved that Crabshaw had been set upon by three masked men, who prodded him with their weapons until he was covered with wounds, each a trifle in itself but the aggregate highly painful, and had driven him before them until the night was nearly spent. As his tormentors had robbed him of nothing, and had exulted at his outcries, the squire was sure that he had been beset with devils; and Sir Launcelot himself was mystified to account for the misadventure until he had returned to the inn. Then he understood, for he learned that immediately after he had been lured away by Crabshaw's cries two coaches halted at the door, armed men issued from them, took Aurelia and Dolly by force and compelled them to embark; after which the coaches departed at high speed along the road to London. There was nothing for it then but to follow without delay, which Sir Launcelot did. Such doubts as he may have had were set at rest while on the road, for the clever Dolly Cowslip managed to send back a letter, in which she advised him, on reaching London, to advertise his whereabouts in the newspapers, so that Aurelia might get definite word to him concerning her own circumstances.

It was evident from this letter that Aurelia had been kidnaped by her uncle, a fact that convinced Sir Launcelot that it would be the part of wisdom to proceed in a leisurely manner, to avoid arousing the suspicions of Sir Anthony, who, if he understood that the knight was making hot pursuit, would perhaps take extreme measures to gain his ends. If the abductors had been the myrmidons of Sycamore Sir Launcelot would have proceeded with the utmost vigor; as it was, before he reached London Sycamore, who had been persuaded by a reckless companion to emulate Sir Launcelot in adopting the accouterments of ancient knighthood, challenged him to mortal combat.

When the challenge was received by our knight he scorned to give it attention. It was no part of modern chivalry, he thought, to stake the love of a fair lady upon the issue of a combat; he was for the nobler forms of chivalry, and he chose to be regarded as a coward rather than recede from his ideals. But Sycamore, convinced that he was a coward, barred the way, and a fight therefore was inevitable. So far as the principals were concerned, the contest was quickly decided. Sir Launcelot unhorsed his man at the first onslaught; and while he forebore to injure, much less kill Sycamore, the latter had the narrowest escape from death on account of falling under his horse. It was quite another matter with the seconds. Captain Crowe, who was always spoiling for a fray, insisted on tilting against Sycamore's daredevil companion. The latter, having no mind whatever to risk his life, had resort to a scurvy trick by which he frightened Crowe's horse, so that the mariner was carried at a mad gallop all over the field except where the fighting was; and, seeing Sycamore helplessly defeated, the companion put spurs to his own horse and fled to London. Meantime Crabshaw had engaged with Sycamore's servant, and neither having any proper conception of the ways of chivalry, their encounter speedily resolved itself to a plain hammering with staves and fists, which Sir Launcelot could not prevent because he was concerning himself necessarily with the injured Sycamore; and Crowe, having at last regained control of his horse, rode up and, in default of his own adversary, pitched in furiously, first in behalf of Crabshaw, and soon, by reason of some hot misunderstanding, against him. So a highly ridiculous belaboring was in progress when Sir Launcelot at last interfered and compelled all to join in improvising a litter on which Sycamore might be conveyed to a place where he could have medical attention. After this the knight and his party continued on their way to London.

Sir Launcelot's endeavors to learn the whereabouts of Aurelia in London, and to make his known to her, were utterly fruitless. He made use of the newspapers, as Dolly Cowslip had suggested, and Dolly herself crossed his path; but the maid could give no clue to Aurelia, for Sir Anthony had dismissed her immediately on her arrival in the city. In the greatest anxiety, Sir Launcelot made a systematic tour of the hospitals and prisons, gaining much knowledge of human affairs thereby, but coming to no knowledge of his lady. He was beginning to despair when one evening a messenger brought him a mysterious letter advising him to be at a certain spot at seven o'clock, if he wished to know what had become of Aurelia. It was then near the hour, and Sir Launcelot set forth hurriedly. Captain Crowe, Clarke, and Crabshaw were all from home, and it was not until several hours had elapsed that they began to wonder what had become of the knight. He was so regular in his habits that, when he did not appear by morning, they were gravely alarmed. They made some search for him, but nobody was found who could give them a clue, and at last they resorted to the ingenious devices of Lawyer Clarke.

What had happened was this: Sir Launcelot had arrived at the appointed spot just on time; he found a coach in waiting, and the driver told him he was to enter and be carried at once to Aurelia's lodging. The knight unhesitatingly complied with all directions, and was deposited at length at a house on the edge of the city. He was shown to a room where presently, instead of meeting Aurelia, he found himself a captive. Worse yet, not many hours elapsed before sounds from adjoining rooms, as well as the impertinent attentions of a physician, convinced him that he was in an insane asylum.

It was a private institution, and nobody connected with it would give the least heed to his expostulations. His very insistence on sanity and freedom were accepted as symptoms of madness. Perceiving this, Sir Launcelot constrained himself to a calm demeanor, but his heart was put into the most violent perturbation by hearing the voice of his beloved Aurelia somewhere in the building. She, too, was a captive there, and each was powerless to help the other.

Clarke's plan for discovering what had become of the knight was based upon his theory that he had been abducted, that being the only reasonable explanation of his disappearance. He advertised a large reward for the coachman who had driven a gentleman on a certain night, and so forth, naming just enough circumstances to attract the attention of the party the advertisement was designed to interest. The reward was so generous that the coachman was induced by it to make known what he had done. Thus Clarke and his friends discovered the house where Sir Launcelot was confined, and after that the release of both the knight and the lady were matters of speedy application of legal measures.

Once again in the presence of Aurelia, Sir Launcelot reverted to the letter of dismissal, and showed it to her, when it developed that this was a letter she had written to Sycamore. She had given it to her uncle to deliver, and Sir Anthony had changed the address, so that it fell into Sir Launcelot's hands. This misunderstanding cleared away, nothing was left to impede the union of Sir Launcelot and Aurelia, especially as Sir Anthony, outgeneraled at every move, at last desisted from his opposition; and the marriage took place, accordingly, as soon after the release from the insane retreat as Aurelia could prepare herself for it. And from that time Sir Launcelot gave over the career of knight-errantry.

HUMPHRY CLINKER (1771)

This story was written in the year of Smollett's death, and it is in the main an account of his fruitless journeys about Great Britain in search of health. Quite apart from its rollicking humor, the book has a spicy interest in that many persons of prominence at the period (the years immediately preceding composition) are mentioned and discussed under thin disguises. Smollett himself appears in the tale more than once, but always in very subordinate relation to the principal personages of the story, which is told wholly in the form of letters addressed by the different members of a party of travelers to their confidential friends. Thus it happens that many incidents are related two or more times, and the reader gets the advantage of different points of view.

ATTHEW BRAMBLE was a gentleman of considerable means whose estate lay in Wales. He was unmarried, and his sister Tabitha lived with him as his housekeeper. She also was unmarried, but she had hopes of the most buoyant nature, as was discovered by every middle-aged gentleman who made her acquaintance. When Squire Bramble was about fifty-five, being much afflicted with gout and other ailments, he went to Bath to try the waters, not with any conviction that they would help him, but as a last desperate endeavor to restore his health to something like its normal condition. This was but the beginning of a series of journeys that took him over the greater part of Great Britain, accompanied at every stage by his sister and her servant, Winifred Jenkins, his own man servant, and two other persons who happened to be added to his household just at the time when he set forth for Bath. These were his niece, Lydia Melford, and her brother Jery, orphans, the latter heir to the Squire.

Jery had just finished his studies at Oxford, and Lydia had left a boarding-school in Gloucester on account of a melancholy accident. She had lost her heart, a matter serious enough, conscience knows, even when circumstances are satisfactory to a maid's guardians, but when, as in Lydia's case, the loss is to

356

a strolling player, the affair is little short of monstrous. The man was known on the boards as Mr. Wilson. He had gained admission somehow to a respectable tea-drinking where Lydia was a guest, and they had been introduced in proper manner, whereupon it appeared that each became immediately the conquest of the other. Nobody accused Lydia of anything whatever except inexperience, for she was as refined and reserved a girl as one could meet in the entire kingdom; but, as there had been the beginning of a clandestine correspondence, it was deemed advisable by all concerned—with the probable exception of Mr. Wilson—that she should retire from school to the closer care of her uncle and aunt. She dutifully conveyed word to Wilson that he must never see her again or send her any sort of communication, and that he must forget her; this expressed in unequivocal terms, she forthwith began to pine because her lover seemed to take her at her word.

Squire Bramble was at first a deep puzzle and a source of great discomfort to his nephew and niece. Jery wrote of him as follows to his friend at Oxford: "My uncle is an odd kind of humorist, always on the fret, and so unpleasant in his manner that rather than be obliged to keep him company I'd resign all claim to the inheritance of his estate. Perhaps I may like him better on further acquaintance; certain it is, all his servants and neighbors in the country are fond of him to a degree of enthusiasm, the reason of which I cannot yet comprehend." The young man grew to comprehend in short order; for he discovered that underneath Squire Bramble's petulant demeanor lay not only a fund of good humor but a source of kindly deeds which was constantly in exercise for the benefit of the needy and distressed. Lydia understood, too, when her brother's severity and Aunt Tabitha's intolerable scolding on account of her heart-sickness drove her to tears. It was Uncle Bramble who then became her comforter. With no sanction for her unlucky passion, he yet manifested such sympathy for her and counseled her so tenderly that he won her respect, affection, and obedience as completely as if he had been her father.

While the party was at Bath a Jew pedler gained entrance to Squire Bramble's lodgings and in a whisper made himself known to Lydia as Wilson. She bade Winifred Jenkins follow the man and learn all possible about him, while conveying from herself a repetition of her command that he should not seek to see her. Winifred returned from this errand in a great fluster. She had found and talked with Wilson, and he had told her that that was not his real name; that he was a gentleman, and that it was his firm purpose to sue for Lydia in his proper character. But what was Wilson's name? Alas! in her flurry Winifred had forgotten, nor could she ever remember it. This circumstance did nothing toward curing Lydia of her infatuation, and, as time passed and no Wilson appeared, either in disguise or in *propria persona*, it availed only to keep the poor girl in a constant state of apprehension and disappointment.

It was Lydia's manifest depression of spirits more than anything else that induced Squire Bramble to take his party to London. He thought to change the current of her thoughts by the novelties she would see there. The journey had hardly begun when one of the horses fell in descending a hill, and the postilion, in trying to prevent the coach from running over the beast, pulled to one side with such vigor that the vehicle was overturned. In the *mêlée* Miss Tabitha's lap-dog, of which she was absurdly fond (this on the authority of both Squire Bramble's and Jery Melford's letters) bit the Squire's servant, whereupon the servant was for killing the beast instanter. Miss Tabitha made such a dismal row about this, and the servant was so impudent, that Bramble, while sparing the dog, was forced to discharge his servant. Moreover, he had to get another postilion forthwith, for Tabitha was as sure as could be that the fellow had upset the party purposely, and not another furlong would she ride under his direction. Badgered to the point of wishing he might take his amiable sister at her word and leave her there, nevertheless the Squire yielded to her whim and made such shift as he could by engaging an ill-dressed young fellow to drive as far as the next village. This unfortunate youth distressed and offended the sensitive Tabitha beyond maidenly endurance by the fact that he wore no shirt, and, there being a rent, or perhaps two, in his nether garments, some slight portion of his anatomy became a feature of the scenery from which the modest Tabitha could by no means withdraw her eyes. According to Jery's letter relating this incident, Winifred Jenkins cried out against the fellow's indelicate conduct quite as loudly as did her mistress, and the Squire felt constrained to call in the temporary postilion for the purpose of reprimanding him.

The fellow's appearance was as pathetic as it was ludicrous. He gave his name as Humphry Clinker, and frankly confessed his shame at going abroad without a shirt; but he offered his excuses with tearful eloquence. He had no shirt; for weeks he had been dangerously ill, and all his belongings had gone to pay the doctors and for such necessaries as had prolonged his miserable existence; meantime he had lost his situation and had not tasted so much as a crust for twenty-four hours. Squire Bramble frowned portentously and summoned the landlord to verify or disprove Clinker's story. When it was verified in every detail, he proceeded to read Clinker a lecture on the crimes he had committed in being poor, and sick, and ill used generally, and fined him a guinea, which coin he placed in the astonished lad's hand. Clinker was overwhelmed with gratitude, and to make short of what followed, he redeemed a decent suit of clothes from the pawnbroker with the guinea and attached himself to the Squire's party, asserting that he would serve his benefactor, whether he was paid or not, as long as he lived; and such were his pertinacity and simplicity that the Squire accepted him in place of the discharged servant.

The Squire's party remained several weeks in London, taking in its wonders, each viewing them in his or her own way. For example, Vauxhall Gardens, to which the Squire felt in duty bound to take his young people, drew from the good man the following comments: "Vauxhall is a composition of baubles, overcharged with paltry ornaments, ill conceived and poorly executed, without any unity of design or propriety of disposition. The walks are filled with crowds of noisy people, sucking up the nocturnal rheums of an aguish climate; and through these scenes a few lamps glimmer like so many farthing candles. . . . In all probability, the proprietors of this and other public gardens are in some shape connected with the faculty of physic, and the company of undertakers," with more to the same effect.

Lydia wrote: "I no sooner entered Vauxhall than I was dazzled and confounded with the variety of beauties that rushed all at once on my eye. Imagine to yourself a spacious garden, part laid out in delightful walks, part exhibiting a wonderful assemblage of the most picturesque and striking objects, . . . the whole illuminated with an infinite number of lamps; the place crowded with the gayest company, ranging through those blissful shades, or supping in different lodges, on cold collations, enlivened with mirth, freedom, and good humor."

Winifred Jenkins, writing to a fellow-servant at home, expressed her first impressions of London in part thus: "All the towns that ever I beheld in my born days are no more than Welsh barrows and crumlecks to this wonderful sitty! Even Bath itself is but a fillitch. In the naam of God, one would think there's no end of the streets, but the land's end. O gracious! my poor Welsh brain has been spinning like a top ever since I came hither. And I have seen the park, and the paleass of Saint Gimses, and the King's and the Queen's magisterial pursing, and the sweet young Princes, and the hillyfents, and the piebald ass, and all the rest of the royal family."

London was a bit of an old story to Jery's eyes, but under his uncle's guidance he found much that was new to him, and with such divergent points of view it may be imagined that the metropolis was thoroughly seen. There must needs be adventures of one kind and another, too. Lydia had more than one opportunity to efface the image of the vanished Wilson and be married forthwith; Aunt Tabitha tried valiantly for an offer, but never had so much as one; but the episodes that were followed with enduring influence on the party had to do mainly with Humphry Clinker. In the first place, that devoted youth had a violent attack of Methodism, from which he never recovered. It inspired him to preach at every conceivable opportunity, his first known outbreak occurring in the vestibule of a nobleman's house whither the Squire had gone to pay a formal call. Eventually he was discovered in the pulpit of the tabernacle, and, stranger still, in his audience, deeply affected by his pious discourse, were Aunt Tabitha, Winifred, and Lydia!

Squire Bramble was much put out by this. He called Clinker peremptorily from the pulpit and bade him choose between working for his acknowledged master or in the vineyards of religion. Clinker replied with no little spirit, defending his course in the jargon of the dissenting ministry, babbling bravely of "the light"; but the Squire, without undue severity, cautioned him that his light was a vapor that would lead to madness, if it had not done so already. In the end Clinker promised to forsake the business of public preaching while in the Squire's service, but he intimated frankly that he could not renounce his religious convictions, which the Squire had no desire that he should do. So this matter was amicably adjusted, but not without protests on the part of the women in the family. Tabitha, as usual, expressed hers loudly, but with much less spitefulness than had been her wont in discussions of domestic affairs, for it was palpable that she had been deeply impressed by Clinker's eloquence, and, indeed, she was ever thereafter of an easier disposition, for which Bramble candidly blessed Methodism.

Lydia and Winifred kept their protests to themselves, save as they wrote to their friends about the extraordinary young man; and, so far as Winifred was concerned, she came not only to piety through Clinker, but to a knowledge of love, for her heart went out to him so fully that only when handsomer men were about was she in any danger of throwing him over. Not that they were engaged; their relations were not formally acknowledged, being rather those of spiritual adviser and devotee; but they understood each other, nevertheless, and Winifred really looked forward to becoming Mrs. Clinker.

This religious affair was the first event in the epistolary accounts of Clinker's adventures; and the second was his arrest for robbery. Little need be made of that matter here, for Clinker was innocent, as was established absolutely when the Squire confronted his servant with the victim of the robbery; but the young man's behavior under accusation was extraordinary. He would not say that he was innocent. "God forbid that I should call myself innocent," said he, "while my conscience is burdened with sin." This sort of remark, though coupled with plain denial of knowledge of the robbery, convinced the magistrate that he was a rogue, and Clinker had to spend some days in prison, where he preached so energetically that the keepers complained because the tap-room had no customers.

As soon as Clinker was set free the Squire's party set out northward. They often left the beaten path to see interesting villages or to visit briefly with acquaintances of Bramble's, and they spent a week or more in such places as York, Durham, and Scarborough. The Squire's health improved noticeably on this journey, although he condemned all the waters he tried at one resort and another. He confessed, however, that the waters of Scarborough agreed with him, meaning the surf of the North Sea, in which he had great delight in bathing; and he would have lingered there indefinitely but for an exasperating blunder on the part of Clinker. One day Bramble had gone some distance from his bathing-machine, and the waves were buffeting him merrily when Clinker, who waited on the beach, saw his master far out and imagined that he was in peril. The faithful fellow immediately waded in, all dressed as he was, grabbed his master by the ear and dragged him to dry land, perfectly naked. So strenuous was Clinker's exertion that Bramble, taken quite by surprise, could by no means free himself until his footing was secure in the sand, although his ear nearly came off with the force of his servant's tugging; but when he was free he cuffed the well-meaning man severely and then pranced shamefacedly back into the sea, whence he entered his machine by the outward end and donned his clothes.

The Squire was ever punctilious in matters of dress and demeanor, and the episode mortified him unspeakably. Nevertheless, while he was dressing, and therefore in the height of his resentment, he was so magnanimous as to reflect that his man meant well; had, indeed, put himself to some measure of peril from motives of loyalty; wherefore, when he emerged from the machine, Bramble apologized for striking Clinker and made amends quite as sincerely as if the fellow had been a gentleman. But the episode made so much talk in a place where everything ludicrous is made much of that the Squire could not endure to observe himself pointed at as the man who was pulled naked from the water, and he gave the order for a resumption of the journey.

When they were near the border of Scotland the party fell in with another traveler who, all agreed, was quite the most original specimen ever encountered. He was Lieutenant Obadiah Lismahago, a Scotchman who had served many years in the British army, and who had now retired on half pay. His service had been mainly in America, where he suffered not only captivity but scalping at the hands of the red savages who inhabit that country. Having survived certain horrible tortures they prepared for him, he was deemed worthy to be the spouse of a chief's daughter, whose betrothed had been killed in battle, and Lismahago married her. By the time her father died he had obtained such a hold on the Indians that they made him their chief, and he had dwelt with them many years as their ruler.

His experiences made Lismahago an interesting companion on a portion of the journey in which he accompanied the party, but he was more talkative on other topics, and he was well enough informed to speak authoritatively on any subject that came to hand. Moreover, he was the most disputatious person imaginable. It mattered not what ground the Squire took on any subject, Lismahago opposed him, and argued with so much sophistication that Bramble was usually worsted. Naturally enough, the Squire's temper was ruffled somewhat at this continual flouting of his opinions, and Lismahago's voice not infrequently took on a rasping pitch; but it was quite remarkable to Jery, who recorded many of their debates, that as Lismahago grew stormy Squire Bramble cooled, and *vice versa*, whereby it fell that never once did the two gentlemen really fall out. Aunt Tabitha found in the war-scarred lieutenant another target for her amorous arrows, and persisted in making up to him as long as he was with them, much to the quiet amusement of the rest of the party; but the old warrior had had similar experiences. He was not to be caught so readily, and when he turned aside to pursue his own journey to the west of Scotland he had not been civil enough to Tabitha to give even her hopeful heart any ground for encouragement.

This was by no means the last they saw of Lismahago. After touring exhaustively and delightedly through Scotland the Squire led his party back to England by way of Northumberland, and there the lieutenant was encountered again. He was now traveling southward, having been disappointed with his visit to his native heath. It was his intention to go to Bristol and there embark for America, to rejoin his squaw and pass the remainder of his days among the savages. He had no sooner reappeared than Tabitha again set her cap for him, and it occurred to both the Squire and Jery that it might not be a bad plan to help the old maid's suit. Sure it was that she never would cease to worry mankind unless some kind man would take her. If she were once married the Squire would be free of his greatest torment, not excepting the gout; and Lismahago, with all his contrariety, was amusing when one did not have too much of him. "If he were settled in the neighborhood," reasoned the Squire, "I could enjoy his conversation when I wanted it, and not have to put up with it when it irritated me." Accordingly, Lismahago was persuaded to travel leisurely with the Squire's party, which he did willingly enough, as there was nothing to induce him to hurry.

Squire Bramble nearly lost his life, some time after this, while his coach was fording a small stream. A heavy rain had fallen the day before, and, a dam bursting inopportunely, the vehicle was overturned in the flood. Jery, Lismahago, and Clinker were riding ahead. They turned at hearing smothered cries of distress and sped back to the rescue. The gentlemen pulled the ladies to shore, choking and drenched. Clinker, of course, gave his attention to his master, who was already unconscious in the bottom of the submerged coach. By the exercise of astonishing strength, Clinker dragged the Squire from the wreck and laid him, apparently drowned, on the bank. By dint of further exertions the Squire was restored to life, and all the victims were conveyed to a mean little tavern in the vicinity. There Bramble was quite overcome with his servant's loyalty and offered him his purse, in which were a hundred guineas. What did the servant do but decline the reward! With genuine tears in his eyes, he protested that his only adequate reward was the continued existence of his master; and he was so positively obdurate in the matter that the Squire was constrained to withdraw the purse, but he called the others to witness that he then and there settled one hundred and fifty pounds a year on Clinker for life. The young fellow was so agitated that he could not express his gratitude, and begged leave to retire for the purpose of praying.

During his absence for this worthy purpose, a Mr. Dennison, who lived in the neighborhood, and who had heard of the accident, came to offer his house for the use of the travelers. Bramble immediately recognized him as an old friend whom he had not seen for more than a score of years. He challenged Mr. Dennison to make the recognition mutual and name him. "Indeed!" cried Mr. Dennison, "I believe you are Matthew Lloyd, of Glamorganshire." At this moment Clinker returned.

"Well remembered!" said the Squire; "I am truly Matthew Lloyd, of Glamorganshire."

Clinker no sooner heard this than he began to caper like mad. "Oh, Lord!" he cried, "I shall lose my senses!" And, being peevishly advised that they seemed already to be lost, Humphry took from his bosom a paper, written by the Squire in his young manhood, and other tokens that proved Clinker to be his natural son. Humphry's mother had made much endeavor to find his father, whom she knew as Lloyd, but certain reasons of family and property had made it advisable for Matthew to change his name to Bramble, so she never had found trace of him, and the son had grown up in unmerited poverty.

The Squire generously recognized his son, and Jery with equal magnanimity took his hand as his cousin. The women of the party were delighted, though Winifred began to have her fears. It was hardly thinkable that the son of the Squire, who was no longer regarded as a servant, would remember his passion for her. But Winifred distrusted her lover without good cause; and although the Squire would have liked to see his son choose his wife from a higher station, events occurred almost immediately that softened his heart and made him uncommonly sympathetic with all lovers. For it proved that Mr. Dennison's son was none other than the mysterious Wilson who had snared and still kept Lydia's heart. The young man had been pressed by his parents to make a match distasteful to him. Rather than yield, he left home and joined a company of players. When the lady his parents wished him to marry chose another suitor of her own motion, he returned and announced his passion for the niece of Squire Bramble. His parents were favorably inclined and bade him make his suit under his proper name. He had gone to London, hoping to find the Squire and his family, but they had already departed. Then the young man was taken ill and had but just recovered.

Now that "Wilson" and Lydia were met again, nothing

would do but they must be married without further delay, and the contracts were drawn with great amicability on both sides. Under the influence of so much tenderness, that scarred veteran of the wars, Lismahago, was brought to a proposal to Tabitha, and she accepted him with so much promptness that the banns for both marriages were published at the same time. And Clinker, also unable to withstand the current of the time, deferentially made it known to the Squire that he would like to marry Winifred. The Squire was quite unable to deny his son, and so three banns were published, and in due course three weddings occurred on the same day. As Tabitha expressed it in a letter to her *locum tenens* at Brambleton Hall—for the weddings occurred in Mr. Dennison's parish—"Heaven, for wise purposes, hath ordained that I should change my name and citation in life, so that I am not to be considered any more as manager of my brother's family." And Winifred, addressing her fellow-servant, wrote: "Providinch hath bin pleased to make great halteration in the pasture of our affairs. We were yesterday made three kiple chined by the grease of God in the holy bands of mattermoney; and I now subscrive myself Lloyd at your sarvice." For Clinker had abandoned the name of the man to whom he had been apprentice and taken that formerly borne by his father.

ÉMILE SOUVESTRE

(France, 1806–1854)

CONFESSIONS OF A WORKINGMAN (1851)

(Confessions d'un Ouvrier)

The high esteem of Émile Souvestre among his countrymen is due less to his greatness as a literary artist than to his profound sympathy with the proletariat and the *bourgeoisie*. He was ever conscious that they were the true backbone of French greatness. To teach them the lessons of morality, right living, and aspiration; to enforce the value of education as a means of material and moral betterment, it is these things which peculiarly distinguish him among French litterateurs. It was lifting the nation from the bottom and not from the top that animated his ideal, and nowhere has he displayed this motive better than in his *Confessions d'un Ouvrier*.

 WAS a true child of the faubourg, and my father, a mason by trade, could have earned a good living, saved money indeed, but for his too frequent indulgence in the pleasures of the wine-shop. Though I spent so much of my childhood in the streets, I always recoiled from the vices of the gamin. It was my nature to be indomitably truthful and honest, less perhaps from moral sense than because somehow it belonged to my temperament. Many a time was I severely beaten by other boys on this account; but buffetings only impressed the lesson more deeply, like hammer-blows on a nail. At ten years old I never had attended school, partly from the indifference of my parents, partly from the advice of the best friend of our family, Maurice Mauricet, a master of the mason's craft, but with all his good sense inimical to the printed letter.

"It is neither the pen nor the inkstand," he was wont to say; "it is the trowel and the mortar-bed that make the good workman."

But Mauricet lost a good contract by his ignorance of writing, and we were wont to share in the pleasure of having a little hunchback read the war-bulletins. So my mother shrewdly reasoned that, after all, a little education was worth while, and I was placed at school, acquiring the arts of reading, writing, and arithmetic, with a little cross of honor for my industry.

My father's death, through falling from a scaffold, made it necessary for me to go early to work, and by Mauricet's assistance I became a mason's helper. I labored zealously, and became such a friend of the journeymen in the yard that they took pleasure in teaching me every nice point in the craft. I began to feel what Mauricet said:

"The true workman regards not alone his account at the banker's. He loves the work of his hands; it is his glory. I never have placed the capstone on a gable without feeling 'something.' . . . Put heart into the handle of your trowel. It's only this that can make the master journeyman."

At an earlier age than common I became a journeyman. Inflated with pride, I celebrated the occasion after the first payday, and spent at the wine-shop the wages of a fortnight. When I returned to work, sullen, mortified, and with an aching brain, the others all laughed, except Mauricet. He walked home with me, and pointed out a certain building, which had a high chimney.

"It was there your father was killed," he said abruptly. "The scaffold was all right, but—but his legs were unsteady, his eyes blurred. When you wish to resume your life of yesterday, Peter Henry, look at it first from this side, and the wine you drink will taste of blood."

In thirty-three years I never have forgotten the promise I then made to myself.

Since making journeyman's wages I had established a comfortable home for my dear mother. It came as a tremendous shock, when, her eyes beginning to fail, the examination by an oculist gave the edict that she would become incurably blind. But there was hope of delaying the evil if Mother Madeleine could live in the fresh air of the country. So I managed to have her placed with a worthy countrywoman, Mother Riviou, who worked a little land near Soujumeau. Never a braver creature ate the bread of the good God, and she cheerfully consented to make my mother as happy as possible, while I remained lonely in the city, and had to live at a lodging-house, saving every sou.

In the common chamber where I slept were two among others, Faramount, a locksmith, and Marcette, a mason. The latter had for years been investing his earnings in land, and with the last payment, then due, he was on the eve of going to the pleasures of the green earth. Before retiring he showed me the bag of francs, and during the night I saw and recognized Faramount in a half-sleepy way, as he began fumbling under old Marcette's pillow. When the robbery was discovered I told what I remembered, and Faramount explained it away as a joke, but he bent on me an eye of deadly hate. Thenceforth I had a bitter enemy.

The first visit I made to my dear mother had a pleasing introduction. As I approached the house I heard an old roundel, which my mother was used to sing, in a charming voice. Then I saw a comely, bright-faced girl hanging clothes on the line. She looked up laughingly and said:

"You are Peter Henry, Mère Madeleine's son." "You are Geneviève," I said, for I had heard of the girl's goodness to my mother.

Thus began an acquaintance that was to sweeten my whole life. My mother had recovered her spirits and would not admit, in her gaiety of heart, that she was blind. They had so arranged a thick cord with a leading-string and knots, that Mère Madeleine could move with perfect ease about the house. Geneviève outdid her mistress in devotion to their lodger, whom many would have found troublesome.

I could hardly express my happiness when I returned to Paris. But I was soon to feel the stroke of bitter hate. I was working one day on a suspended scaffold, when just above me, peering through the joists, looked the fiendish face of Faramount, who had been employed to set some ironwork there. There was no one about, and quick as a flash he unknotted a rope, the planks gave way, and I was precipitated forty feet on a mass of rubbish below. There was only my word to prove the crime, and the would-be murderer escaped punishment. But God lives. A few months afterward he was clubbed to death by an accomplice in a robbery, in the desire to secure the entire booty. I was in hospital two months before I recovered from broken bones and could return to work. But my restiveness and discontent were put to shame by the saintlike cheerfulness and optimism of a paralyzed cripple on an adjoining cot, who never could cease praising *le bon Dieu* for His goodness. Mauricet, who came to know him from his visits to me, was wont to say:

"Such men ought to be placed on the top of a column, to be seen by everybody. When one looks at them it makes him ashamed of being happy, and that gives the wish to merit it."

When I returned to the trowel I was apathetic, and it was as if water had been mixed with my blood. It remained for an instructive episode to inject life into my spirit. Mauricet took me one day to the dwelling of a great contractor, for some instruction which was to be put in writing. I entered the most magnificently furnished house I ever had seen or dreamed of. Hung among the splendid paintings was an ugly little portrait of a workman in his blouse, holding a pipe and a compass.

"That's the gentleman," said Mauricet, "and he is not ashamed of it either."

Then my spirit rose in repining and I broke out in bitter words: "Why have you not, friend Mauricet, a mansion as well as he who dwells here? Are you less meritorious, less brave? If he has succeeded better than you, is it not all a stupid story of chance?" I ended my diatribe with: "Why is it that these carpets, these silks, these velvets belong to him rather than to us?"

"Because I have earned them," interrupted a blunt voice from behind.

It was a little gray man with a commanding face, who bade us accompany him to his office. This was a room filled with colored designs of buildings, models, and instruments of scientific construction. He handed me a plan.

"That building," said he, "is to be modified by a contraction of three meters without lessening the number of windows, and retaining the staircase. Make me a colored sketch."

I said I couldn't design.

"Then examine and verify this estimate. There are three hundred and twelve articles to discuss."

I responded that I lacked information about prices and couldn't name the measurements.

"Then tell me the formalities to be gone through for the three houses I have in hand now."

"I am not a lawyer," said I.

So he went on to confound me. The matters he had mentioned were only a few of the things that a great contractor needed to know.

"Finally," said he, "as you know nothing, except what a thousand other journeymen know, you are only like them, good to handle the trowel and the hammer. If you wish society to treat you like me, do as I have done. Work all day, study at night, watch everywhere for instruction, as a merchant watches for profit. When you know things and men, should you still live in an attic, come and complain. I will listen. Remember," he said in parting, with a return of good nature, "comrade, don't fume against those that are higher than you; rather climb a rope to join them. If I can ever aid you, I will lend you the first bit of hemp."

This momentous talk rearoused all my ambition. I went to the great man again, and he sent me to a surveyor who gave lessons in geometry and drawing, where I was taught gratuitously.

My mother had been losing strength, and we all knew her end was near at hand. I had been sent for, and I overheard her broken tones talking with Geneviève:

"Why don't you wish to marry him?"

"It is not for me or you to decide," said the embarrassed girl; "he ought to choose according to his taste and will."

"I waited yet for this joy upon earth," was the plaintive answer.

I sprang to the bedside and said: "You shall have it, for your choice is my choice." So we were betrothed. As I had dreamed, so I found Geneviève after marriage the most loving, faithful, and wisest of wives. Mauricet had already gone into business for himself in taking small contracts, and I followed his example. I was without capital, but obtained credit, as my exactitude and activity inspired confidence.

My wife's nephew, Robert, of whom she was fond, though

he was a worthless scapegrace, was a thorn in the flesh. During my absence in Burgundy to bid on a contract, he came to her with a terrible story that he had laid himself open to prosecution for perjury. He worked so on her fears that she gave him all the money I had saved to insure him against the galleys. We learned afterward that this was all a conspiracy of robbery, but it was too late. It prevented me from paying certain notes then coming due, except by sacrificing all my immediate prospects, and thus I was forced to join again the great regiment of the needy.

By and by Mauricet returned to Paris on business, told me he had been very successful, and insisted on lending me five hundred francs, which enabled me to undertake a small but profitable subcontract. Bad luck was still armed against me; for a lawsuit, involving the chief contractor, postponed my hopes, and I was put to all sorts of expedients to keep bread in the cupboard. To sum up our misery, our darling child died. Geneviève and I were benumbed with grief. But the trouble of another seemed to arouse me from the paralysis of my own. One night Mauricet arrived suddenly in Paris. His face was clouded and haggard, for he was in great financial distress. He asked me to go over his papers and memoranda, and a careful study of these proved that his liabilities were double his assets. There was a deficit of thirty-three thousand francs, which implied ruin. That night poor Mauricet left the house with so wild a look on his face that my wife and I followed him. He went to the Pont du Châtelet, and we saw him take off his coat, his lips murmuring as with a prayer, while the river rushed and swirled below. I seized him by the middle and barely held him from the fatal leap. Then Geneviève clasped him round the neck and pleaded with him to think of wife and children. The desperate man was melted, and broke into sobs. He was saved.

He then told us all; he had been crazed for a week. I understood exactly how it came about. His inability to keep accounts, as he was carried away by the current of a big business, had left him unwarned of breakers ahead, and open to the tricks of swindlers. He was wrecked before he suspected danger. I could do for a friend what I could not do for myself. I went to the millionaire contractor, whose enterprise appeared to embrace all France, told him about Mauricet, and put the papers in his hands. When he had examined these he pronounced my calculations correct.

"I will take charge of the affair," he said, with gruff kindness. "Tell Mauricet to come and see me. He is a brave man, and we will find him some employment that will suit him."

It behooved me to liquidate my own affairs after the arranging of the Mauricet affair. When the lawsuit was ended it left me an honest man, with all my debts paid to the last sou, but penniless. It happened then that an architect under whom I had worked proposed that I should settle at Montmorency, where he was superintending important enterprises, as master mason. There was only one mason there, and he a surly brute, employed because there was no other.

"It is better," said he, "to be a tree among bushes than a bush in the great forest."

We took humble quarters in Montmorency, and the very first night I had to go to the baker's shop, which proved to be a sort of rendezvous of working people. There I heard a big, angry-looking man declaiming.

"He names himself Peter Henry, called the Conscientious," the fellow bawled; "but you may wring my neck if I don't change his name into that of the Famished."

I announced myself, and after a brief altercation in which Jean Ferou heaped up invective, there was a personal encounter wherein I got the worst of it, owing to tripping over the doorsill. That night my heart full of rancor vented itself in vengeful dreams, but these were dispelled by a clangorous alarm of fire. As I ran into the street they told me it was at Jean Ferou's yard. The flames were rapidly spreading, the house itself blazing. The owner, in a drunken stupor, had locked himself in. At last the wretched man himself appeared at a window shrieking for help. As no ladder could be found, I climbed to the cornice of the first story by aid of a shutter, and the mason, sliding down over my body, reached safety. When he recognized me he could only stammer out some incoherent and shamefaced words. The result was that the townspeople gave me their cordial esteem, and Jean Ferou, whose cruelty to his family had made him unpopular, was tabooed more and more till after two years he suddenly left the country.   The turning-point had come.   Abundance of profitable work flowed in on me, and God gave us two beautiful children to reconcile us to the loss of the first.   The money came to my box of itself, and good luck shone on us like a cloudless sun.

Mauricet, who had become prosperous again as an overseer of mason work for the great contractor, came to see us and asked to be godfather to our little new-born girl.   A wealthy neighbor had taken a great fancy to us all and had offered to be godmother.   The graciousness with which she consented to share the function with a working mason, when we told her how dear Mauricet was to us, furnished the finest proof of the real great lady, whom money and social position could not spoil.   Mauricet, too, bore himself with the manners of a prefect, and, when he went away, said with tears in his honest eyes:

"Should I live a thousand years, I could never forget this hour.   You have not been ashamed of your old comrade, and have risked for him the loss of a rich patronage.   It was brave, it was just.   God will recompense you."

Mademoiselle Lefort was, indeed, very fond of our little Marianne, and her daughter, Caroline, nearly the same age, was devoted to her.   Thus our little girl enjoyed many advantages of education and training above her station.   Her godmother would have taken her altogether as an adopted child, but to this our hearts would not consent, for we never would have Marianne grow ashamed of us.

As years went on, a painful experience came to checker my happiness.   My patron, Monsieur Dupré, who had induced me to settle at Montmorency, had always been very good and helpful to me.   Unhappily, he was easily susceptible to pleasure and extravagance, and finally he became badly entangled in his affairs.   His credit suffered first, then his reputation.   A Parisian company had placed under his charge an extensive brickyard and quarries, the business of which he greatly developed, on paper at least.   But the profits were far from corresponding.   It was thought that an oversight of the operating details was indispensable, and M. Dupré consented, with a little hesitation, to my selection for this duty.   Cursory examination showed workings in good shape, splendid machinery, and a first-rate working force. But I probed more deeply, and unmasked a good deal of embezzlement, amounting to twenty thousand francs. I noticed M. Dupré's disturbed face, when I told him; and wondered when he asked me to keep it secret. A quick suspicion and I recoiled, while he carried his hand to his forehead with a gesture of despair.

"Don't be indiscreet," the wretched man begged, "and in a few weeks I will make good the loss."

I told him I could not ignore the trust placed in me. I would resign my place as overseer from that day. If by my lending him twelve thousand francs, which would pauperize me, he could make up the rest, the loan was at his service. At last he refused; "for," said he, "I should ruin you without saving myself. You do not know all."

It was a sad farewell, for I could guess the consequences. I went to Burgundy, where a grand opportunity had been offered me, but I was none the less shocked when the man whom I had wished to save had, at the thought of public dishonor, killed himself.

Many years have passed since then, and affairs have gone with me very prosperously. Geneviève and I are growing old, to be sure. But life resembles a ball; when one is too old to dance he looks at the others, and their joy makes his heart laugh. We find ample consolation in the pleasures of the young people. I sometimes asked myself, in my unhappy hours of old: "What profit comes in living rightly?" Now there is one which I know —that is, the power of growing old with impunity. Age thus becomes a certificate of honor. My son Jacques is the first workman of the country, a true leader of men and organizer of enterprise. Our Marianne is a charming good girl, and I see in her the youth of her dear mother. What more could a man desire? God has been very good to me.

FRIEDRICH SPIELHAGEN

(Germany, 1829)

HAMMER AND ANVIL (1869)

The idea of writing this novel was suggested by Goethe's strange lines:

*Du must
Leiden oder triumphieren,
Hammer oder Amboss sein.*
("Thou must do wrong or suffer wrong,
The hammer or the anvil be.")

For this ferocious individualism the author would substitute "hammer and anvil," mutual solidarity in good and in evil, in joy and in pain.

THE entire destiny of my life, with its troubles and their compensations, was influenced by my comradeship with Arthur von Zehren at the gymnasium. This dainty, aristocratic lad, the son of the Steuerrath von Zehren, was so charming in all his ways, that I, George Hartwig, the son of a subordinate official of the Customs, worshiped him as a superior being, and felt it an honor to be asked to lend him my pocket-money, fishing-rods, and other such things, although I knew the dear fellow would be sure to forget to return them. When, therefore, he invited me to play truant in his company and have a sail on the steamboat of his uncle, Commerzienrath Streber, I was flattered. Yet I was not without dreadful misgivings. What would my father, a parent of the old Roman type, who considered the slightest infraction of domestic discipline a crime, say when he heard of this bold defiance of the authority of Professor Lederer, Director and Ordinarius of the Gymnasium? Even on board the stately vessel I was not happy.

There were two very pretty and very young ladies among the guests, and Arthur had promised that one of them, whom I had lately kissed at forfeits, should be left in my charge. But there the coxcomb was, flirting with both of them, and never thinking of introducing me to his friends. I sat down in a remote corner, very melancholy, and, after a time, very hungry. We had just rounded one of the long headlands that run out from this part of the Baltic coast, when I saw a cottage that recalled a flood of pleasant memories. This was the cottage of old Pinnow, the blacksmith, the most remarkable person of my acquaintance, father of my stanch friend, Klaus Pinnow, whom I had not seen for more than four years as he had been away learning the trade of locksmith.

Just then a hatchway rose, and to my surprise I recognized the face of honest Klaus, all grimy with coal-dust. While we were giving each other a joyous greeting, a lovely little girl of eight came out of the deck-cabin, but at sight of the black face she vanished in terror. This was Hermine, the commerzien-rath's only child. It was some hours before Arthur remembered me, fortunately in time, however, to enable me to take part in the banquet given by his uncle. The feast was protracted, and I was not the only one that drank to excess; but I blush even now at the many ridiculous things I was guilty of on that occasion. Just as Arthur and I were having a tipsy quarrel on our return, which was about to end in violence, I noticed on the coast of the island we were nearing an old and picturesque ruin—all that remained of Zehrenburg, the ancestral seat of the Zehren family, which in former times had enjoyed large possessions on the island. I little thought how soon I was to see it again.

After the return of the party to Uselin, I found Professor Lederer with my father. The contemptuous laugh into which I broke when the Professor accused me of corrupting "the mis-guided boy" Arthur—for I knew "the misguided boy" better than he—aroused my father's indignation to fury. In a voice quivering with passion, he said:

"You will instantly ask pardon of your teacher for this additional insolence."

"I will not," I replied.

"Instantly!" thundered my father.

For the second and third time I repeated my refusal.

"Begone!" he said, slowly and firmly. "Leave my house forever!"

I was about to say something, perhaps to ask pardon, but my heart was like a stone in my breast, my teeth were clenched like a vise; I could not speak. I moved silently toward the door. The Professor hurried after me and seized my arm, no doubt with the kindliest intentions. But I regarded him as the cause of my disgrace, shook him off roughly, and ran into the street.

I was hastening across the heath to Pinnow's cottage, when I met on the way Klaus and pretty Christel Mowe, a waif from a shipwreck, who had been adopted by his father. I had interrupted a tender scene; they were evidently lovers. Klaus was greatly affected by my story, and did his best to persuade me to return to my father and ask forgiveness. Seeing I was not to be moved, he went to the town, and I accompanied Christel to the cottage. I was surprised at the agitation of the usually merry creature, especially when she burst into tears and said I must not go with her to *his* house, for *he* would certainly not lodge me.

I knew the blacksmith had a shady reputation; still we had always been good friends, particularly when I was in funds and could pay extravagantly for the loan of a boat or a gun. But he refused me admission, and when I tried to enter he threw himself upon me with a fury that rendered all my strength useless. I was quickly on the floor, and his grip of iron was on my throat.

"For shame, old man!" cried a sonorous voice, "he has not deserved that of you," and a pair of strong arms tore the smith from me.

I rose and confronted my deliverer. After a supper calculated to tempt a far more fastidious appetite than mine, I related all my recent adventures to this mysterious stranger, who gave me a warm invitation to stay with him until I was reconciled with my father. Before I could answer, he left the room with Pinnow. Some words of a very vehement dialogue reached me from outside.

"I will have it so!" said the stranger.

"And I say no!" retorted the smith. "It is my affair."

"And mine as well."

I heard a rustling in the room, and turned round. It was Christel.

"Don't go with them," she said, "and go away from here."

"But, Christel, why not? Who is the gentleman?"

"I dare not tell you. You will know soon enough, if you go. But don't go."

The girl's warning produced on me the exactly opposite effect of that intended. Besides, my new acquaintance had already acquired a strange power over me. Soon Pinnow and I were with him in a boat. A storm arose, and my conduct met with his approval. When, in answer to his question, I told him I was nineteen, he said:

"You are a man."

I had never felt prouder in my life. After landing, he led me by the hand to a mass of buildings surrounded by a grove of immense trees.

"Where are we?" I said, on entering the hall.

"At Zehrendorf," he answered, "the house of Malte von Zehren, whom men call 'The Wild.' Do you regret having come with me?"

"That I do not," I replied.

When I awoke next morning in a magnificent but sadly dilapidated apartment, my first thought was: where am I? my second: what is to become of me? Then I found myself looking with a sort of superstitious reliance to a man whom I had just learned to know. But "The Wild Zehren" had held a place in my imagination since boyhood, with Rinaldo Rinaldini and Karl Moor, and I had envied Arthur the possession of such a romantic uncle. I had heard, too, of his daughter, Constance, who was said to be very beautiful but of somewhat dubious morals. While rambling about the grounds I met her, a charming, gipsy-like brunette, who told me she had been ordered by her father to take charge of me. She was very frank about herself. The Wild Zehren had met her mother in Spain, had carried her off, had been intercepted by her brother, whom he had slain, and had then refused to marry her. She had pined away at Zehrendorf, and, when Constance was three years old, had committed suicide.

Constance said I must always stay with her, and be her faithful George, and slay the dragons for her sake. And indeed, after this conversation the thought of going away now fell heavy

on my heart. And then came other thoughts: the strange connection between the nobleman and the smith, Christel's warning, the night sail in the terrible storm, the solitary situation of
the place, upon a promontory extending far into the sea. I had
often heard my father speak of the profits made by smugglers
along this coast. Was this the solution of the mystery? Oh,
no, such doings are for the rabble. A Pinnow—yes; but a Von
Zehren—impossible!

A few nights afterward, while my host was playing faro with
a few gentlemen of the neighborhood, I went into the park.
Suddenly I heard someone breaking through the paling at a
short distance from the windows of Constance's chamber. I
ran to seize the intruder, but I had hardly cleared the rails when
I saw a rider galloping madly across the open. Who could it
be? Doubtless someone who had been attracted by the light
from her windows, and not to-night for the first time. I had
too much respect for her to believe that it was a favored lover;
but my former happiness had vanished.

So far, I could see nothing calculated to confirm the suspicions
I had heard of Von Zehren's occupation. To be sure, the people
on the estate looked as if they were not accustomed to honest
industry. One of them especially—Jock, the Herr's confidential
man—had villainy written on every line of his countenance.
But the cotters on the estates around were a rough, uncouth set
also, and every one of them had the air of a pirate. Even if
Von Zehren were as bad as reported, his neighbors were no better.
These high-born gentlemen made no scruple of filling their
cellars with wine they knew to be smuggled. After all, I was
bound to him by the firmest ties of gratitude, and, even if he were
a smuggler, I was determined to stick to him. But first I would
have the truth from his own lips. Yes, every rumor about him
was based on fact, and the reasons he gave for his present mode
of life had a powerful influence on my youthful imagination.
The Lords of Zehren had levied sound dues for centuries. Had
their rights ceased with their fallen grandeur? "Does my right
to levy tolls and taxes in a different form lapse," he said, "because every tree in yonder forests now belongs to that plebeian
brother-in-law of mine, your Crœsus, the commerzienrath, well-
named Streber [Striver]? I see that stockfish still, distorting

his crooked mouth as he counted down the pittance on the table and crammed the contract into his pocket." He also told me tales of many incidents in the history of the great house, and of their feuds with my native town, that kindled my fancy. This was truly a kingly man, and the idea of the foxy-faced commerzienrath being one day lord here in his stead thrilled me with anger.

The next day, as I was strolling along the shore, the broad, honest face of Klaus stood before me. He was on a visit, with his father and Christel, to his Aunt Julchen at Zanowitz, and was determined not to leave without seeing me. The news he brought was not comforting. Everyone in my native town considered me a castaway, leading the most shameless life with a degraded nobleman. Worse than all, I was supposed to be the lover of Constance, about whom things were said by my friend Arthur that it was impossible to repeat. Klaus was terrified at the effect his account had upon me. I swore that I renounced forever that treacherous friend and would be most bitterly avenged upon him. The next morning I called at Aunt Julchen's cottage to bid Klaus good-by; for he was to pass two years in the commerzienrath's workshop in Berlin. I witnessed a tearful parting between him and his sweetheart.

I had just crossed the summit of the highest dune on my return, when, to my surprise, I saw Christel crouching in a little hollow. The secret she revealed to me when I drew close to her showed that Herr von Zehren was on the brink of destruction. She had awakened at daybreak and heard voices in the kitchen. She listened. The speakers were the blacksmith, Jock, and Customs-Inspector Blanck. What she heard left no doubt that Von Zehren was betrayed.

"He has been so good to me," said the young girl. "He has left me in peace ever since the Herr swore he would shoot him if he ill-treated me. But afterward, he has sworn frequently that he would bring the Herr to the gallows."

I knew that Von Zehren was absent; so I hurried to the house of his loyal and bibulous friend, Herr von Trantow, and related to him everything.

"I know you deeply respect and love the Fraulein von Zehren," I said. "It was only yesterday her father told me how your ancestor and namesake had rescued him, a prisoner in Uselin, after a message brought by a faithful squire. Well, now, I am the faithful squire, and you and I will cut him out as they cut out the Malte von Zehren of five centuries ago."

"That we will!" he cried. "If they shut him up, we will blow up the prison."

"No," I answered, smiling, "we must get to him before anything happens; we must frustrate the plan founded on Pinnow's and Jock's villainous treachery."

Ah, but the question was, where to find him. We decided to visit Constance, who might have some information. As we approached the castle we saw a carriage driven from it with such speed that in a few minutes it vanished in the mist. At the gate we found Christian, an old retainer, lying on the ground, with blood trickling from his forehead. When we had revived him, he told us he had tried to stop the flight of Constance with her seducer, the young Prince of Prora, who had struck him with the butt of his whip as he was trying to shut the gate.

I rushed into the house. The doors were all standing open, even that of Von Zehren's bedroom. Within it was the housekeeper, old Pahlen, a sinister hag whom I had always distrusted and detested. She was trying to force the lock of the escritoire with a hatchet and a crowbar. As I dragged her back, she glared at me with impotent rage.

"Where has she gone?" I thundered.

"Now he begins," she screeched. "Didn't they make a fine fool of you, you blockhead? You thought you were her man, while the other one was with her every night. Oh, you donkey! How often we have laughed together at your stupidity!" and she burst into hideous laughter.

After driving the creature from the house, I charged Hanne, the only other male servant left, and whom I knew to be honest, to take care of Christian, unchain the dogs, and on no pretext to admit the old hag, from whom I expected mischief.

To relate the motives and events that led me for a time afterward to believe in the loyalty of Pinnow and Jock, a belief that had fatal consequences, would take up too much space. For the same reason I cannot enter into the conflict between Von Zehren's vessel laden with a priceless cargo of dutiable goods from China, and the government revenue cutter. I must content myself with saying that the incidents of that encounter were most surprising and sensational. At last the smuggler craft reached the shore unmolested, and Von Zehren with eleven carriers was at hand to bear away the heavy packs made up for their convenience. But there was a twelfth pack, which would have to be left behind if there was no one to attend to it. I volunteered. As I was bearing it on my shoulders from the ship, a boisterous laugh resounded behind me. It came from Pinnow. Then it flashed upon me, "He is a traitor, after all!" and I said to myself, as I closed the file headed by Von Zehren and Jock: "Now it will soon be decided."

We had passed the dunes and struck across the marshy heath, when my ear plainly caught a clicking sound like the cocking of a gun. I ran to the head of the file and touched Von Zehren on the shoulder.

"We are pursued!" I whispered.

"Nonsense!"

"Halt!" cried a powerful voice behind us.

"Forward!" commanded our leader

Then a dozen bullets whistled over our heads. In an instant the whole party threw down their packs and scattered. The next moment Herr von Zehren and I were alone. Behind us we heard the ring of iron ramrods in the barrels. Our pursuers were reloading.

"There must have been treachery at work," said my companion.

"Yes, Pinnow and Jock."

"I see. They were the very ones that advised this route."

The darkness was now intense, and it began raining. In spite of my protests, he insisted on going back to Zehrendorf. We had taken a few steps in that direction when we saw flames that towered above the gigantic trees. The castle was on fire.

"That is smoking the old fox out of his den with a vengeance," he said, with a hideous laugh.

But I knew it was not our pursuers who had done this. I recalled the threats of old Pahlen and certain words about "the red cock crowing from the roof." But the hunt was up again, and we were begirt on all sides.

"Into the morass," whispered Von Zehren.

We leaped among the tall rushes that bordered it, and at the same time three men in ambush sprang upon us. One of them was Jock.

"Dog!" hissed my companion. He raised his pistol, and long Jock fell to the ground a dead man.

I fired also, and another sank down with a loud cry, not dangerously wounded, I am glad to say. The third took to his heels. I never have been able to understand how an old man like Von Zehren, wounded, too, as I discovered, was able to go through the fearsome adventures that taxed even my youthful strength. At last we came to the dunes. Then he commanded me to shift for myself, for he felt it was impossible for him to go farther. I answered that I should stay with him to the end. To obey such a command was to cover myself with disgrace.

"Well," said he, "get me a draught of water from a spring I know to be in yonder ravine. It will keep me from fainting. Make haste."

I set off at a run. When I returned with the water, all was over, he must have died instantly. The Wild von Zehren knew where a bullet must strike, if the wound was to be mortal.

When I recovered from my stupefaction, I wandered aimlessly for several hours, starved and almost crazy. Then I went to the castle of Hans von Trantow, and was received there with open arms. After I had satisfied my ravenous appetite, he told me I must remain concealed in his house until the first heat of the pursuit was over. Food, drink and sleep quickly restored my old strength. After three or four days I learned that the chase after me, so far from slackening, was hotter than ever, that my father had been accused of sheltering me, and that his house had been searched. I decided that the only manly course for me was to escape to Uselin in disguise and surrender myself to justice. After many adventures, some perilous and some comical, I accomplished my purpose. My trial resulted, of course, in conviction, and I was sentenced to seven years in the penitentiary.

On my way to prison I learned that the Arthur I had so

dearly loved had in his evidence laid to my charge crimes that
I never had committed; that Constance had been deserted by
her princely lover; and that the governor of the jail to which I
was being hurried was the brother of the Wild von Zehren.
Seven years! Well, I was resolved it should not be so long.
What Baron Trenck and other noted jail-breakers had done I
could do also. Yet, after I had examined my cell, I thought
that if all the prisoners were so well lodged there were many who
fared much worse when at liberty. It was neat and comfortable, better furnished than my garret at home.

I heard a rustling outside, the key was turned, and a man
entered of tall stature, slightly stooping, with delicate, kindly
features. This was the superintendent. He laid his hand on
my shoulder, and in soft, deep tones said:

"Poor youth, how I pity you! It is hard and cruel that you
should be punished for a crime which, whatever it may be in
the eyes of the law, merits in mine a milder name. I am the
brother of the man for whose fault you are suffering."

How deeply must the prison air have already poisoned my
heart when neither his words nor the manner in which they were
spoken moved me! I rejected his sympathy scornfully, rejected
the dishes and wine that he sent me, and when, some days afterward, he asked whether I had any wish it was in his power to
grant, I answered roughly:

"No, for you could hardly give me a day's shooting over the
moors of Zehrendorf."

Having decided that I should owe nothing to this soft-man-
nered jailer, I demanded to be treated like the other convicts.
My demand was granted, and for a fortnight I had been doing
the very hardest work in the establishment, the superintendent
thinking it was the kind of work best suited to my exceptional
strength.

It took two months for the long-suffering kindness of my
benevolent jailer to wear out my churlish stubbornness. But it
wore out at last, and an event occurred that brought him very
close to my heart. I had a hint of a conspiracy—confined to a
few of the prisoners—to murder two of the keepers and escape.
I could hardly believe this at first. The prison was a model of
everything that such an institution should be, and the prisoners

appeared to worship their superintendent, whose humane and wise treatment had undoubtedly worked a reformation in the great majority of them. He often said: "Hammer *or* anvil! No. Hammer *and* anvil. Mutual understanding, mutual sympathy—these laws must eventually reclaim humanity."

In the struggle between the conspirators and the keepers I saved the superintendent's life, but was myself wounded almost to death. I owed my return to life to the careful nursing of one of the most angelic beings that have ever visited the earth, Paula, the fifteen-year-old daughter of the superintendent. But I owed something greater to this wise and tender-hearted young maiden, the recovery of the health of my soul.

Two other incidents in which I took a prominent part would undoubtedly have abridged the term of my incarceration, but for the interference of the prison chaplain, Von Krossow, a strictly orthodox and hypocritical type of his class. He hated Von Zehren for his broad and liberal views, and hated me because I was his disciple and his favorite. The death of the superintendent a few months before the time for my liberation enabled him, with the aid of the new official, to procure an extension of my punishment for six months, by methods which certainly appeared inconsistent with his ostentatious piety.

The superintendent had been my teacher for nearly six years, and never had pupil a teacher so kind and wise and patient. He had discovered my capacity for architecture and engineering; so I spent most of the time in his office, learning the use of the compass and ruler, drawing plans and specifications. When I left prison, then, I was fairly well equipped for the battle of life. My first journey after regaining my freedom was to my native town of Uselin. I might catch a glimpse of my father through the open door; for to enter, to throw my arms about his neck, as my heart yearned to do, I dared not hope. Alas! he had died a week before, died expressing his love for me, a love that was the deeper because of the austere and stern demeanor that concealed it.

How I worked in the factory of Commerzienrath Streber, becoming eventually foreman, chief manager and inventor of machines that revolutionized his business; how I married Hermine, the little maid who had once been frightened by the sooty face of Klaus, now my right-hand man and happily married to Christel; how I succeeded to the Von Zehren property on the island in virtue of the succession of my wife, and founded factories there based on profit-sharing and the copartnership of the workmen—in other words, based on the brotherhood of man— may be read in all their minutest details by such as care to have recourse to the longer narrative in which I have fully described every incident of my life.

HARRIET PRESCOTT SPOFFORD

(United States, 1835)

AZARIAN (1864)

This romance was suggested to the author by the history of a friend, a young flower-painter, whose work was valued by the Brownings and others, and who was cruelly neglected by her lover, himself an artist of note. The friendship of the heroine and the actress Charmian was suggested by the friendship of the actress Charlotte Cushman and the sculptress Elizabeth Stebbins. The story was published in 1864. The day it was issued, Mr. James T. Fields, the publisher, wrote the author: "I see money in the clouds; before it falls *dew* I send the enclosed," accompanying the letter with a large check. We present the author's own briefer rendering of her story.

LIFE strung no summer on Ruth Yetton's thread brighter than that filled with the boy Azarian's infinite variety, half forgotten now with her childhood. Her father, a man of dreams, moving to the city found his dreams fail, and became an old man in his prime.

Ruth took the burden on her slender shoulders, an accident revealing the value of her work in water-colors. What visions were hers at that moment! Wealth and its possibilities rose around her like an exhalation and made her radiant. She felt the quick glance of Azarian over the portfolio, as a flower feels a sunbeam.

Her home was in two rooms, which she had made pleasant in a house on an empty square. Sometimes she went with the old man into the country; sometimes into greenhouses, where she feared his bewildered soul might be lost among the enchanted odors; sometimes into a concert-room, where the music's dreamwork shaped itself to color and design; sometimes they leaned over the bridges and watched the green light flicker below. All fed her art. For she had found an art in which at the time she

388

stood alone; she handled her pencil with decision, and there was courage in her color, whether painting the things that call the wild March sponsor, the tree-blossoms crowding into life before the leaf, or the heart's blood of the year in autumn leaves.

She was at work one day, with Charmian beside her—a young actress who, in a sudden inflorescence, might some day dazzle to blindness the world of footlights. "I am not in the after-piece," said Charmian. "So I will bring Constant Azarian to see you."

"Constantine Azarian!"

"He used to know you. And now he would like to know you again."

"Constantine—"

"Really, I don't know about it. He is so charming outside —and as shining and hollow as a glass bubble."

"Oh, no!"

"He has talent. There are dark hints of a tragedy in his life. He has modeled a little—patience for the day, money for the plaster, but not genius enough for the marble. He has painted—portraits; he has a brush like a scalpel—lays bare your hidden sins. His portraits don't pay. Meanwhile, he has some practise as a physician. So be warned, be armed—good-by."

"Azarian," Charmian had occasion to say that night, "unless you conduct yourself with more propriety, I will not bring you again!"

"I can come alone," he said, and, possessing himself of a portfolio he listened to the story of each sheet from the lips of the delighted old man.

"He will pay more deference to my opinion when I return. I am going away, Ruth. The contract is signed—a golden opportunity! How can any latent power develop in such a searching wind of criticism as *he* breathes! But in the tropical nights, under the passionate plaudits, the soul blossoms."

"Ruth," interrupted Azarian, lifting one of her arabesques, "where did you find these winged faces? I will take you to see some Fra Angelicos—"

"You needn't be taken unless you wish," said Charmian.

"But I do! I have dreamed of them. Once, when I was in trouble, I dreamed of laboring through a field of stubble, and two angels came with great rosy wings and lifted and bore me over it all."

Azarian, looking in Ruth's face then, perceived the exquisite beauty of her dark eyes and delicate features, on her cheek not so much the blush of the rose as the purple pink of the rhodora. As he told her afterward, he felt she was one of the last drops of the earth's pungency, strong enough to turn a man's head.

Presently Azarian, following this last fancy, had Ruth with him at the play, driving in the country, walking with him down lonely ways, till at last, as they one day sat alone together, Ruth suddenly found her hand in his, and as suddenly—she never could tell how and Azarian never could tell why—she was drawn and wrapped in a clasp that checked her pulses.

Happy Ruth! She walked on air, and a rosy cloud enveloped her. As for Azarian, he too was abandoned to the flight of time. The cup was in his hand; and all the years to come would offer him nothing of more virtue than this elixir at which he only wet his lips.

The tide of Ruth's happiness swept her out to richer performance. Someone said that only Nature and Miss Yetton dared use such tints. "Little woman," said Azarian, "you have a pact with certain tipsy dryads; they had such a head of color on when they told you their secrets that they reeled."

As time passed Charmian returned, and Ruth and she renewed their old affection, Ruth beginning to see glimmeringly that perhaps it was not in Azarian's nature to be a tender lover, while the flood of her own love had deepened the channels of her being and made her wants wider. Happy with Charmian, she forgot how often high spirits presage misfortune.

Azarian was brilliantly handsome on the night when he came with a casket and a violin-case, his face overspread with a shining pallor, his lips curved in mocking smiles, his steel-blue eyes sparkling, along his straight brow the hair in smooth waves of gold. Never had he been so radiant, so varying, so charming with a seducing sweetness! Love kept bubbling up in Ruth's heart; and after her father had gone to sleep she sat at her lover's feet, silent in sheer happiness.

"I saw her—Charmian—to-day," said Azarian abruptly. "We had one sharp thrust of words. If that woman darkens your doors again, I never will. The stronger love must conquer. Hers or mine!" Then he grew kind, bent with endearments and caresses, wrought wizardry with his violin, till at last she felt it would be a light sacrifice to lay her very life at his feet.

The next day Ruth and Charmian parted. "If you ever find Azarian's love less worth than mine," said Charmian, "come to me. Mine will be always waiting."

Azarian did not again mention the affair. He had confessed to himself that his infatuation was a folly; now he must make the best of it. Retarded on the road to wealth and fame by an impetuous moment, he had a right to assistance from Ruth, and his first requirement was separation from the actress. But always it is some stir that completes crystallization; and since Charmian's season in the south he had not seen her play.

Azarian gave Ruth a week or two of great devotion, and then he turned to his work. Ruth was content to miss him by day, his coming gave such cheer at night. One evening he opened the forgotten casket and showed her the vase he had carved; on its processional curve circled camelopard and lioness and wood-gods in a merry crew. "I shall set the blanched beauty outside the walls of heaven when I go in," he said. "And never part with it till then. It is the Witch of Atlas's story, that topmost piece of pure fancy of the mysterious stars." And while Ruth read the poem Azarian's bow hovered in murmuring music over the strings.

So the evenings went; the nights when Azarian failed to appear were a blank of lonesome longing, and time was all the blither when he came at last.

Azarian had acquired some renown through performing an operation from which few had ever recovered. His hand was tremorless, his eye pitiless, his knife the instrument of a defiant curiosity; he dared beyond his duty and he commanded success. There were those who worshiped him as if he were a young god with the gift of immortality in his hand.

Rumor of this reached Ruth; and she was touched that he made no mention of marriage. But with the summer Azarian had a new fancy, a bladelike boat that ripped the water with a gash, and afforded an intimate satisfaction to the demands of his temperament. In it he lay in wait for morning, chased the

sunset at dewfall, lingered at midnight to surprise the solemn
rites of turning tide. As he lay miles from any shore, a star
looked down from far above, a star looked up from far below;
the glint passed, leaving him the sole spirit between the immense
concaves, shut in like the flaw in a diamond. By and by the
blood-red fragment of a waning moon might lean up the horizon, but now it was dusk; above, a wide want and hush; beneath,
a mystery; and from every side the muffled music, the everlasting
fugue of the sea; and alone, akin to the wild Thing about him,
he sought that for which there is no language. Thus gradually
all Ruth saw of him was in broken bits of time, and at last he
came in to say good-by, off for a trip to Labrador.

In Azarian's absence Ruth's father died. The bond between
them had been of peculiar sympathy, and her grief was overwhelming. A bitter instinct told her that with all his skill
Azarian should have known this might come, and not have left
her to meet it alone. Unnerved, oppressed with ghastly fears,
she felt the need of help; searching, she found the darkness instinct with deity, and peace fell on her heart like dew. What
happiness when she should impart to Azarian this heavenly
experience!

But when Azarian came he brought with him Madame Saratov, an exile who hoped to find a career for her two sons in
America, a woman with a patrician preservation, a sparkle of
wit, a strain of mystical piety. When Azarian came again, and
Ruth would have spoken of the recent past: "Purr!" he exclaimed, "the cat is gray! You weren't made for this rôle,"
he added. "You haven't a moonstone rosary blessed by the
Patriarch."

Years afterward, Azarian saw the glance of those dark eyes
in his glass, in the ashes, on the night.

"Give me my violin, Ruth," he said, "and you shall have
a *Fantaisie Glaciale*"; and the weird crispness of his strains
took her among glittering iceberg tops till all ended with a pair
of chasing scales in another measure. "That was two cubs
tumbling after their mother who snapped her jaws at me.
Pictorial music—good for the critics. Now to good-night,"
said he.

It was a time of financial stringency; people had no money

to spend; and Ruth was growing thin under her deprivations added to Azarian's neglect. The Baroness Saratov, indeed, gave Ruth some satisfaction. She could not blame Azarian for dallying where it was so delightful; and she recognized a kinship of race between him and the foreign woman. In Ruth Madame Saratov found a new experience and valued it. Once she told Azarian he reminded her of those vampires who thrive on the heart's juices of young girls. His black brows drew a line over the icy brilliancy of his eyes, they lightened once, and he said no more; neither did Madame Saratov. But she made Ruth a part of many little adventures, and Ruth learned to love her and the two boys.

One evening she took Ruth to the new play in which Charmian had scored a triumph; and that night, fired with joyous excitement, Ruth made drawings of Charmian in her crucial scenes, perfect in pure form, and drawn with a clarity of line as if a diamond had etched them on crystal. Not long afterward the etchings were in the shop-windows, and Azarian in a rare rage came in with a handful of them, finding the room steeped in fragrance and strewn with Charmian's flowers; upon which a longer absence than usual was Ruth's chastisement.

Azarian never made excuses. But when he came in, humming one of the Miltonic quatrains, it was impossible not to feel him as part of their beauty. At this time he said to her: "You are imposed upon and neglected, sacrificed to selfish pleasures, is it not so? Yet I never condescended to concealment."

"Oh, no, no!" sobbed Ruth.

"No? Then kiss your heartless wretch! What! Blotting the new leaf already? We may as well have it out," taking her hand as the surgeon keeps his finger on the pulse in the hall of torture. "Black moments visit all," he said. "Then all turn to the fireside. You bewitched me once. When the thrall loosened—ah, to pretend mad passion would be ridiculous; but to separate from you would give me more uneasiness than I care to encounter." They dined with Madame Saratov, and Ruth, strung to brilliancy, so sparkled that Azarian congratulated himself on his work.

Madame Saratov kept Ruth with her that night. "Will you tell me," she asked when alone, "as your friend, as one who sees

you do need help—it pains me the heart—why you marry?   It
is because you are ambitious, because—"

"Oh, Madame Saratov, because I love him!"

"*Pauvre petite!   Les roses tombent, les épines restent.*   I remember me of men, the imps of self, whose ruin marriage completed.   One has the palm of martyrdom.   But he?   He becomes a degraded soul—"

"Madame Saratov," cried Ruth, "if you play with fire you
will be burned!"

"What have I done?" cried the Baroness.   She drew Ruth
to the window.   "Striking one," she said, and continued:

> "*Vous qui pleurez, venez à ce Dieu, car il pleure,*
> *Vous qui souffrez, venez à lui, car il guérit,*
> *Vous qui tremblez, venez à lui, car il souvit,*
> *Vous qui passez, venez à lui, car il demeure!*"

After this, Ruth was absorbed with illustrations of the
Garden Song for Madame Saratov.   And as in a fortnight
Azarian did not come, she took them to the Baroness.

By an oversight she was not announced.   Madame Saratov
was holding the white Witch Vase.   "You make me of com-
pliments!" she was saying.   "For me?   *Pourquoi pas pour elle?*
No, no!   But—do you know that someone's body is wearing
so thin that the soul arrives to look through?   My good friend
Azarian, if you have need of the child, why do you break her
heart?"

Azarian's anger passed in a flash, and with the old mocking
smile and bravado he said: "I don't know that I do need her."

Just then Ruth touched his arm, and the vase fell from
Madame Saratov's grasp in twenty pieces.   Azarian dropped
the black fringes over his luminous eyes and laughed.

"What have we here?" he asked, possessing himself of
Ruth's work.   "Apples of Syria and Turkish quinces and
myrobalans.   By Jove, you are a genius, Ruth!"   He rested
his hand on her hair.   "You are going?" he said, by and by.
"Well, then, expect me for sentence later."

"Surely, Azarian?"

"As sure as twilight!"

Ruth held herself rigidly till sheltered in her own room.

Then, bursting every bond, she cried, "I don't know that I do need her!" and fell upon the floor, her whole nature roused with clamorous longing, the black side of the universe turned upon her. When again those words fell on her consciousness like ice-drops, she penciled along her drawing-paper: "Till you need me, Azarian, till you need me."

Azarian had promised to come at twilight. But twilight passed without him. In the highly wrought state of her nerves his coming had become a matter of life and death to her. Darkness fell; she strained her gaze where the gaslight flickered in the black rainpools. No one came; a wild, wet night—few braved it. A stir then in the solitary space. A footfall? The spark of a cigar? The lessening shadow—that was he! She ran to light her candles and waited with her breath between her teeth. All was silent. Her heart sank down a sickening gulf. She blew out the light. The clock struck nine iron strokes. Eagerness, impatience, fear, fevered her; her pulses throbbed with liquid fire. She threw up the window and leaned out into the gale. There was a shadow far down the distance—could it be—ah, no! only the flaring gaslight in the empty square. "Oh, Azarian, how can you treat me so!" she cried aloud.

The clock pealed ten. A noise of wheels—ah, to be sure, he would not walk in the storm. Her heart shook the chair she sat in; she forgot reproach; she sprang to meet him with passionate welcome; the coach rolled by. Then suddenly life surged up again, for a key rattled in a lock. Now he would come in, flushed with the weather, eyes shining beneath the slouched hat, open his arms and shut her in under all the raindrops, feel her heart beating, and all the night's trouble for nothing. Then the heavy step of a lodger went up higher. Half maddened with the reverse, she leaned out in the last fierce shower, and let the torrents dash about her, or walked the room like one possessed. She would not look for him again; but the next step found her searching the flashes of the desolate lamp through the expiring storm.

Twelve o'clock of a starlight night. She expected nothing more. She was in a maze of misery. The day broke over the dark wet roofs, the fresh azure bloomed above; but it was noon before she stirred. All her love was beating its life out; all her

wrongs would drown the struggling passion. Her breath came
in little gusts of flame. She was half beside herself with inani-
tion and despair. "I have not the strength to live and let him
leave me," she said, when night came again. "Live? Where
is the need? Oh, God, why don't you take me?" Take her?
Why not go! Let her bury her sorrow out of sight!

A white, cold horror overwhelmed her; her forehead was wet;
her heart struck her side in great blows.

Slowly, sweetly, the peal parted the air, fell softly down,
lingering and loitering into silence. It swam still upon the air
when Ruth was flying to find her fate.

This was the place. She searched the lucid dark of the far
horizon, whose transparence seemed full of unknown light; and
even then, through all the madness of her purpose, came the
thought of how beautiful must be the hand that made its work
so fair. An instant and the pain shut down again. God had
forgotten her. A moment—and then sleep. Suddenly she
turned and looked up; there was nothing but the velvet, violet
heaven, the great immensity of bending space. Scalding tears
blurred her eyes. How beautiful the hand! Tender as beautiful! God never had forgotten her! The old worship wrapped
her.

A breath; one of those swift miracles that weld our wish with
the eternal will. Her selfish ecstasy of pain passed; the nerve
had ached out. A wind caught the dust and whirled it in clouds
about her, a passing light fell over her, and Azarian, drifting in
a boat below, remembered with a heart-beat the two upbuoying
angels of which she had once spoken. He shot down the stream,
secured his boat, and climbed to the spot. The sheltering
clouds of dusk hid the slight phantom flitting away.

With quick spasms of apprehension Azarian sought Ruth's
door. It was open. He found a candle. All was as she had
left it; on her painting-desk were the words: "Till you need me,
Azarian—till you need me."

"Charmian," faltered Ruth, at the stage door, "I have
come!"

Falling, torn and bleeding, the arms of a strong affection
can support one till health returns. There were three foreign

years in which Charmian's embracing spirit lent vigor to Ruth's. Then the death of Madame Saratov gave Ruth and Charmian her boys to take to their hearts. Ruth soared with her art on new wings; she had her work, her satisfactions; these were her children.

Did one who, with a start, paused in passing, and gazed into a lighted drawing-room, divine anything of this? Was that Ruth in the firelight, his Ruth, who three years ago had gone away into the night? With such light in her dark eyes, such bloom on her cheek, such smiles about the mouth he used to kiss? Was it Paul Saratov, the youth with the mien of a young Norse hero, looking down at her and at the dark-eyed Ivan at her feet? Had she set these boys in his empty shrine? Ah, no, that chamber was sealed! There was serenity of gladness in those trusting glances.

As he gazed his bitter gaze, the happy eyes were lifted, looking quietly at him. The night without, the light within, the pane between, made him viewless. He was of less substance than any film of the darkness.

A queenly woman, with her purples gleaming under the golden drip of the chandelier, swept forward and dropped the shade. "The curtain falls," said Azarian, striding on his way alone. "The play is played out."

THE THIEF IN THE NIGHT (1872)

This story was first printed serially in 1868 and afterward in book form in 1872. It has perhaps the first treatment in literature of the possibilities of a canal across the Isthmus of Darien, which was a suggestion of Mr. Richard S. Spofford, husband of the author. The following is the author's version.

THE garden sparkled in the first light of a June morning. A heaven everywhere a field of rose and azure soared over it. A breeze that was living fragrance rifled its roses. Everything bloomed and glittered; everything spoke of life and the luxury of living; nothing spoke of death or desolation. Through the casement of a sumptuously appointed room on the ground floor a level sunbeam smote a globe of red roses and laid a crimson stain on the face of a sleeper there, a sleeper lying as a dead man lies, a man murdered in his sleep.

A lady, beautiful, of gracious presence, came down the marble staircase into the garden. A gardener followed. With a start, the man went back and into the room, but came out whiter than the thing he had left.

"Mr. Beaudesford—" the man began. "Oh, Madame, this note is for you. I took it from his hand! And this little knife—"

"It is mine," she replied.

"It is the knife with which Mr. Beaudesford was last night murdered in his bed!"

Mrs. Beaudesford swept by him like one defying fate. But she shivered as she crossed that sill. Now it was daylight. Last night she had crossed it stealthily and in the dark. As she caught the stare of those icy eyes she fell senseless to the floor. In a moment the alarm was given and the room was full; her will perhaps asserted itself, and she stood at one side of the dead man's pillow while Major Gaston stood at the other.

Gaston did not speak. But even in that moment she felt his

gaze. Yet with that note secured she was safe. Twice and thrice a murderer, she would rather Gaston thought her, than once a false wife. Her husband's honor lay in that hidden scrap of paper. She met Gaston's gaze with triumphant eyes.

"The radial artery opened?" said Dr. Ruthven, when he came. "A night attack? It has not been an hour since! It may be yet—"

Major Gaston followed the dead man's gaze to a portrait where a painted lady appeared to lean far from the frame, commanding worship. To her worship? Her, who finding her husband murdered keeps her powers about her? Strong nerves! Strong nerves were needed last night! Her, who loved another man, who knew she was beloved again, whose husband knew it all, who had reason to wish the man where he now lay, that man who had found him there! Gaston's brain was like a cave full of flapping vampires, and yet his blood beat toward her; in spite of sin or shame or life or death he loved her!

Dr. Ruthven laid his hand on Gaston's arm. "There are various ways of committing a crime," he muttered. "This hand of Arnold Gaston's is just as guilty as if it had driven home the knife!"

Beaudesford and Gaston had been one in every thought. The first, wealthy, a prodigal, had kept his personal expenditure on the level of Gaston's purse. Young, rich, handsome, with troops of friends, Beaudesford would have exchanged identities and circumstances with Gaston. They were on a trip along the coast when they met Catherine Stanhope, whose father had been Beaudesford's guardian—she, with her sister Rose, cut off from shore by the tide—and she saw life gleaming for her again from Gaston's eyes as he lifted her into the boat.

Before many days Beaudesford had asked for Catherine's hand. "When he has not known me a week!" she said indignantly.

"Do I look like a disappointed lover?" Beaudesford asked afterward.

"No," Catherine replied, "but like a disappointed purchaser!"

One day at twilight they were all coming off the water to-

gether. "How the wind freshens down there in the white line
of breakers!" said Gaston.

"A dance of death by beautiful ghosts," said Catherine.
And in a moment they were flying out to sea again, soaring and
sinking among foam-phantoms in starlit darkness. Suddenly
the tiller snapped, and the boat was drifting on the breakers
when Gaston, thrusting his arm through the hole, held the rudder with a grasp of iron, and the boat passed into safe water.

Gaston went up the bank with Catherine; under the fragrant
boughs he took her hand, and in the spell of midnight and dew
and hush their lips touched in one long thrill of passionate surrender. Let Catherine have her night's joy in remembering
that throb of bliss! The next time she saw Gaston she had been
two years the wife of Beaudesford.

Gaston had gone away the morning after that mad embrace.
When, under Mrs. Stanhope's stress of urging, Catherine had
married Beaudesford, they had all gone to live at Beaudesford's
house. After a while her husband took her away into strange
countries. Under his tender care she became satisfied enough
with life. When she returned to her home the first person she
saw on her threshold was Gaston. "She was an airy nothing
when you knew her," said her husband to his friend. "Now
she is Beaudesford of Beaudesfords."

Catherine always reminded Beaudesford of light. He was
struck anew with the thought, seeing her in a gold-colored fab-
ric, her hair gold-colored, her eyes shining. She sang that night
a sorrowful song; and as she looked at him among the cushions
that lent his face a flush and deepened the tint of his yellow
curls she thought his head was like that of the Capitolean gods.
Then, seeing Gaston's darkening eyes, his scar, his gloom, all
thought of the other went out like a blown candle flame. Beaudesford woke her in the night to ask what her song signified.
"Be content," she said, laying her hand on his eyes. And lest
the touch should cease he did not stir.

"Catherine," said Beaudesford one day, coming in with a
book, "you must hear Gaston's journal," for he had insisted
that Gaston should remain as their guest. "Strange as if kept
on another planet. One day he was the guest of an emperor.

Here it is: 'My interview with the Emperor to-day was all I could desire. I told him that when engaged on private enterprise I found greater opportunity, and came to him as one whose sight reached beyond his kingdom. He admitted that whoever owns the canal uniting the Pacific and the Atlantic has the keys promised to Columbus in his dream.' Here's something more: 'To-morrow I go ashore and begin my work, a bequest Columbus left me, perhaps, to make Atlantic and Pacific one; a part of that most immense of all the testaments when he willed away a hemisphere.' Oh, Gaston made famous headway till a revolution there made things impossible. Listen again: 'Government has no forecast. When my ditch is digged, there is its barbican; the long outlying fortress, the island that is to take tribute of the nations, commanding the argosies of the Orient as they flock by, gathering into free ports the wealth of the world. The Queen of the Antilles must belong to the power that holds the interoceanic strait, or else at the center of the Great Republic of the Archipelago; another Venice, rising in the west, recovering the maritime glories lost when the Alexandrian highway was closed by one which will be abandoned for this ecliptic of commerce, she will herself possess it!' There, read the book yourself!" And Catherine could but couple Gaston thenceforth with such lofty enterprise that he towered transfigured in its grandiose splendor.

Months later the great house was full of guests and a wild snow-storm was raging. There was inquiry for Gaston, who had employed himself on some neighboring engineering. "He cannot breathe an hour in this gale!" said Beaudesford. A wild white gust blew in, but not till he had seen a woman's face as wild and white looking out with him. Then Gaston staggered up and fell across the doorstone. "I thought I had lost you, Gaston!" cried Beaudesford. "My God, how black the world grew!"

Gaston's face grew livid. "My friend," said Dr. Ruthven to him later, "you must have some hell-fire in you, since all this storm has not chilled it."

That night Catherine, listening to the great cry of the elements, felt her small personal equation open into one of sin and tumult; and she cowered shivering and weeping half the night long.

The next day, looking from her window, she saw Gaston on his restive horse pull the creature up till, poised and outlined on the dazzling snow, horse and rider might have been hewn from black marble; and as he glanced up he caught her wild and eager gaze again. Then she heard Beaudesford singing in his golden tenor, as he came through the gallery, a hymn they had lately heard; and she felt like the transformation of some vile eft as she listened. "I am not base!" she cried. "I will not live in bondage to sin! I will conquer or I will die!" and as she faced Beaudesford, her locks of palest gold fallen, her cheeks vivid, her eyes flashing, he stood transfixed with her beauty and thought only of her innocence.

As spring came on Beaudesford was full of mounting gaiety. Catherine followed him everywhere, trying to fill her waking and sleeping thoughts with him, till Mrs. Stanhope stroked her sleek fur, thinking she had known what was best when she had made Catherine marry Beaudesford. But after every endeavor of Catherine's to forget the dark, scarred face, it would rise as she had seen it first, with death at her feet on the point of rock; and she saw life and heaven only in Gaston's eyes.

One day she went into the conservatory, taking with her a legend of the Middle Ages that Beaudesford had been reading. Suddenly a long brown finger stretched before her on the page, and Gaston read aloud the treacherous knight's words of eternal parting. His voice trembled; a tear fell on the leaf. She looked up, under the shelter of the broad banana leaves. Since he was going, then—since this was all—the first time and the last—his head bent; then a footfall was heard, and Beaudesford stooped to lift the fallen book.

If Beaudesford had been blind, he was so no more. That bending, that uplifted face, that start, that defiant turn, those streaming tears, were like flashes of light. He plunged into his own den, and walked and bounded there like a caged leopard. He writhed at distrusting Gaston, at suspicion of his treachery, with rage, with grief, with love for Catherine. That night, three years before, when she and Gaston went among the breakers— if they had but spoken then! He would have forgotten himself; he would have compassed earth and heaven for them! It hurt more than it enraged him. And how was it possible to have such fancies concerning his white-souled wife! And why had he exposed her? What woman ever withstood Gaston! Though he recalled the branding blush with which they met the day she returned home, the wild, white face searching the storm, her looks, tears, words—he tried to convince himself that his suspicions were groundless. He went out at last, declaring he must have been mad, nor would he insult wife or friend with another doubt. But suspicion, once aroused, has its head erect and hissing ever after.

Everyone in the great house felt the ferment. Beaudesford was continually putting two and two together. Nothing escaped him. Bitter things were bringing his better nature to naught.

Catherine saw now, with the assurance of one who faces a terrible consequence, that Gaston must go. The family were all in the garden one day, and Beaudesford strolled down a path to meet them. "My poor boy," said Mrs. Stanhope, "I am worried about you, you are so pale. Those houses in the Great Wood are reeking with typhus."

"You are too good to me," he said. "What a kind and wise little woman! But for all that you have made some mistakes in your life!"

"Come, come," said Rose, "look at these treasures," for an Italian image-boy had brought his wares inside. "Shakespeare for a dime, Cæsar at half the money! Here is the Princess Phèdre—for two shillings!"

"And dear at any money!" said Beaudesford. "Tell me the value of any representation of perjury and passion! Are unfaithful wives so rare that they should be sealed in amber? What was Phèdre? One with the sole claim that she is the ideal of every woman that is, that ever will be, false to her husband!"

Hope left Catherine as she heard Beaudesford. She could not appeal to him to take her away. She feared him—feared that should she abase herself he would trample her into the dust.

It came to this at last—she must implore Gaston to go. And since this closed all, and rolled the stone against the tomb, she wrote that which later she would have given her hope of the hereafter to recall. For, whether it was passionate acknowledgment of what once was but was no longer, or whether they were slight and feeble phrases of request, to her proud soul upon reaction, the mere penciling seemed shame. But with the writing in her handkerchief she went down to dinner, radiant now, persuaded she was safe. To her dismay, when Gaston should have had the note, it was Beaudesford who received it; and she felt that she had signed her death-warrant.

Beaudesford's face was as pale as Catherine's when he came into the drawing-room that night. He had been making his will, having been down in the fever region. "I have left you half my fortune, old boy," he said to Gaston. "It is not your fault if you survive me. The other half I leave, as the will says, to my dear and honored wife." Perhaps they understood the sarcasm.

When that night Catherine entered the old room on the ground floor, to which Beaudesford had returned, she hardly saw the corpselike whiteness of his face, or the rigidity of his movements, as if the nerves of volition were strained to their utmost, so madly did she desire to possess herself of that writing of hers before he should have read it—that paper which was not written to save her happiness but to ruin Beaudesford's! Suddenly she asked herself what odds how long Gaston stayed? Was she not Beaudesford's wife, honored and honoring? Had not Beaudesford the dignity, the nobility she loved? What loftiness! he was willing to go and give the thing most valued to him who would have despoiled him of it! He had displayed a majesty of which the other, traitor that he was, was destitute and naked. And as Beaudesford's nature assumed in her thoughts its peerless proportions Gaston's shrank to recreancy.

"You are ill," she said. "I cannot keep away! Beaudesford, if you love me!"

Catherine never could remember those moments as mere remembrance; she was wrapped in it like a whirlwind, caught in his arms, pressed close to his convulsive heart, covered with kisses. "Good-by, good-by, my darling!" All bitterness melted away. "God knows—God knows I love you!" and the door was closed between them.

As Catherine paced the hall outside, the starlight companioning her with strange shadows, she heard no sound. He slept; after such slumber he must wake well. All would be right should she but recover that note—for honor did not sit on him so lightly that he would violate a paper belonging to another. That done, what a life of blessing lay before them! With what joy she would go to Beaudesford and tell him this happiness she had learned since purple twilight had shut down over the rosy world! She answered proudly the challenge of those half-glimpsed portraits on the wall, those honorable wives—she also was an honest Beaudesford! She stole out at last under the stars that from their vast heights saw the dawn, and through the open casement in the dusk. The note was gone. But something compelled her to stay, to drop a kiss on his forehead light as a flower-petal.

Beaudesford gave no sign. From him the world had already begun to recede. The agony of renunciation was past; and now not all his great freeholds, his manhood and strength and beauty and troops of friends would hold his spirit down. He stretched his arm with its clenched hand till the veins stood forth, and the little knife did its work. The wind that blew in and lifted the lock upon the ivory brow swept out again into the garden; for there everything told of life and joy, and here all things waited for death.

As Gaston stood then that next morning beside the bed he felt the majesty of Beaudesford in that helpless sleep superior to life, Death holding state in that dust. A living flame heated his memory; all his days with Beaudesford stalked like black shadows through the fiery furnace. The wrongs he would have done him stared with evil eyes. Remembrance of Beaudesford's long service of loving-kindness was like a poisoned blade in a festering wound. But through all the confused and terrible phantoms—for honor that runs along the flashing of a soldier's sword had ceased to exist for him—came one thrill of delicious pain: whether Beaudesford were living or dead, he and Catherine and Gaston loved each other! For, although it were her hand that had done to death this man—the hand of a fair fiend, ah, heavens, how fair!—yet be she however false, be she twice as foul as she was fair, he loved her!

Yet when he would have challenged Catherine came recoil, as if the sunshine had grown blood-red, the earth were but a vapor, the doubt that she could have done this deed. His smile had been triumphant as a sunburst; it fell before her shudder. "Stop!" he cried, and his effort to be calm seemed turning him into iron. "Do you mean to say you never loved me!"

"Never!" she exclaimed. "Let me say it, even here and now. If ever any delirium disturbed me, I escaped it! I have loved only my husband. Oh, Beaudesford, so lofty, so serene, so pure, what is death between us? For oh, I love you! I love you, Beaudesford!" And she fell upon her knees, creeping up to lay her mouth on his lips, pouring between them the warm breath of her breast laboring on his with sobs.

"It's the last resort," cried Dr. Ruthven, hurrying in again. "If I can get some cordial into him with this tube, and then apply the battery—faint from loss of blood—suspended animation—Boerhaave gives a case of six hours—"

"Come here! Come here!" Catherine interrupted, springing to her feet, overlaid with a burst of sunshine. "His heart beats! Oh, it beats! He breathes!" And then the doctor had the battery along the whole course of the nerves, wrestling in all his might with Death.

You might as well ask the great angels who watched the Almighty hands fashion the red day upon Aornos when the first man entered into the sacrament of life, as have asked Catherine what took place in that hour. She seemed to herself entering into the secrets of eternity, a witness of awful rites of preternatural powers; to have seen the form of indestructible spirit. And when a long tremor vibrated through Beaudesford's body, a shiver shook the ashy lips, the great eyes opened bewilderedly and then rested on hers, she felt heaven descending into the room.

"I heard it all," he whispered, as she clung to him. "I could not move. The weight of my grave was on me. I could never have come back to life had you not made such pulses leap, had you not set my heart beating to yours, Catherine, my wife!"

And then his eyes rested on Gaston's, with a recognition blasting as that of the judgment-day. It was the last blow for Gaston. The currents of his blood had been reversed when Beaudesford's death had been announced; his head had whirled when he found Catherine free; his temples had beat like triphammers with thought that the deed was hers. He had believed her hand red, and found it stainless.   He had seen a dead man gaze—great God, how dead men gaze! Something was bursting in his brain; he turned away with a low and idiotic laugh, a maniac.

When, after a long season, Gaston was a reasonable man again, his face still dark and scarred, his head iron-gray, his youthful fires and furies burned away, the two friends had made all right between them; and presently he sought the tropical regions, where he is still at work with a scheme as grand as the mountains he shall penetrate.

But as for Beaudesford, happiness had become his atmosphere. "Do you know," he said to Catherine one evening, "I have grown so still that I think the time I died I must have been made over. If you were not at hand, if those airy creatures yonder should disappear, I should sink! Listen to the murmurings of our anchorage here!" And, kneeling beside two little beds, they thanked God for their lot, and for the perpetual youth in life that children bring.

FLORA ANNIE STEEL

(England, 1847)

ON THE FACE OF THE WATERS (1896)

This work is not only fiction but history also. Mrs. Steel lived many years in India, going there at a time when memory of the Sepoy Rebellion was fresh in the minds of all residents. She had access to all official documents bearing on that episode, and she examined other sources of information such as native newspapers and private letters. In making the history a basis and background for her story she was at pains not to distort the slightest historical fact, and the many real persons who figure in the story say and do there only what it is known they said and did in real life. The Sepoy Rebellion occurred in the summer of 1857. Mrs. Steel begins her story about a year ahead of that date and covers all the events that had a bearing on the causes of the insurrection and the progress of the conspiracy that lay behind it. The greater part of the book is concerned naturally with the siege of Delhi. The Englishwoman who, in the story, was hidden in Delhi during the entire siege had her counterpart in real life. A striking feature of the book, considered as history, is the rigid impartiality with which the writer presents both sides of the question without expressing comments on British blunders, or her personal condemnation of Indian atrocities.

AJOR ERLTON, stationed at Lucknow, was said to be a good soldier, and that he devoted much energy to horse-racing was not counted against him, as there was plenty of time for sport while the country was peaceful; but there were those who could not approve his open attentions to women other than his wife. In the summer of 1856 his frequent companion at the races, and in rides or drives about the country, was Mrs. Alice Gissing, the pretty, frivolous wife of a contractor. Mrs. Gissing, indeed, turned the heads of many men, but it was plain enough that her preference, such as she had, was for Major Erlton. The Major's wife suffered in dignified silence. Her one son had been sent to England, the mother making this sacrifice earlier than might have been advisable had educational considerations alone been held in view, because she could not bear the thought that the boy should be aware of family differences, or influenced by his father's faithlessness. So neglected was she, so certain that circumstances never could arise to restore her husband's love to her, that the future of her boy had come to be her only serious interest in life.

This concentrated regard for her son led her to send for a certain man named Grayman, of whom she had heard as a professional horseman, after a race in which Grayman had lost by reason of "crooked" work on the part of Erlton. Grayman, she understood, intended to lay charges against Major Erlton before the Jockey Club which would bring about his eternal disgrace. Dismissal from the army would be a mere detail in the catastrophe. It was not that that counted. What Mrs. Erlton dreaded in behalf of her son was that the boy should have to blush for his father's reputation. She resolved, therefore, to offer Grayman her diamonds in compensation for his losses if he would promise not to press the fatal charges.

Grayman had been cashiered from the army years before as the result of a scandal in which a woman was concerned. Since then he had given his attention mostly to racing and to trading horses. He called on Mrs. Erlton at her request. They never had met, and the moment she saw him she perceived that she could not deal with him as she had intended. This was not a man to whom she could offer diamonds in reparation of a wound to his honor. He was not only a gentleman in appearance and demeanor, but honest almost to the degree of brutality. She sought to touch his compassion; but this man, who had not been treated compassionately by the world, spoke from his bitterness and refused to shield her husband. "Major Erlton is a knave," he said in effect. "No hiding of this particular offense can possibly prevent knowledge of his real character from eventually coming to your son." He even doubted whether any son of Major Erlton could become an honest man, no matter how situated.

Mrs. Erlton sadly admitted the logic of his attitude, but pleaded still. "It is always possible for a man to redeem himself," she said; "give my husband one more chance," and, strange as it seemed to Grayman himself, he yielded to this argument. It meant—for of course he would not think of taking the lady's jewels—that he must sell his stable to pay his debts, when the pressing of his claims against the Major would have relieved him; it meant that he did a magnanimous act without any reward whatever, not even of his conscience or of his judgment. The latter, indeed, was against his decision, and he confessed that his conscience, if stirred at all, was against it also. But he did it. Mrs. Erlton's cold eyes had softened, thus giving a glimpse of that commonplace, indefinable womanhood which makes or wrecks men's souls. It wrecked Grayman's business; sent him adrift; penniless, he sought and obtained government employment as a spy.

When he undertook to supply the authorities with information, he asked to be enrolled under his right name, James Sholto Douglas. There was abundant need for services such as he could render, although the government officials were strangely slow to appreciate the danger that hovered over the country, and apparently incapable of estimating wisely the many signs of discontent among the natives.

Douglas, in the course of fifteen years of horse-trading, had become proficient in more than one dialect of the East. Deeply tanned by constant exposure, he could pass anywhere, when properly costumed, as an Afghan. He had a roving commission, and from one place and another he sent word to the officials concerning the agitation against British rule. He furnished documentary evidence; he patiently expounded the situation from the native point of view; and yet nothing was done. Numerous false charges of British tyranny were insidiously spread abroad by the Indian agitators, and these were as little heeded as were the grievances that were real, from the native point of view, which a wise administration could have rectified without sacrifice of British dignity. For example, the Sepoy soldiers were exceedingly disturbed because a new cartridge had been issued which had been smeared with fat. In those days it was necessary to bite the cartridge when loading the rifle; the Sepoys, both Hindoos and Mohammedans, maintained that to bite the greased cartridge made them lose caste. Their friends and relatives never would eat with them again if they had tasted fat. Douglas perceived, and some of the military officers admitted, there was no real necessity of biting the new cartridge. The drill could have been altered to fit the new contrivance without appearing to yield to heathen prejudice; but no; the superior intelligence of the British authorities declared for unchanged discipline, despising the silly superstitions of the Sepoys and fatuously depending on dogged British stubbornness and courage, of which there was always an abundance, to overcome if not wholly to avert any disaffection in the ranks.

Douglas tired of his fruitless occupation at last, and returned to horse-trading. Nearly a year after his meeting with Mrs. Erlton he was in Meerut, about thirty miles from Delhi. He had been attracted thither by a crisis in the discontent that seemed to threaten an immediate outbreak, but the crisis had passed apparently without trouble, and he set out to return to Delhi in the early morning, leading his horse, for the animal had been drugged with opium so that she could not have borne her rider. Why this trick had been played upon him Douglas did not know. He believed he could save the beast by walking her to a point where he had a remount half-way between Meerut and Delhi.

At that time the greater part of the British forces in that part of India were stationed at Meerut. Major Erlton's command was there, though his regular station was now at Delhi, where his wife lived, as did also Mrs. Gissing. This lady's husband had been absent from home for a long time, and was due to return in a month. In the preceding interval the Major's attentions to her had been constant, and, so far as his own home was concerned, there was no pretense at love for his wife, or anything but neglect of her. While he was at Meerut Major Erlton learned from Mrs. Gissing that her condition was such that she must leave her husband and throw herself upon his protection. The Major immediately wrote three letters: one a resignation of his commission; another to Mrs. Gissing, bidding her come to him; another to his wife, informing her of what he was doing and suggesting that she would better get a divorce. These letters were despatched just previous to the departure of Douglas for Delhi.

The crisis that had brought Douglas to Meerut arose from the prejudice of the Sepoys against the new cartridges. Eighty-five men of first-rate record had refused to bite them when the order was given. They were tried by court-martial, convicted of insubordination, and sentenced to ten years' penal servitude in the Meerut jail. That was the British way of dealing with a religious prejudice. Intimate observers like Douglas had supposed that the other Sepoys would refuse to fasten the chains on their comrades, or conduct them to jail; but discipline had prevailed and the mutineers were safely locked up. If Douglas had known the reason why discipline prevailed he would have remained in Meerut. The fact was that the conspirators had planned a general uprising all over India to begin two weeks from that date; and all the Sepoys were pledged to submit to every imposition until then. It was the jeers of loose women that brought on the insurrection ahead of time and perhaps restricted the rebellion to lesser dimensions than had been planned for it. The Sepoys who had escorted their comrades to jail wandered into the women's quarter of Meerut only to be assailed with cries: "We have no kisses for cowards!" Inflamed by this feminine disdain, the Sepoys burst open the jail and freed not only their comrades but all criminals confined there. The revolt spread faster than fire, and a horrible massacre of Christians in Meerut followed, to be succeeded by an immediate march on Delhi.

As soon as Major Erlton realized what was afoot he mounted his horse and galloped away on the Delhi road, intent upon warning the garrison there and saving Mrs. Gissing. He was a very heavy man and his horse was unequal to the strain of carrying him at top speed the whole distance. Some of the rebellious Sepoys were ahead of him, and, although he feared his horse would not last, he turned from the road hoping to ride by them unperceived. Douglas, overtaken by the Sepoys, had also turned aside, and the two Englishmen came together at a ford where they undertook to cross the river. It was no time for personal animosities to count, and Erlton apprised Douglas of the situation. It was clear to Douglas that Erlton never could reach Delhi ahead of the Sepoys; but he himself, being much lighter, could do so if he had a horse capable of running. Douglas's horse was still suffering from the effects of opium. He suggested that they change animals as the only way to assure carrying the warning to Delhi in time. It was impossible for

Douglas to get his remount, for the Sepoys were already at the half-way house where the animal was stabled.

"You know the country, and I don't," said Erlton. "I've been thinking of that ever since I saw your cursed face. You know the lingo, and I don't. And you're a deuced sight better rider than I am, too, damn you! But for all that, it's my chance, not yours."

"It's yours more than mine," the other replied slowly, "but it isn't ours, is it? It's the others'—in Delhi."

Erlton gave an odd sound between a sob and an oath and dismounted. "Look after her," he said. "I don't mean my wife. She's safe in the cantonments, but in the city—you know."

Douglas knew, as did every man, that Major Erlton's first care was for Mrs. Gissing. "I'll do everything you could possibly do in my place, Erlton," he said.

An hour later, while Douglas was still far from Delhi, his horse put his foot in a rat-hole and came down heavily, incapacitated for further progress; and while the rider was trying to help the beast the advance guard of the Sepoys passed on the road near by. So he had been right. It was neither Erlton's chance nor his own. The gates of Delhi would not be closed against the rebels, and the first man in would set the whole city in an uproar of insurrection with slaughter unspeakable of women and children. Foreseeing the tragedy, but desperately determined to fulfil his mission for Erlton if he could, Douglas left the horse and proceeded toward the city on foot.

When Mrs. Erlton had read and pondered her husband's letter, she drove from cantonments to Mrs. Gissing's quarters in the city. It was impossible to accept her husband's dictum that the situation could not be helped. For the sake of their son it must be helped, and the letter had not made clear to her that Mrs. Gissing's condition had made the question one of honor that, to a man, could be answered in only one way. Mrs. Gissing received her visitor with surprise, but tranquilly, for she never was one to become excited, and the argument began; but it had proceeded no further than to a revelation of the final cause underlying the Major's action when a servant entered with news that there was an outbreak in the city and that slaughter of the English had begun. Mrs. Gissing tried to quiet the servant's fears, and to pacify her left the room to get her husband's revolver. The next moment a piercing scream came from the garden. Mrs. Erlton, running to a window, saw a five-year-old boy, son of her friends, the Seymours, fleeing before an old native who carried a spear. The child, known by all his acquaintances as Sonny, was a great favorite with Mrs. Erlton, but she needed not that fact as incentive for such help as she could give. She tried to unfasten the French window, but the bolt stuck, and with every second the aged native gained on his little victim. While Mrs. Erlton was frantically working at the window-fastening Mrs. Gissing emerged from the house, crying: "All right, Sonny, all right, dear!"

She seemed no more than a child herself, her slight form garbed in light, girlish raiment fluttering with gay ribbons. One moment she paused to steady her right hand against her left arm. Then she fired. The spear wavered, the native seemed to hesitate. In that critical instant, when the spear was almost against the child's body, Mrs. Gissing caught him in her arms and turned toward the house, running for her life. There was a clatter of hoofs in the street; an Afghan who rode like an Englishman leaped from his horse; Mrs. Gissing tripped and fell headlong; a shot came from the newcomer's revolver, and the native staggered and fell across Mrs. Gissing; his hands let go the spear haft, but its head was buried in Mrs. Gissing's breast.

Mrs. Erlton had at last forced the window open, and the Afghan was kneeling beside Mrs. Gissing. When he spoke she recognized the voice of him she knew as Grayman. The servant came whimpering into the garden. Douglas had kicked aside the body of the dead native and tenderly lifted the woman. She was not unconscious.

"Don't be a fool," she said to her servant; "take care of the boy."

Douglas bore her swiftly into the house, but she was dead before he laid her on a couch. The man's heart swelled with admiration and regret, but he was all action. He gave Sonny to Mrs. Gissing's servant, saying in the dialect: "She charged you to take care of him. Don't forget!" Then, in English: "Mrs. Erlton, it is the lad's only hope for safety, for this Indian woman has friends in the city and you have none. Rebellion has broken out. You must get back to the cantonment, but I must reconnoiter first. Wait here."

He was gone but a few minutes, and when he returned it was to say breathlessly: "The game is up. There's only one chance for you, and that's desperate—quick!" He made her climb to the saddle before him. The regiments in the city were shooting their officers, he explained as he set spurs to his horse and galloped away. "I'm going to ride through the thick of the devils with you as my prisoner. Slip down a bit across the saddle-bow. Don't be afraid, but scream! scream like the devil! Then let your arms fall slack as if you'd fainted."

He made straight for the crowd that lay between him and safety, and as his horse pressed in among the frenzied rabble he shouted jests which fortunately Mrs. Erlton could not understand. He used the flat of his sword on such as would not budge, ready to slay right and left if the crowd refused to take him in the spirit he feigned. Coarse laughter and exultant shouts greeted his sallies. The mob gave way for the Afghan with his fair Christian prisoner, and, still at a gallop, he bore her to the main guard, the one spot where the rebellious Sepoys might be effectively resisted. There he left her, believing her safe, and went away to look after his own affairs.

Everybody, Douglas included, supposed that the force at Meerut would come promptly to the relief of Delhi, and all eyes were strained upon the road, looking for the cloud of dust that would announce their approach. Many clouds of dust arose, but they heralded always the advent of fresh mutineers. For reasons known only to the military authorities, the force at Meerut did not approach Delhi for many days, and before that first day was over orders that had to be obeyed caused the desertion of the main guard. That is, the troops were marched to another part of the city. In the confusion Mrs. Erlton was overlooked and left behind. She remained hidden in a shed till night and then crept out, eluded the rebels, and made her way to Mrs. Gissing's house. She took this course merely because it was her most direct way to the magazine where she hoped to find refuge, but as she approached the house of her dead rival she was forced to hide in it because the road ahead was full of fighting men. There was just time to dart into the room where the dead lay. Shouting, shots, groans, fierce yells were all around, and Mrs. Erlton stood silent till the sounds ceased. Then she tried to go forth, and found that every door and window had been barred from the outside. She had been locked in during the fighting.

A little before dawn the mystery was explained, for Douglas came to dispose of Mrs. Gissing's body so that it should not suffer mutilation. He had been in the fighting at the door. The bodies of his victims lay there obstructing entrance. It was he who had managed to bar the doors and save the house itself from destruction. Amazed to find Mrs. Erlton again in peril, he unquestioningly took upon himself the burden of protecting her. There was now no possible way of taking her to the quarters of such loyal troops as were in or near the city, but he knew how to prolong her chance of life if she would consent to his devices. There was no disposition on Mrs. Erlton's part to question his methods. Before the full light of day came he had hurried her to one of several rooms he rented in the city. They had been useful to him when he was acting as a spy, the rental enabling him to claim possession for months. Believing that relief from Meerut was but a matter of hours, or at most of a day or two, he thought of shifting his quarters every night, leaving Mrs. Erlton locked in one of his rooms during the daytime. This plan was pursued until, desperate at the failure of the relieving column to appear, and convinced that this hide-and-seek game could not continue indefinitely, for every venture upon the streets was a dangerous risk, he hired a roof apartment and installed Mrs. Erlton there with a native woman as her companion and servant.

There Mrs. Erlton remained for months. Troops came from Meerut after a time, but they could not enter the city. Delay followed delay. Reënforcements were necessary, and when added troops came there were still not enough, for the disloyal soldiery within the walls outnumbered several times those without them. There was frequent fighting, but all to little purpose. The Sepoys could not dislodge the beleaguers;

the British could not force the walls. The magazine within the city, held by nine British soldiers, was deliberately exploded to prevent the enemy from profiting by it. The nine soldiers went to destruction in the wreck, but a thousand rebels went with them. Disease decimated the ranks of the investing force.

Douglas, roaming the city freely in his character as an Afghan, heard no news to quiet the impatience of his spirit. The prolonged failure of his countrymen to attack decisively passed his comprehension. Meantime, his personal situation, and that of Mrs. Erlton, was of the strangest. She, dressed as an Afghan, her face and hands painted brown, was supposed to be his wife. And the servant who attended her was secretly in love with Douglas. This servant had all of the Hindoo's idolatrous loyalty to her master, and therefore was a trustworthy guardian for the white woman.

The semblance of family life was heightened one day when Mrs. Gissing's servant staggered in with Sonny. The boy was dressed and painted as a native child, but the old woman who had cared for him was dying. She had shrewdly suspected the identity of the Afghan's "wife" and had brought the child there for his further safety. So, until the child's irrepressible prattling in English threatened to betray them, he remained and was posed to the occasional native visitors, who could not altogether be avoided, as the son of the family. At last Douglas had to trust his secret to a conjurer whom he had employed when he was acting as a spy and who undertook to smuggle the lad to the British camp. Drugged with opium, Sonny was carried in a bag to a trader's stable, put with bundles of freight on a horse's back, and conveyed outside the city, eventually reaching the camp and his own people unharmed.

Once when Douglas was absent, the neighborhood was invaded by a party bent upon finding Christians who were supposed to be in hiding thereabout. They burst in the door to Mrs. Erlton's roof. She had just time to slip over the parapet and let herself drop to the roof of the adjoining building. When the invaders had gone she could not climb back, and it was hours before it was possible for her to gain the street and so return to her dwelling. Meantime Douglas had returned, found her gone, and, believing that she had been killed, or possibly escaped to the British camp outside, himself left the city, gained the British lines, and there fell desperately ill. His servant eventually found Mrs. Erlton on the roof and, still strangely loyal to her master, conveyed the Christian woman, in the guise of a penitent, to a shrine where for fifteen days she knelt with her face to a wall, perfectly safe from so much as a spoken word. At the end of that period, the servant led her to a door in the walls and let her go forth believing that the white woman would be killed before she could cross the space between the city and the British outposts.

But chance favored Mrs. Erlton, and she crossed unharmed. She found her husband one of the most daring fighters in the army, for the circumstances had induced the withdrawal of his resignation and given him insatiable ardor for killing. Their meeting was surcharged with embarrassment, but Major Erlton took her to his tent, congratulated her on her escape, told how Douglas had gone back to the city to find her as soon as he had recovered enough strength to stir, and then, having said all there was to say, the Major went to his post of duty for the night. Within an hour a stray bullet killed him instantly.

"He was a fine soldier," said the General in command, to Mrs. Erlton; "he leaves a good name to his son."

At last the rebellion was quelled, and Delhi again was occupied by the British forces. Then came Douglas's servant to Mrs. Erlton with word that her master was dying. "Everything has been done; you cannot help," said the Indian woman, but Mrs. Erlton hastened to the familiar roof. Under her nursing, or rather under the influence of her presence, Douglas recovered sufficiently to journey to Scotland, his native country, and there, two years later, Mrs. Erlton received a letter from an army acquaintance, congratulating her on her betrothal to the brave Douglas. The chance that he had taken for her, not once but many times, was united to hers for life.

STENDHAL

(MARIE-HENRI BEYLE)

(France, 1783–1842)

RED AND BLACK (1830)

The fact that Beyle spent his early manhood in the armies of Napoleon, from Marengo till after Moscow, accounts for his idolization of that great soldier, which appears in all his literary work wherever it is appropriate. Despite his fecundity in biographies, books of travel, and essays, his fame to-day—and he said he should not be appreciated till 1880—rests chiefly on his four novels. The second, *Rouge et Noir* ("Red and Black"), meaning the army and the Church, aimed to depict the conditions in France after Napoleon. In Bonaparte's day the only career for the ambitious was that of the soldier; in 1830, the priesthood offered the best opening for ability to gain power and wealth. The struggles, successes, and temptations of the hero of *Rouge et Noir* —so like Stendhal himself in morbid introspection and energy, but tainted with unscrupulous selfishness—are shown with unrelenting vigor, while his worship of Napoleon, his hatred of the Jesuits, his cold-blooded triumphs with foolish women, and his strange, tragic end make a startling picture of the sordid conditions of French society at that period.

THE Mayor of the pretty manufacturing city of Verrières was Monsieur de Rênal, owner of the great nail-factory down by the River Doubs. His imposing mansion and extensive gardens were the finest in the neighborhood. When our story opens he had engaged young Julien Sorel, son of an old peasant carpenter, as tutor to his three boys, the eldest aged eleven.

Julien was different from his father and elder brothers, was fond of books, and was studying Latin with the curé, preparatory to the priestly seminary. He could teach the boys, and it would be fine to have them walk out in charge of a tutor—something that Monsieur Valenod, the ambitious superintendent of charities, had not for his children.

Madame de Rênal was tall, well formed, with beautiful

eyes, and a simple native refinement, placidly accepting her lot as the wife of a wealthy, rather vulgar, but important man, and the mother of his children. She had been unavailingly made love to by the loud-voiced, handsome M. Valenod, but had gently declined his attentions.

Old Sorel despised Julien as a good-for-nothing, and that very day had beaten him for reading instead of mill-tending, but he now sent him to the Mayor's. Julien was eighteen years old, his delicate features and slight figure looking even younger. In his boyhood he had been wild to be a soldier, having had a friendship with a retired army-surgeon who filled him with worship of Napoleon. But, when Julien was fourteen, interest in a new church at Verrières, and unjust judgments rendered by a magistrate to please an influential young vicar, decided the boy to become a priest. Ambition was his passion, and, already an intelligent reader, he sought the Abbé Chélan, who taught him Latin as well as theology. Obeying his father, Julien went to the Mayor's.

Meantime Madame de Rênal, who never had seen young Sorel, had pictured to herself a vulgar, slovenly priest, who, because he knew Latin, would be empowered to scold and perhaps flog her dear sons. She was stepping out to the garden when she saw a young peasant timidly standing near the entrance-door. His complexion was fair, and his big black eyes were as soft as a girl's. She looked toward him and asked:

"What do you wish, my child?"

Julien turned, and, his sensitiveness responding to her kindness and beauty, he said:

"I am the new tutor, Madame," and the tears started. Madame de Rênal was so happily surprised at this turn to her fears that she gaily laughed, and led him in.

He gradually regained his courage, told of his home, his studies, his ignorance of manners, and asked forgiveness for unintentional faults. Meantime, as the lady talked, he thought that he ought to kiss her hand. That frightened him; then he braced himself, feeling that not to do what he had intended would be cowardly: he *must* do it. And when she besought his kindness for the boys, he said:

"Never, Madame, will I lay my hand on your children; I

swear it in the presence of God," and he took her hand and raised it to his lips.

She was astonished, and even offended, but said nothing, as just then M. de Rênal emerged from his study, and after some commendatory words, paid Julien his first month's salary and sent him to the tailor to be clad in a suit of black.

When presented to the children, Julien had them one after another open his Latin New Testament, and read the first few words of any paragraph, when he recited from memory the rest of the page; he knew the whole New Testament by heart. This astonished everyone; even the servants lingered at the door. M. Valenod called, and was dazed by such learning; and in the evening the neighbors came in. It was a triumph for M. de Rênal; while Julien maintained a quiet but lofty air. Within a month be was respected by the whole house; as to his passion for Napoleon—now execrated by all loyal Frenchmen—he was shrewd enough to speak of his idol in terms of horror.

The children adored their tutor, while he had no love for them. Cold, just, yet interesting, he was a good preceptor. He hated the frequent dinner-company, despised their insincerities, but kept silence. Elisa, Madame de Rênal's maid, promptly fell in love with him, but he treated her with kindness only. Madame de Rênal, since marriage, had learned nothing except a fatuous love for her children, who monopolized all her tenderness. Her husband had laughed at her religion and motherly anxiety, so she presumed that all men were alike hard, money-loving, ambitious, and she became indifferent to anything beyond her children and her one friend, Madame Derville, a former companion at the convent.

In Julien, however, she found a peculiar charm, on the one hand correcting his rustic manners, and on the other admiring his vigorous intellect and his sensibility. She had no more knowledge of love than a child, and, happy in caring for Julien's welfare and in her children, she never dreamed of self-reproach.

Elisa had some money left her, and in confessing to the Abbé Chélan told her desire to marry Julien. He communicated this to Julien, who calmly declined the proposal, giving the Abbé to understand that his reasons involved a third party—

practically an imputation on Elisa. He had no notion of tying himself to a girl of her class, although he would not say that.

M. de Rênal sent his family every summer to his château at Vergy. Here, they all chased butterflies and impaled them in frames, while the lady kept Elisa busy with her changes of dress, in genuine innocence making herself as young and lovely as possible. She also brought her friend, Madame Derville, to visit her. Julien now enjoyed life, with his pupils, the ladies, and a retreat among the rocks for hours of reading.

One evening the young women and Julien were sitting under a shadowy linden, when he accidentally touched Madame de Rênal's hand, which she quickly withdrew. This did not please Julien; it offended his *amour propre*; he thought it his due that her hand should not be withdrawn when he touched it. That evening, sitting beside the ladies, he was violently excited—now daring, now fearing to act—and he desperately took Madame de Rênal's hand. She withdrew it. He took it again, resisted her effort to release it, and finally thrilled with beatitude when she suffered it to remain. Not that he loved her; but he had carried his point; and now he was terrified and talked on, excitedly and entertainingly. As for her, she enjoyed an innocent delight.

Shortly after this Julien received the Mayor's permission to be away several days, and visited his friend Fouqué, a young wood-merchant, in the mountains, who besought Julien to become his partner. But ambition beckoned our youth to Paris and to fame; so, veiling his desires under his vocation for the Church, he returned to Vergy. For two days he had not even thought of Madame de Rênal, whom now his suspicious nature watched for signs of despising him as a peasant. But, reflecting that he owed it to himself to be successful with one so far above him, he took her hand that evening, and when she asked:

"Will you leave us? Will you go away?"—for that was her dread, he replied with a sigh:

"I must, for I love you passionately—and what a crime—in a young priest."

Knowing nothing of love, or of its depiction in novels, Madame de Rênal spent a happy night, thinking of their serene and pleasant intercourse. Frightened by his own boldness, Julien now tried to arrange a plan of action. One evening he whispered in her ear:

"Madame, this night at two o'clock I shall visit you in your chamber. I have something to say to you." And he trembled lest she should assent.

She answered with unfeigned indignation, and he continued in general conversation with the two ladies until bedtime, mortified and depressed.

When the château clock struck two he was miserable indeed, for he felt that he *must* pay the announced visit, and he entered her room, where a night-lamp was burning. She leaped from the bed, exclaiming "Wretch!" and he fell at her feet and embraced her knees. She severely reproached him, and he burst into tears.

Some hours later Julien left the chamber. Between reproaches and embraces and final abandonment she had given herself to him, while he, amid it all, thought only of himself, his obscurity, his victory, his superiority. And when alone in his room again he thought: "*Mon Dieu!* to be loved, to be happy— is it no more than that?" And then: "Was I attentive to what I owed myself? Did I play well my part?"

After a few days and nights, however, Julien did almost forget his rôle, and found himself really in love; and, as the months passed, they had many happy hours together, she instructing him in social matters, and he often thrilling her with his keen observations and eloquence. Madame Derville, seeing the affair, had left her friend, and, while Julien did not neglect his preceptor's duties, he spent much time with his mistress.

But it befell that little Stanislas Xavier, the youngest of the children, came down with fever, and his mother was smitten with remorse, thinking it God's punishment for her love. Julien could hardly prevent her confessing her sin to her husband or to her confessor. At last the child grew better, and, although their relations continued, she incessantly reproached herself.

Elisa, consulting M. Valenod on a small lawsuit, confided to him her suspicions about the man who had rejected her and the woman who had turned from M. Valenod, and shortly afterward an anonymous letter to M. de Rênal opened the husband's eyes. Hideously angry, the poor man was distracted. He had nowhere a friend: the poor hated him for his meanness, the rich for his success. If he killed his wife he would lose a valuable social asset, and would miss the large legacy expected from her dying aunt; to kill Julien would be equally a scandal and a quarrel with her. Amid his perplexities his wife brought him another anonymous letter, addressed to her (prepared by her and Julien), advising her to be rid of her little peasant and to remember that the writer held her secret, and would compel her to walk his path. She showed it to her husband, insisted that he should discharge Julien, who, even if innocent, was the occasion of this insult, and intimated that the author of both letters was Valenod (whose earlier love-letters to her she now showed him), inspired by Elisa, who hated Julien for rejecting her. The result was that Julien was sent to Verrières for two weeks.

Meantime, however, Elisa had confessed other sins than her own to the Abbé Chélan, who sent for Julien, saying:

"I ask you nothing; you will tell me nothing. Within three days you set out for the seminary at Besançon, or the abode of your friend Fouqué. Go you must, and not return to Verrières for one year."

Julien decided for the seminary, bade farewell to Madame de Rênal—who felt as if she were about to die—and with a letter of commendation from the Mayor, set out for Besançon. He was deeply affected at parting, but soon began to anticipate the pleasures of the great city.

In Besançon he stopped at a café for a roll and cup of coffee, and attracted the interest of the elegant young woman presiding at the *comptoir*, who gave him her address on a card as he went out. Thence he sought the seminary with trembling. He met the stern-eyed director, the Abbé Pirard, who had received from his old friend, Abbé Chélan, a kindly letter about Sorel, and, after conquering his fright, Julien really surprised the director by his knowledge of Latin and the Scriptures. He was finally sent with friendly admonitions to his cell—a tiny chamber, eight feet square—and fell asleep, without supper or prayers, awaking next morning on the floor.

In the seminary Julien spent months, amid petty jealousies

and puerilities, but bore himself sturdily and studied hard. Finding that not diligence but obedience, not acquirements but exercises of ascetic piety, were the secrets of success, he changed his habits—but without making friends; his white hands, his cleanliness, his bad habit of thinking, all made him unpopular. One day the director sent for him, and before leaving the seminary—for he was suspected of Jansenism, and this Jesuit seminary had become too inimical for him—he appointed Julien tutor for the Old and New Testaments. They parted with an embrace, and Julien found his new station vastly advantageous.

But the Abbé Pirard had been for years aiding as counsel in a lawsuit, which the Marquis de la Mole of Paris was pushing. Learning of Pirard's difficulties, the Marquis sent for him and gave him a wealthy parish near Paris, meantime asking him to be his secretary, for he had vast business interests and valued the Abbé's integrity and ability. The Abbé declined, but spoke of young Sorel, who, with his energy and intelligence, would fill the place satisfactorily. And Julien, summoned to Paris, joyfully left the Seminary.

On his way he stopped at Verrières. A league from town he bought a ladder, and at night he went to M. de Rênal's garden, finding entrance at Madame de Rênal's window. She was horrified, but when she learned of his going to Paris it was too much. He spent the night and the next day in her room, but about two o'clock the following morning M. de Rênal came to the locked door. Julien leaped from the window and escaped, while she indignantly opened to her suspicious husband.

In Paris he sought the Abbé Pirard. Receiving much wholesome counsel, he was presented to the Marquis de la Mole, who was friendly and courteous. Madame la Marquise was tall, fair, and haughty, regarding only high descent as of any worth. The son, Comte Norbert, was a gallant officer, who was polite to Julien and took him riding. The daughter, Mademoiselle Mathilde de la Mole, was a beauty, but intelligent, contemptuous of the brainless fops of "society," and deeply romantic, cherishing the memory of that Boniface de la Mole, the lover of Marguerite de Navarre, who was decapitated in 1574 on pretense of a political conspiracy, and whose head the love-sick

Queen begged from the executioner and buried with her own hands. Her name was Mathilde-Marguerite, and on every thirtieth of April she wore mourning in memory of De la Mole's execution.

Julien gave satisfaction to the Marquis—docketed his correspondence, wrote his letters, straightened his accounts, and much reduced his employer's worries. He dined with the family, was present at receptions, and gradually acquired social customs, never intruding upon conversations unless sought, when he usually did himself credit.

During these months, while becoming a Parisian in dress and air, Julien had maintained a cool indifference to Mademoiselle de la Mole. Without showing it, she admired his cleverness, so different from the titled men that paid court to her. One night, at a ball, he was honored by her with a confidential talk of irony concerning the stupid people about her. The next morning she found him in her father's library, where he usually worked, and talked with him. She sought him, in short, while he, always suspicious, withheld himself from friendliness until their conversations and walks in the garden · convinced him of her sincerity. She displayed with him a frankness and enthusiasm in striking contrast with her usual cold and often ironical manner.

Once or twice she tried to resume the tone of great lady with him; but he met that with scant courtesy, and at last he began to think that she must be in love with him, finally saying to himself:

"Well, she is beautiful. I will possess her, and will then go away," and his heart beat like a trip-hammer.

On the other hand, while Mathilde admired Julien's ability and his pride, it was with surprise and romantic joy that the idea suddenly flashed across her: "I am in love! Other men weary me, but in Julien I find everything that they lack except a name and fortune, and these he will achieve." The romance stirred her imagination.

Always distrustful, he suspected a conspiracy to disgrace him, and assumed a cold, repellent attitude toward Mathilde, whose beauty and wit nevertheless grew upon him. Anxious to get away for thought, he obtained permission to visit Languedoc for inspection of an estate there; but before going he received from Mathilde a note—in short, a frank declaration of love. Julien was in an ecstasy of bliss. He swelled with pride —he, the carpenter's son, to have distanced counts and dukes! Suspicion still dogged him, however, and, to make sure of Mathilde's letter, he hid it in the cover of a Bible, which he sent to his friend Fouqué.

He answered the letter, but with ingenious phrases. She replied; and he rejoined; when she wrote:

"I *must* speak with you this night. At the stroke of one, take the gardener's ladder and ascend to my chamber-window. It is moonlight, but no matter."

Still Julien feared a conspiracy and determined to depart in the morning. "But, if Mathilde should be in good faith! She will think me a poltroon, and I shall miss not only a mistress— they are plenty—but the divine pleasure of seeing myself preferred to men of birth and station." He passed a miserable evening of doubts, but at one o'clock, pistol in hand, mounted his ladder, and the casement opened to him.

He frankly told Mathilde his suspicions, and she admired his bravery in coming into such possible danger; but she now bitterly regretted her rashness in summoning him. Still, here he was, and she reflected that he must be made happy or she would be wanting in strength of purpose. At a zero temperature they discussed it. Finally, violating her own feelings, she yielded herself to him. In the morning, as he galloped off to the forest, he found his astonishment greater than his felicity; while she wonderingly asked herself: "Can I have been mistaken? Do I not love him?"

For several days she avoided him, and he hungered for her; and for weeks they treated each other with alternations of affection and coldness, until she broke out upon him with reproaches, and vowed she never loved him.

Advised by one of his friends, Julien now thought of paying attentions to some other woman to bring his loved one to terms. He selected the Maréchale de Fervaques, a frequent visitor at the Hotel de la Mole, a widow, beautiful, wealthy, and a champion of virtue. For six weeks he offered devotions by letter and in person to the austere lady—the letters being rather philosophic than amatory, and the personal devoir not much more zealous—to Mathilde's uneasiness. At last she saw the porter bringing a letter, and informed Julien that she was his wife and he must not correspond with other women. However, seeing several of Madame de Fervaques's letters in his desk, unopened, she fell at his feet, crying:

"Ah! forgive me, but love me, for without you I cannot live."

He did not yet treat her tenderly, eagerly as he desired to, but still held her off, asking what guaranties she offered that she would not reject him again. But when she told him that she was about to become a mother he was really touched. She proposed to write to her father the fact, and then with Julien to depart. He forbade this at first, fearing its effect on the Marquis—his friend and benefactor—and dreading the necessary separation from Mathilde, for he loved her. Mathilde wrote pathetically to her father, bewailing his disappointment and grief, but assuming responsibility for beginning the attachment and declaring her readiness to go away with Julien, who would support them by teaching.

The Marquis loaded Julien with reproaches, and, when Julien offered to kill himself or to be killed, drove him away. Mathilde scornfully rejected any secret accouchement, and the Abbé Pirard, whom Julien now sought, persuaded the Marquis that an open wedding and departure would be best. Her father gave her ten thousand livres and presented them the Languedoc property, but hesitated long about the marriage, mortified that his daughter should become merely Madame Sorel; then he procured a commission in the hussars for M. le Chevalier Julien Sorel de la Vernaye, demanding that he should join his regiment at Strasbourg.

Julien gaily joined his regiment, but two days later he was summoned by Mathilde to return. "All is lost," she wrote; "come immediately. Rely on me. I love you."

The Marquis had received a letter from Madame de Rênal (to whom he had written on Julien's own suggestion), saying that her duty constrained her to tell him that the man he inquired about had, by the seduction of a weak and unhappy woman, striven to rise in the world; that he was devoid of principle, and that his settled policy was to secure foothold in a family by seducing the woman there whose credit was the greatest.

The Marquis had gone, writing that he forbade Mathilde's marriage, but would give Julien an income of ten thousand livres to live abroad; concluding: "Cut loose absolutely from the villain, and you will regain a father."

"I cannot blame Monsieur de la Mole," said Julien. "What father would do differently! Farewell!" and he ran to a post-chaise standing in the street, sped away to Verrières, bought pistols, went to the church—it being Sunday morning—found a seat behind Madame de Rênal, and, when all heads were bowed at the elevation of the host, fired at her, and missed; then fired again, and she fell.

Julien was arrested. Madame de Rênal was not seriously wounded, but was grievously disappointed. Deprived of Julien, she had long wished to die, and the letter had been written at her confessor's dictation.

Julien confessed his murderous intent, saying: "I have merited death, and await it." He wrote to Mathilde, announcing his deed, and asked her to marry Monsieur de Croisenois a year after his own death. "You have my last words, with my adoration."

But Mathilde came swiftly to Besançon, where he was confined, and visited him every day. Madame de Rênal also, recovered of her wound, came with forgiveness and love, visiting him twice a day. The two women—separately, for they never met—lavished effort and money to employ lawyers and to influence jurors. Their labors might have succeeded but that Julien, at the trial, feeling all his love for Madame de Rênal revive, and his dutiful affection for Mathilde grow cold, made a speech in which he repeated his confession of intent to murder, and then insulted the jurymen, declaring that he was a peasant who had achieved success, while they were but discontented *bourgeois*, and he was not on trial before his peers. He was convicted, and condemned to the guillotine.

Refusing to appeal, he was duly executed, one sunshiny day. His ending was without affectation or bravado. Fouqué went at midnight to inter his remains, at Julien's request, in a grotto on the mountain above Verrières. But Mathilde accompanied

him, bearing in her lap the head of her lover. After twenty
priests had chanted the service in the illuminated grotto, and all
had departed except Mathilde and Fouqué, she buried the head
with her own hands. The grotto was afterward adorned by
Mathilde with costly statuary.

Three days after Julien's death, while embracing her children, the heart-broken Madame de Rênal breathed her last.

THE CHARTREUSE OF PARMA (1840)

This romance, which may be fairly estimated as Beyle's masterpiece in fiction, was begun in 1830, when the author was consul at Civita Vecchia. It attracted very little attention on its publication or for years afterward, although Balzac wrote a fervent eulogy of the work in *La Revue Parisienne*. But his conclusion that it never would be read by more than fifteen hundred people, comprising diplomats, statesmen, and the *élite* of society, must have had a rather depressing effect on Beyle. According to Paul Bourget, Beyle did not expect his story to be widely circulated before 1880. He was a true prophet, for after that period it began to be almost universally recognized as a world classic.

THE family of Del Dongo, one of the oldest and wealthiest in Lombardy, consisted, in the early part of the nineteenth century, of the Marchese, a sour-faced and sordidly avaricious fanatic who hated Napoleon and was the abject slave of Austria; his beautiful and long-suffering wife, the Marchesa; his widowed sister, Gina, the Countess Pietranera, a lady of surpassing loveliness, indomitable energy, and elastic morals; his elder son, upon whom the entire fortune of the house was entailed, and who gave promise of being a worthy successor of his detestable father; and his second son, Fabricio, Marchesino del Dongo, to give him the title customary at Milan.

At the age of sixteen Fabricio was a handsome, intelligent youngster, though hardly able to write his own name. But he was a superb horseman, an inimitable fencer, and was idolized by his aunt the Countess. Most of his time was spent at his father's magnificent château on Lake Como, and here he was the leader in all the expeditions and forays of the peasant urchins of the neighborhood. Indeed, this good-looking and gifted scapegrace was continually getting himself and his youthful aunt into difficulties by indulging the impulse of the moment.

From his earliest years Fabricio had been an enthusiastic admirer of Napoleon. As soon as he learned of the hero's return from Elba he decided to offer him the succor of his arm. His mother and his aunt were in despair; but, as they could not turn him from his purpose, they gave him all the money they had and sewed ten diamonds, worth about ten thousand francs, into the lining of his coat.

Our young hero made such speed across the Alps that in a surprisingly short period he was in Paris. He wished to have an audience with the Emperor; but, though he went regularly every morning to see Napoleon review the troops, he failed, and this astonished him very much. At last he left Paris, where he had been robbed of all his ready money by some young Bonapartists as enthusiastic as himself, and, after selling two of his diamonds, set out for the frontier. In his exalted disinterestedness, he believed that his valiant right arm would play an important part in repelling the allies. Still, his controlling impulse was to witness a genuine battle and to immortalize himself with the Corsican hero. Such was his fixed idea, and, in his naïve inexperience, he thought all he had to do was to join one of the French battalions, never suspecting that there were any formalities to be observed before enlisting under the French flag. Owing to an absurd passport, which described him as a dealer in barometers, and his almost total ignorance of the French language, he was soon arrested as a spy, and would have been shot within twenty-four hours but for the compassion of the jailer's wife, who did not like to see so pretty a lad killed, and one who paid so liberally for all he had. After concealing him for a few days in her own room, she gave him a huge cavalry saber and the uniform and papers of a hussar who had died in the prison, to which he had been sent for stealing a cow and some silver spoons, and dismissed him with a warning not to speak, as his Italian accent would betray him. An hour after parting from his benefactress, Fabricio bought a skeleton-like horse from a peasant and pushed on to the front. Rigged out in his ill-fitting habiliments, he at length arrived in high spirits at the battle-field of Waterloo. About five o'clock he heard cannonading; it was the overture of Ligny. He fell in with a good-natured vivandière, who was touched by the youth and handsome appearance of this "seventeen-year-old weanling," as she called him. She procured him a decent horse, made him swallow a few glasses of brandy, and cautioned him to be less free with his money than he seemed inclined to be. She also told him to throw away his clumsy saber and pick up a gun and cartridge-box: "Though," she added, "I'll lay a bet you don't know how to bite a cartridge." Poor Fabricio had to make the mortifying confession that his new friend was right.

His steed, evidently a war-horse, galloped with him excitedly in the direction of the firing, and then the horrible sights that met the eyes of the young enthusiast turned his naturally pale complexion to a sickly shade of green. But he overcame the involuntary terror excited by the sad spectacle around him, and burned with renewed ardor to throw himself into the middle of the bloody conflict: he would witness a real battle of the Grand Army, no matter what happened.

An incident that now occurred promised to satisfy his desire. His horse, which had probably belonged to some superior officer, dashed forward wildly after a passing escort, and Fabricio quickly found himself dragged among a group of hussars who were following Marshal Ney. In their company he passed through several corps and even managed to kill a redcoat. Now he began to think he was a real soldier and engaged in a real battle. He was intoxicated by the smell of powder and imagined himself the exact counterpart of the warriors of Tasso surrounded by noble and sympathetic souls, in whose company it would be sweet and glorious to die. But alas! all these fine dreams were to come to naught. A general, whose horse was shot through the head, fell quite close to him. Then Fabricio felt himself seized by the feet, grasped round the body, lifted out of the stirrups and moved backward over his horse's croup. His captors let him drop, and he struck the ground in a sitting posture. The general climbed into the saddle and rode off, followed by his men. Fabricio, boiling with anger at such perfidy, rose to his feet and started in pursuit, shouting: "*Ladri! ladri!*" ("Thieves! thieves!") It was a queer spectacle to see this tender youth chasing a regiment of robbers on a battle-field.

After a variety of adventures comical-tragical and tragical-comical, Fabricio was so exhausted that it was impossible for him to keep up with the beaten army in its retreat. But the guileless youth had learned a thing or two from his experiences.

Seeing a soldier treating three horses to a feed of wheat, he covered him with his musket and declared he would blow a hole in him if he did not surrender the best of the steeds. The frightened soldier obeyed, and Fabricio generously flung him three five-franc pieces.

On his return journey to Italy his wounds troubled him, and he was sometimes obliged to take to his bed. He incurred danger also from the spies of the triumphant Bourbons. But he was always affectionately tended and protected by the wives and daughters of his hosts at the inns where he put up; for Fabricio was fated through life to be the pet of women.

The rapturous delight of his mother, and especially of his young and beautiful aunt, when he entered the Del Dongo palace in Milan cannot easily be described. Indeed, the Countess Pietranera took such an intensely affectionate interest in her engaging nephew that a scandal of the worst kind might have ensued had it been reciprocated. But it was not, and as for the lady she never wilfully cherished an irregular or guilty wish.

Before Fabricio was a week in Milan, he was driven almost to frenzy on learning that his elder brother, the Marchesino Ascanio, had denounced him to the Austrian police. The influence of the Countess with Baron Binder, head of that body, obtained a modification of the decree that banished him. He was allowed to live in an old palace of his family in Romagnano, providing he should attend mass every morning, never associate with philosophers or men of enlightenment, eschew all reading-matter printed since 1720, except, at the utmost, the novels of Sir Walter Scott, and select a pretty and pious young woman of the neighborhood (belonging to the aristocracy, of course) for a mistress.

With Fabricio away, the Countess felt the need of novelty and consolation, and became an assiduous frequenter of the opera. She had quarreled with her odious brother and had taken up her abode in an apartment in a fifth story, determined to live on her pension of fifteen hundred francs a year.

One night at La Scala, Count Mosca della Rovere, the Prime Minister of Ernesto IV, Prince of Parma, was presented to her and fell desperately in love with her. He was almost forty-five years old, but a fascinating talker, and he amused and interested

Gina. He had such a charming air of simplicity and gaiety that he would have been good-looking still had not his freakish and truculent master forced him to wear powder in his hair as a guaranty of his political orthodoxy.

The Count discovered excellent reasons for his folly as long as his charmer was before his eyes; but when he came to reflect on his age and the cares that darkened his life, these reasons appeared less cogent: "The Prince, a man of ability, deluded by his fears—he looks under the bed every night for conspirators—gives me a splendid existence and money in abundance to serve him as his minister; but suppose he dismisses me to-morrow, what am I? A poor, penniless old man; that is to say, the most despicable object on earth—a fine offering, truly, to make the Countess!" But the Countess was beginning to think that age was not an obstacle in a man who possessed the art of pleasing, and, when the Count made his proposal, he was accepted. He explained to her that there were three courses open to him: first, to fling ambition to the winds and live with her at Florence, Milan, wherever she wished, on the wreck of his fortune; second, to purchase an estate near Parma and dwell there. She would be received at court. But there was one objection. Count Mosca had a wife living; Gina was a widow; and the Prince was a man of strict principles. The Count then laid before her his third proposal. The Duke of Sanseverina-Taxis, an amiable young fribble of seventy, dapple-gray, immensely rich, but of plebeian origin, had been so maladroit as to manifest Liberal opinions, and for two years past had been sitting in sackcloth and ashes. He had been unable to obtain the Grand Cordon of the noblest order of the principality, and for lack of it had been wasting away visibly. The Count had concluded this singular bargain with him: he was to marry the Countess Pietranera, to receive the Grand Cordon, the want of which had been hurrying him to the grave, to be appointed envoy at a foreign court, and to promise on the morning of the marriage never to set foot again in Parma.

Three months afterward the new Duchess of Sanseverina-Taxis was the cynosure of every eye and the observed of all observers at the court of Parma. She had conquered her elevated position by her serene dignity of manner and easy affability; her house was by long odds the most attractive in the city, and she was afraid she had succeeded only too well in pleasing the Prince, Ernesto IV. This sovereign had the reputation of a monster, an ogre, because now and then he took it into his head to hang a Liberal or two. But he was really an amiable personage, led astray by a mania for imitating Louis XIV.

The tide of the Duchess's successes was for a time checked by the intrigues of the notorious Marchesa Roversi, the head of the faction opposed to Mosca. She was niece to the Duke of Sanseverina, and feared that her expected inheritance was menaced by the charms of the new Duchess. But the position of the latter with the Prince proved too strong to be shaken; it became stronger than ever, in fact; and Count Mosca was raised to the seventh heaven of bliss; it was a glorious epoch in his life, and was destined to exert a powerful influence on Fabricio's future.

That young gentleman was still at Romagnano, confessing his sins, hunting, reading nothing, and assiduously making love to a lady of quality, in pursuance of his instructions. This was not a useful sort of life for a young man of eighteen, however, and was the occasion of serious anxiety to Mosca and the Duchess. After many discussions it was at length agreed between the exemplary pair that the proper vocation for a youth of a high, aristocratic house, who was suspected of Liberalism, and more than suspected of libertinism, was the Church! Fabricio refused firmly at first to enter a profession for which he had not the slightest inclination. His desire was to go to New York and enter the American army.

"The worst mistake you ever made in your life!" exclaimed the Duchess. "You would see no fighting, and the Yankees have no theaters, no opera, none of the refinements of life." She told him of the worship of the almighty dollar in the United States, and of the consideration exacted by the porters and hod-carriers, who make and unmake men by their votes. Then she showed him that three members of the Del Dongo family had occupied the archiepiscopal see of Parma in the seventeenth and eighteenth centuries. Why should not Fabricio do the same in the nineteenth? He consented, with a sigh, to abandon the voyage to the United States and to spend three years at the

Naples theological seminary instead. After all, life could not be duller at Naples than it had been at Romagnano.

The year which passed pleasantly enough for Fabricio was a trying one for the Duchess. On three or four occasions the Count was within an inch of ruin. His rival, Rossi, Minister of Police, became the Prince's prime favorite. The Duchess clung to Mosca with passionate tenderness in his hour of peril, and Fabricio was almost forgotten. At last the Count won the battle. His first step was to secure the nomination of his bitter enemy, General Fabio Conti, to the governorship of the citadel where the political prisoners condemned by Rossi were immured. "If this so-called Liberal treats his prisoners kindly," said Mosca to Gina, "he will be disgraced as a Jacobin. If he shows himself strict and merciless, he will cease to be the leader of his party. He has not the brains to extricate himself from the dilemma in which I have placed him, and, in either event, my stability is strengthened."

Four years passed, filled with events as insignificant as those we have already recorded. The Duchess and the Minister had now and then to open their purses to pay for an occasional escapade of Fabricio's, but otherwise he followed pretty strictly the line of conduct laid down for him—that of a *grand seigneur* pursuing his theological studies, and not counting entirely on his virtues to make his way in the world.

In 1821, having passed all his examinations, after a fashion, he set out for Parma, traveling—for he was now a Monsignor—in a carriage drawn by four horses. After praying at the tombs of his three archiepiscopal congeners, he proceeded on foot to the palace of the Duchess. She was astonished to see him. When he was leaving for Naples he had the appearance of a neck-or-nothing steeplechaser. Now he was affable, dignified, a polished diamond, yet with no loss of his youthful fire. As soon as Count Mosca entered the apartment, he expressed his gratitude for certain favors so gracefully that that veteran statesman said to himself: "He'll do!"

Yet when the Count looked at the Duchess and saw the rapt expression of her face, a pang of jealousy tortured him. She never had given him any real cause for complaint. He knew that she had declined the pressing attentions of the Prince, who at the time had made a remark that afforded food for thought. "But with what face could I present myself before the Count," she said laughingly to him, "should I accept your Highness's devotion?"

"I should be almost as embarrassed as you," was his reply. "The dear Count! my friend! But it is a difficulty that could be easily got round. I have thought it all out. We would clap the Count into the citadel for the remainder of his days."

The Duchess had been maneuvering for two months to procure a private audience for her protégé; it would be a distinguished honor and would at once mark the young man's position at court. Although his Highness yielded, his feeling toward Fabricio was the reverse of friendly. He tried to entrap him by talking Jacobin politics. Among the remarks Fabricio made in answer to the feigned Liberal sentiments of the Prince were such gems as: "The people owe blind obedience to their rulers"; "The terms *liberty, justice, the greatest good of the greatest number*, are infamous"; "Everything that has been done since the death of Louis XIV in 1715 is not only a crime but a blunder"; "The man who distrusts the Bible or the laws of the Church is lost."

The Prince soon tired of the contest and showed his ill humor by dismissing him abruptly and turning on his heel.

"The animal doesn't like me," said Fabricio to himself. Then he waited on the aged Archbishop Landriani.

This prelate was a man of broad views, a scholar and a saint; but he had one overpowering defect. Being of the very humblest origin, he had got it into his head that persons of noble birth had all the virtues. Therefore he never could say no to the Prince or even to one of his ministers. When he discovered that Fabricio had been kept a quarter of an hour, without his knowledge, waiting in his anteroom, his despair was pitiable. A Del Dongo! whom he intended to appoint his vicar-general, and afterward his coadjutor with right of succession!

Although Fabricio, guided by the politic counsels of the Duchess, paid assiduous court to the good Archbishop and frequented the most aristocratic and dullest houses in Parma, he did not deny himself all amusement. He secured a box in the third tier of the theater, where he was not likely to be recognized.

There he saw a very pretty and graceful young actress whose natural and unaffected acting in one of Goldoni's comedies quite charmed him. He was surprised to learn that her name was Marietta Valserra—Valserra being the family name of the Del Dongos. His curiosity was aroused and he called three times at her lodgings. This excited the jealousy of a frightfully ugly varlet called Giletti, who played small parts in the company and was in love with Marietta; and the jealousy of this squint-eyed giant was to have disastrous results for our amiable hero.

Shortly afterward intelligence reached Parma of the death of the Duke of Sanseverina-Taxis, and the Duchess and the Count were thus enabled to regularize their situation by marriage. The Duchess determined to spend a goodly portion of the immense fortune bequeathed to her by her late husband in erecting a monument to his memory. But the misfortunes that soon overwhelmed her nephew necessitated a different method of employing the money.

Fabricio, who had imbibed a taste for digging for antiquities at Naples, had been sent by Mosca to superintend certain excavations that were being made at Sanguigna. The farmers of the district looked with no friendly eye on these operations or on the long trench that was being driven across their fields, and Fabricio's presence was useful in restraining them from violence, and also in seeing that the laborers did not pocket the coins and medals that were now and then turned up. While he was about to reload his gun he descried a ramshackle vehicle in the distance, and, as it approached nearer, he saw that it contained Marietta, Giletti, and the old woman who played the part of Marietta's mother.

The jealous Giletti took it into his head that Fabricio had posted himself in the middle of the road with a gun in his hand to attack him and to carry off Marietta. He jumped from the carriage, flung himself on the young man, and, as his strength was the greater, wrested the gun from him. Then he struck at him with a long sword he was in the habit of using when enacting certain characters. Fabricio took to his heels. As he was passing by the open door of the vehicle he heard Marietta say to him in an undertone: "He will kill you if you don't look out. Take this!" And she dropped a big hunting-knife into the road. Our hero stooped and seized it; but at the same moment received a thrust in the shoulder from Giletti's sword. After receiving a few more thrusts and parrying several others, he bounded on his enemy with his knife held low and pointing upward. The blade entered Giletti's chest and came out at the shoulder. He was dead. Fabricio's own wounds were only skin deep. But he saw half a dozen men marching deliberately toward the scene. "These are gendarmes," he reflected; "they will carry me to Parma. That would be a dainty morsel for the Roversi woman and the courtiers who hate my aunt!"

He jumped into the carriage and promised the *vetturino* four gold napoleons if he managed to get him beyond the Po before the gendarmes overtook him. But there was no pursuit.

When they were near the river, the old woman asked how he expected to get on with the Austrian police if he had no passport. She advised him to take Giletti's, which she surrendered "for a consideration." But the passport of the unfortunate actor was full of discrepancies. Fabricio's stature was barely five feet five, which was materially different from the five feet ten recorded in the descriptive list, not to speak of other differences. After incurring the greatest dangers, he was so fortunate as to be recognized by a retired and pensioned coachman of his aunt, the faithful Ludovico, who was ready to encounter any peril in his behalf. He procured a disguise for the fugitive, whom he accompanied to Ferrara, giving out that he was his elder brother. There Ludovico hired two small rooms in the house of a Jew. Fabricio was attacked with fever the next day, and the leech who was called in declared, on seeing his wounds, that he must inform the police. So Ludovico, after burning Giletti's passport, hired a *sediola*, and the pair set out for Bologna in the guise of tourists. Here Fabricio regained his health.

One day he met Pepe, his aunt's confidential man, at a restaurant. He had been looking for the Marchesino everywhere for the past week; he had a supply of money for him and three different passports, one in the name of Joseph Bossi.

The year spent by Fabricio in Bologna was not unpleasant and was agreeably diversified by a few duels. But, though Count Mosca used all his influence, and his wife expended immense sums in her nephew's behalf, it was learned that their enemies had triumphed; that a verdict had been returned against the little Marchesino, and that he would be sentenced to death or the galleys for the murder of Giletti.

Then the Duchess played her last card. Putting on her traveling costume, she demanded an audience of the Prince. As she was about leaving his dominions forever, she wished to thank his Highness for the favors she had received during the past five years. She was going to Naples.

The Prince was greatly concerned. Not only should he lose the most brilliant ornament of his court, but, with her cleverness and persuasive powers, everyone would believe whatever she said. He would owe to her the reputation of being a silly tyrant who employed none but corrupt judges, and who was in the habit of rising at all hours of the night to search for conspirators underneath his bed. He consented to quash the sentence against Fabricio on condition the Duchess remained at his court.

But, owing to a mistake of Count Mosca, he was enabled to punish Fabricio without actually violating the letter of his promise. He issued a decree, to be kept secret for the time, by which his Serene Highness in the clemency of his heart commuted the sentence of the Marchesino del Dongo to twelve years' imprisonment in the fortress of Parma.

When Fabricio received this news at Bologna the idea of seeing again the Duchess and the Count delighted him beyond measure. In spite of all that Ludovico could say, he hired a horse and was off like a shot.

No sooner had our poor hero entered the dominions of Ernesto IV than he found himself handcuffed and on his way to Parma, escorted by eight gendarmes. After entering the citadel he was grossly insulted by the Governor's clerk, Barbone, although he had called his attention to the fact that he was Grand Vicar of the diocese and that his birth and station entitled him to be treated with respect. After the handcuffs had been removed, the clerk became so offensive that the young prelate bounded over the rail and landed his fist on Barbone's nose to such good purpose that the latter tumbled off his chair and fell against the legs of the Governor-General Fabio Conti.

Fabricio spent nine months in the fortress, feeling like a

caged lion. Fortunately, he had a friend in the Governor's daughter, the delicate, high-minded Clelia Conti, whose pity for him quickly changed to love. Barbone had been bribed by the Rossi and Roversi faction to poison him, and nothing but the devotion and ingenuity of Clelia saved him from a horrible death on at least two occasions.

It may be imagined that the Duchess was not idle. She lavished her money in every direction, bribing everyone susceptible of bribery. Through her assistance, and with the indispensable complicity of Clelia, Fabricio made an escape from his high tower—one of the most marvelous escapes that ever have been recorded in history. Relays were posted by the Duchess on the route he was to follow, and at length he found himself a free man in Piedmont.

After the death of Ernesto IV, and the succession of his son, Ernesto V, Fabricio could safely return to Parma. He was named coadjutor by the good Archbishop Landriani. On the death of the latter he succeeded him, and his exemplary morals, piety, and eloquence were so remarkable that the virtues of the late prelate were soon forgotten. His elder brother, too, had departed, and the family possessions had descended to our hero. But the death of his faithful sweetheart Clelia, a few years after her marriage, affected him so deeply that he resolved to retire from the world. He signed papers assuring to each of his servants a pension of one thousand francs and reserving an equal allowance for himself. He divided his estates among his mother, his aunt, and an unhappily married sister. Then he retired to the Chartreuse of Parma, a monastery situated in a forest near the Po. He died after a year spent in the Chartreuse, and the Duchess, who continued to adore him to the last, did not long survive him.

ANN SOPHIA STEPHENS

(United States, 1813–1886)

FASHION AND FAMINE (1854)

This novel had an immediate and great success. It was republished in London by three houses, and three translations appeared simultaneously in Paris.

ONG ISLAND sends to Fulton Market some things that are fresh and inviting besides fruit and vegetables; and Dame Gray, although only a huckster-woman, was one of them. When little Julia Warren crept anxiously past the stalls, looking for someone to whom she would not be afraid to speak, she was at once attracted by the cheerful, tidy dame. Her plaintive voice told her pitiful story of an old grandfather and grand-mother, breakfastless, at home, and asked for some berries and flowers that she might sell in the streets. Gladly Mrs. Gray filled her basket, and she sped away, promising to return at night and make payment.

"Oh, how glad grandfather will be!" she thought, as she raised her sweet voice and offered her tempting wares.

Wandering on, she found herself at the wharf just as two steamers came puffing up to their respective berths—one from across the sea, and one from the South. To the passengers streaming forth the little flower-girl presented her basket, but she became so absorbed in looking at a beautiful woman from the European steamer that she almost forgot to cry "Straw-berries and violets, just fresh." The woman was followed by a tall, awkward man, who performed the duties of a servant, but was often addressed in a manner that suggested a confi-dential attendant rather than a menial. The lady noticed the flowers, and, beckoning the little girl to the carriage, took a liberal supply, dropping a coin into the basket. Then she drove away.

Soon afterward a man of distinguished presence came by, half guiding a young and lovely girl toward the carriages.

"Oh, see those beautiful moss-rosebuds!" she exclaimed.

"Step in, lady-bird," said the gentleman, and he, too, summoned the flower-girl and dropped a coin into the basket, now nearly empty. Such success proved the beginning of more sales, and when Julia Warren hurried back to the basement that she called home, she had paid for all her stock and had a fortune —in her opinion—with which to purchase food for her beloved grandparents. For the lady's coin had proved to be a half-eagle, the first she had ever seen.

Besides this wonderful good fortune, she had an exciting adventure to relate. As she was turning away from the second carriage, she had picked up a gentleman's fine handkerchief, and had tried to overtake the carriage to see whether the tall, handsome man had lost it. While she was looking and wondering, the lady's carriage had come back, evidently for some lost object, and Julia had run to the window and shown the handkerchief to her first patroness. The lady had looked at the corner, and then, to Julia's astonishment, had opened the door and almost lifted her inside. Swiftly she was taken to a far more beautiful house than she ever had conceived of, and the lady had placed her in a lovely room, asking her to tell exactly where she found the handkerchief. The facts were soon told, and then, as the lady fell into a deep reverie, Julia stole out softly and ran home.

Ada Leicester had learned from that handkerchief and Julia two important things—William Leicester, her husband, was in New York and had arrived with a beautiful Southern girl. With these clues her servant, Jacob Strong, soon learned, further, that he was at the Astor House and that the young girl was not with him. The rain was pouring in torrents; but within an hour a hired coach, with Ada Leicester inside and Jacob on the box with the driver, was at the hotel. And so strong was the love of adventure in the heart of the libertine Leicester that it was quite in keeping with his habits to obey the invitation of the servant to enter the carriage, though entirely ignorant who was his companion on the rapid drive that followed. The lady did not speak, and Leicester felt something so mysterious about this affair that his usual free audacity was held in check. Not until the carriage stopped was a word of explanation uttered. Then the lady led him to a small room, furnished with the greatest plainness, in striking contrast with the luxury that had greeted Julia's astonished eyes, where, throwing off her wrappings, she revealed her face.

"You know me, William?" she asked.

"Yes," he answered coldly. "I thought you were dead. Where have you been so many years?"

"You know—you know—" she faltered. "Why ask that cruel question?"

"Now," he said, still with an indifference that crushed her, "tell me all your history since we parted, and your motive in coming here."

She sat mute and pale under his cool stare.

"I am waiting, Ada—waiting to hear why you abandoned your husband—and child."

"My husband left me."

"For a journey."

"Yes—such as you had taken before. You had a companion. You left me in debt and temptation. You drove me away. My child I sent to my parents."

Leicester had no desire to prolong this scene. His only wish connected with his wife was to discover whether, by any means, she had received any of the vast wealth of the man to whom she had referred when she spoke of the temptation that she had been forced to meet alone. He inferred from the plain furnishings of the room, her simple dress, and the hired coach, that she was poor, perhaps in debt still. He rose to go.

"You have sought this interview," he said, "and it is over. It must never be repeated."

She started up.

"You do not mean that, William," she faltered, as she fell senseless across the bed.

Leicester was not wholly satisfied that he had divined the whole truth about his wife, so, with a cunning in which he was an adept, he bribed her servant—the fellow seemed to lend himself readily to the scheme—to watch her and report to him. Then he returned to his hotel.

A few weeks after these events an old farmer and his wife, in Maine, were surprised by a visit from a tall, awkward man who made many anxious inquiries about the former owner of the farm. When he learned that Mr. Wilcox and his wife and granddaughter had been gone ten years, and that no one in the vicinity knew where they were, he abruptly departed without explanation. On receiving his report, it seemed to Ada Leicester that her cup of sorrow was indeed full. Her drop of comfort had been the hope that she might find her parents and her child, and that, devoting herself and her wealth to their happiness, she might atone in a measure for her youthful flight with Leicester. His fine presence and winning manner had captivated her, and she had loved him passionately until his conduct had destroyed her confidence. His crowning act was to go away with another woman, leaving her completely in the power of a man of great wealth, of whom he had borrowed large sums. From that position she had fled, sending her child to her parents. But, failing in all her efforts to support herself, she had finally, at the entreaty of her husband's creditor, returned to him. At his recent death he had left to her his immense estate, and she had hastened to New York, hoping to find her parents in her old home. Now this hope had failed, her husband had met her with scorn, and she was desperate. She closed her New York house, and again went to Europe. Jacob did not accompany her, but applied to Mr. Leicester for employment and was engaged as his personal attendant—an arrangement that suited the clever servant well.

In a small, artistic house, near the center of the metropolis, but embosomed in flowers, Leicester had placed the young Southern girl whom he had brought to New York. She was the daughter of a rich planter, and had been permitted to leave home only on condition of obtaining the advantages of instruction, which Mr. Leicester promised to secure.

As companion, Leicester had established his mother in the house, a weak woman who understood perfectly, and greatly feared, her unscrupulous son. Florence Craft had been perfectly happy at first, for she loved her betrayer with utter devotion, and was too innocent to realize her position. Not until he became neglectful of her did she perceive the full character of her surrender to his passion. At first a pretense of instruction had deceived her, and she, of course, hoped for a proposal of marriage. But as time passed, and lonely, humiliated, and hopeless, she saw no prospect of any other fate, she was wretched indeed. She had one friend, a young man whom Leicester had trained to be an expert penman and who, on the pretense of teaching her penmanship, came sometimes to the house. To him she spoke of her loneliness. One day when he was with her the servant, Jacob Strong, brought in a note from his master. Florence opened it sadly, but a glow lighted her face instantly.

"How could I doubt him?" she exclaimed. "See," and her face was lifted to his, "we are to be married next week."

Robert Otis remained silent, and Florence exclaimed again: "Why do you not congratulate me?"

Otis had already begun to distrust, for reasons of his own, the man in whom Florence felt implicit confidence, and he could only say that he hoped she would be happy. Happy! she had no doubt of that, and went about singing like a bird—a bird caught, alas! in a snare.

New York was now surprised by the magnificence of the entertainments given by a Mrs. Gordon, just arrived from Europe. She outrivaled all leaders of fashion in her balls. The world knew her as "Mrs. Gordon," but she was in reality Ada Leicester. She learned again of Leicester's presence in the metropolis, and determined to show him, in a most dramatic manner, that she was the mistress of the vast wealth that he coveted. She knew nothing of Florence Craft, nor of the intended marriage; but had she known, she would have known the truth—that the marriage was but a scheme to obtain money. For Leicester had received the news—he received all the letters intended for the young girl—of the death of the old planter, and that in two years Florence would come into possession of a handsome fortune. This fact accounted for the sudden determination to marry this latest object of his fancy.

To carry out her purpose of taking her husband by storm, Mrs. Leicester gave orders for the most magnificent entertainment ever given in New York. Her splendid apartments were converted into veritable fairy palaces, each room unique and complete, and yet all mingling in a harmonious whole. It was to be a fancy-dress ball, and she was to appear as Ceres, the Goddess of Plenty. Her gems had all been reset to simulate fruits and flowers, and she was a dazzling vision as she stood to receive her guests. Leicester had been invited, and signified his intention to be present at "Mrs. Gordon's" ball. But it chanced that this was the very evening of his proposed marriage to Florence, and he had still other matters on hand, which were demanding his attention. He was expecting to leave for Europe on the steamer at that hour lying at the pier ready for an early start. In order to live during the two years before Florence should come into her property, he must have money, and he had put into execution a scheme for which he had laid plans long before. He had, in fact, forged the name of Robert Otis's employer to a check for ten thousand dollars, and had given it to the young man to be cashed for him. His plan was to leave in the morning, believing that suspicion would fall at once on Otis, and that the numerous checks and notes on which he had made the youth practise, and which were, as he supposed, in the young man's desk, would prove him guilty beyond a doubt. The plan looked sure; but he was nervous and anxious to be off. Robert was to bring him the money between the ceremony and the ball. Just as he was entering the house for his marriage, he met the little flower-girl, and remembering that his mother had refused to act as a witness, and that he must have one besides his servant, he impressed her into the service, and so it happened that one of the witnesses to his illegal and treacherous marriage was his own child.

When he returned to the hotel Robert was not there. He was nervously walking the floor, and cursing the "rascal" for not coming, when the door opened and the young man appeared, with the full amount in gold. Gold! Not a trace would be left. His heart gave a bound of relief, and he made his preparations for an hour or two at the ball with a feeling of intense self-congratulation on his cleverness. If he had known where that gold had come from, he would have had different sensations.

When Jacob Strong entered the service of William Leicester he did so with the sole object of avenging the wrongs committed by his so-called "master" upon the beautiful Ada Wilcox, whose protector he had been when, a boy, he worked on her father's farm. He now understood Leicester's purpose in training young Otis to copy the signatures of merchants and bankers on notes and checks, whose significance the boy had not for some time known. He knew all about Florence and the letter from her home, telling of her expected inheritance. And he had been a witness at the false marriage. He had seen the forged check pass from Leicester to Robert Otis, with the request that it be cashed in the afternoon and that the money be brought to him at a certain hour in the evening. When Robert left the room with the forged check, he met him, told him the truth about the check, and appointed a meeting with him later. It was not from any bank that Robert Otis brought the money, but from Ada Leicester, procured from her by Jacob Strong, who had kept the check as evidence. But of the trap into which he had fallen Leicester knew nothing.

When he entered the ballroom he looked about him in amazement. He was accustomed to scenes of display, but this surpassed anything he had ever seen.

"Where is the hostess?" he asked of a masked youth.

"Don't you know her, the incomparable Mrs. Gordon? There she stands, a vision of beauty," was the reply.

Leicester looked and looked again. It was Ada, his wife. Every gem that she wore seemed to fix its value on his mind. His resolution was taken. He would claim her and all this splendor; the law gave it to him. He confronted her, but with cool self-possession she waved him off and laughed and danced with others till he was maddened. At last the guests were gone, and he sought her alone.

"Tell me, Ada," he said almost tenderly at first, thinking his game would be much more surely won by that play, "is this real? Is this house, are these splendid furnishings, yours?"

"They are mine," she answered with scorn—"yours, if you will, since the law makes them so." She saw the gleam in his cruel eyes, and she continued: "But listen," and she told him the story of her inheritance.

"Your confession in no way interferes with my ownership," he said, with cool insolence. "But, madam, it gives me the right to rid myself of its incumbrance. I shall apply for a divorce."

Instantly Ada realized how completely she was in the power of her husband.

"Mercy, mercy!" she shrieked; "will no one save me from this man?"

At her cry a door opened and Jacob Strong came in.

"*You* here!" exclaimed Leicester, eying his servant with rage and an undefined suspicion.

"Yes, and the young lady you have just pretended to marry is here too," was the quiet answer.

"Do you mean to say you have been a spy in my service?" thundered Leicester, paling fearfully.

"Yes, a spy. I know your most dangerous secrets. I know all about the letter from Georgia and Florence Craft's inheritance. I have the forged check, which I saw written, in my possession. Villain, I am your master. Five minutes you have here for deliberation, and till noon you are safe from arrest. But men are placed everywhere to watch you, and escape is impossible."

At last Leicester was foiled at every point. But an idea occurred to him. He knew where Julia Warren lived. He would seek the old people—whose true name was Wilcox—demand his child, and then obtain from his wife whatever he chose to ask as the price of her child. He sought the poor abode, and endeavored to browbeat the old man into a prompt resigning of the child. But the grandfather was firm.

"If the law forces me to give her up, I must obey," he said; "but nothing else shall deprive me of my daughter's child."

It was nearly noon, and a prison cell already was opening before Leicester's eyes. Seizing a carving-knife from the table, he plunged it into his own breast, and fell lifeless to the floor.

There was no witness to the deed except the old man, and, as it was soon proved that he had ample reason to hate the dead man, the jury that tried him brought in a verdict of "Guilty." Ada Leicester, overwhelmed with grief, sought by all the means that wealth could employ to procure a different sentence, a fair trial. But the law cared little for the life of a poor old man, innocent or guilty, and every means failed. Indeed, when her father learned from his daughter's penitent lips the source of her wealth, he protested against its use in his behalf. The day was set; but sorrow had already enfeebled the worn body, and when the hour for execution came he was dead, a peaceful smile upon his thin lips.

"Mrs. Gordon" never again appeared in the gay world. The costly furnishings were sold and were replaced by plain, comfortable ones. With her servant, Jacob Strong, in attendance, she went into the highways and compelled the poor to share her comforts. But her affections were centered on her aged mother and her lovely child. The benevolent huckster-woman found in her a devoted friend, and Robert Otis, who proved to be the nephew of that kindly dame, shared in her benefactions.

Three years after the death of old Mr. Wilcox a simple wedding took place in the boudoir in which Julia Warren had first told to her unknown mother the story of her father's handkerchief. The bride was the little flower-girl, and the bridegroom was the nephew of Dame Gray, her first benefactor.

SERGIUS STEPNIAK

(SERGIUS MICHAELOVITCH KRAVTCHINSKI)

(Russia, 1852–1895)

THE CAREER OF A NIHILIST (1889)

In writing this narrative, Stepniak had the personal experiences of his own career upon which to draw. When twenty years of age, after his graduation at the St. Petersburg School of Artillery, he founded a society called the Nihilistic Circle, and actively spread revolutionary ideas among the workmen in the capital.

ELEN ZUBOVA, or Lena, as she was commonly called, hurried from her modest dinner in the cheap Geneva café frequented by Russian exiles to take to Andrey Kojukhov the letter for him which the white-haired old watchmaker had handed her a short while before. She was as eager as Andrey himself to get news of Russia and of the revolutionists there. Andrey had been compromised in his work among the peasants in Russia three years earlier, and had fled the country. Ever since then he had chafed under his enforced exile, and he longed for the day of his recall. Lena had been in Siberia, and on her return had also left Russia for a time.

Andrey was a thoughtful, good-natured young man of twenty-six, with a strong, graceful figure; his earnest face a little careworn. This letter from his friend George recalled him to Russia and told sad news. Andrey had smeared the ostensible letter all over with a liquid that effaced the writing completely. Then rose to the blank surface letters, words, phrases, like soldiers hurriedly falling into ranks at the bugle-call. Toward the second part of the missive long passages began to appear in cipher. George, the correspondent, had employed the double cipher of the League. The original figures had to be changed into others, and then these were subjected to another key, which gave the words. It was a two or three hours' task to work it out. Lena was a great help, as a sort of intuition enabled her to guess some baffling combinations.

The letter told of the recent arrest of Boris, one of the ablest young men of the revolutionary party, at Dubravnik. Zina, his wife, had gone there to see what could be done to enable him to escape. In a few days money and a passport would reach Geneva for Andrey, whose services were desired for this purpose.

"You must write to me and Vasily when you are in the whirlpool again," said Lena, with a sigh.

Vaska Vasily Verbitzky was her friend. His good-natured, swarthy face was half hidden by an abundant growth of auburn hair.

A young Jew, David Stirn, engineered the passage of revolutionists across the frontier, whether they were departing from Russia or returning to it. Andrey's impatience had brought him to a small village near the frontier ahead of time; and he had to wait four or five days for David. Then he was promptly transferred to Russia, a few copper coins more than sufficing to render the guard insensible to his passage. He set out at once for St. Petersburg, and on arriving found his poetic friend, George, elegantly attired, waiting for him at the station. They jolted away in a droshky to George's lodging, for although two revolutionists avoid living together, lest the arrest of one may lead to that of the other, George could not deny himself the comfort of entertaining his friend for a few days under his own roof-tree. George mentioned a girl he wished Andrey to meet, Tatiana Grigorievna Repina, the nineteen-year-old daughter of a famous barrister. George described her as beautiful and enthusiastic, but with great practical judgment. When this young girl became of age she would be wealthy. Her father was a sympathizer in the cause. Andrey suspected that George was captivated by the girl. Although he did not think a revolutionist should not fall in love, he thought he should try to avoid doing so. He and Zina, the wife of Boris, both met Tatiana at her father's that evening. Zina was a strikingly beautiful blonde, with clear gray eyes and a delicately modeled forehead. It was

impossible to believe that her calm and poise were only due to
her will.   In the world to which she belonged, at least one in
every three persons has a heart torn by a misfortune like hers.
If nerves were not kept in good order their work would become
impossible.   Zina took part in the conversation in the simple,
natural way in which she fulfilled every other duty.   Andrey
talked a good deal with Tatiana, and was more favorably impressed than he realized.

That night Repin's house was visited by the gendarmes.
This was not due to the conspirators' presence that evening, but
he thought it best that Tatiana should acquaint them of it.   She
found at George's, not only Andrey, but Lena Subora, who had
just arrived from Switzerland.   Vasily had also come, and
joined them later, together with Zina.   They were both wrought
up to a high pitch of indignant feeling on hearing of a needless
outrage committed by the Dubravnik prison authorities, who,
pretending a need of precise personal description of every inmate of the prison, had stripped a young girl in the presence of
jailers and gendarmes.   Everybody agreed that this should not
go unavenged.   Zina and Vasily resolved to go to Dubravnik.
A woman was needed there who could conduct a lodging for
conspirators.   Lena was to take Zina's work—propaganda
among educated young persons and workmen, and secret correspondence with prisoners in the fortress.

Everything had been prepared for "settling the account"
with the Dubravnik official who had ordered the outrage, when,
panic-stricken, he fled.   It was then determined to make an attempt to liberate Boris and his companions, Levshin and Klein,
who were awaiting trial in the Dubravnik prison.   In the mean
time, Andrey continued his propaganda among the workmen.
This, according to Lena, was the one form of activity to which
revolutionists ought to devote their efforts.   She was a "peas-
antist," or "propagandist," pure and simple.   In the two months
he had devoted to this work, Andrey had awakened to the fact
that he was madly in love with Tatiana, who had been in the
position of a warm sympathizer in the cause of Zina and George
ever since she had known them.   She was instantly converted
to the cause by hearing at Lena's one evening of a simple, heroic
young Russian, who had screened a man of immense value to the

movement at the expense of his own life.   The radiant beauty
of this dark-eyed girl's kindling enthusiasm had wrought in
Andrey's soul an intense conviction of his love for her.

At this juncture a letter arrived at headquarters from Zina,
declaring that the task she was engaged in had complications that
rendered Andrey's presence advisable in Dubravnik.   Arranging his affairs quickly, he departed.

He found Zina, with Annie Vulitch, a keen, spirited girl of
nineteen, and two sisters Dudorov, in Dubravnik.   The political prisoners, who had cells in the upper story of the jail, had
won the coöperation of two common criminals, whose cell was
on the ground floor.   A subterranean passage from the cell of
these two had been laboriously worked at by them until nearly
completed.   At the proper time the political prisoners would
make their way, by using skeleton keys, out of their cells, and
descend to the floor where the common criminals were confined.
The guards had to be eluded, and there was a sentinel near the
point where the passage opened outside.

"Of course, any escape is risky, but we have to do the best
we can," Zina remarked.

Vasily lived at an inn where his horse was kept, and he was
to drive the carriage in which the prisoners were to be taken
away.   Andrey was supposed to be his master, and his arrival
had been arranged for by Vasily.   Passport and suitable dress
had to be secured by Andrey.   David Stirn was in Dubravnik
and was a go-between.   Vasily never visited Zina, who lived at
a little house in the suburbs.   After the escape Andrey and Vasily
would be secreted in Zina's house long enough to let the excitement subside.

The conspirators met only in the public parks, or streets, or
at Rokhalsky's.   He was a man of means, friendly to the conspirators, and his house was considered a very safe refuge.
But an experience of Andrey's on entering it and finding the
police actually up-stairs, led to his staying at Zina's that night.
She took him around to the prison and showed him where Vasily
would wait with the carriage.

There was a delay in the proceedings, however.   A prisoner,
whom Berkut and Kunitzin suspected of being a police spy,
had been put into the cell, and they dared not work at the

passage until, by their annoyances, they had caused him to plead for removal to another cell. A bitterer disappointment was the guard's discovery of the secret passage itself, through a sudden invasion of the cell, owing to a dispute.

Then Andrey proposed a more daring scheme, which had enough possibility of success to induce Zina to acquiesce in it. This was to attempt the rescue of the prisoners when they should be taken to their interrogation; and arrangements were made at once on this new basis. The warder of the prison, who was a revolutionary, was to get revolvers to the three prisoners.

On the morning of the day when the attempt was to be made, Zina received an official request from the committee in St. Petersburg for its postponement for three days. Andrey, in his bitter disappointment, voted to neglect this and go ahead with the plan; but Zina, calm despite her own personal bitter regret, soon won them to a better frame of mind. They wished to give the unfortunate men who were buoyed up with hope of escape some sign that the attempt was deferred, and this was only possible by placing themselves where they could see them on their way to court.

As Boris, who appeared strong and healthy, with his long chestnut beard blowing in the breeze, approached with his two worn-looking companions, Zina, under a sudden inspiration, stepped under a porch and began knocking at the door. She conveyed to her husband, in the prison-knock alphabet, the message: "Get another examination." A hardly noticeable jerk of Boris's head intimated that he had understood. When the maid opened the door Zina sweetly asked whether Colonel Ivan Krutikoff (the first name that came into her head) was at home, and apologized when she learned of her mistake in the house.

The day for the attempt arrived. The signals were posted. The four gendarmes, with the three prisoners, were nearly at the point in the road at which the attack was to be made, when a friendly movement made by Andrey was misinterpreted by Levshin, who instantly drew his revolver and discharged it at the gendarme nearest to him. Despite the premature start, the two men were rushed into Vasily's carriage, which he had driven up. But Boris was left struggling with his guard. Andrey, too excited by the critical moment to be perfectly cool, madly charged the gendarme, who was bowled over; but he dragged Boris down with him. A few priceless moments were thus wasted, and when Andrey had pulled his horse round, Boris, between the two gendarmes, looked down the street, livid with fury.

"Save yourself! The police!" he shouted, in a voice that Andrey never forgot. He rushed his horse toward them, emptying his revolver. But the hurry and excitement nullified the desperate attempt, and at last he spurred his horse away, bullets whistling about his ears. To have delayed a moment longer would have been to throw away his life.

He escaped, but repaired, sick at heart, to the new retreat prepared by Vasily, who had engaged it a fortnight before and had represented that Andrey, a clerk, was to have one of his rooms. They had to remain there quietly for some days after the attempt. Andrey's usefulness in any further efforts to release Boris was over. He was too well known in Dubravnik. Zina remained; her love for her husband would not permit of her leaving.

So Andrey returned to St. Petersburg. Tania Repina had joined the revolutionists, and a strange fate had deputed the two to work in the same district. Andrey was certain now that he was madly in love with this beautiful girl, whose fine character and generous nature seemed greater than ever in her new sphere of action. They worked together, and he could see how his encouragement and advice helped and cheered her. Then she told him one day that she and George were going to Moscow to work there. Andrey could not endure this. He tried to absent himself from the girl, but he could not. He was even impatient and hard with her in his intense preoccupation and efforts to dissemble his passion. At last, one day, she spoke so movingly to ask the cause of this, she pleaded so simply to be told what had made the change, that his soul burst forth.

"Are you blind, then?" he asked, almost rudely. "Do you not see that I love you to madness?"

Her eyes softened, her bosom heaved quickly, and she stretched her arms toward him; then, sobbing, flung herself upon his neck.

"You love me!" he gasped. "Tatiana, my own!"

Within a fortnight they were married. They took a small apartment and resumed their work, and their joy in each other mellowed into the happiest peace and trust.

Then came a bitter blow. Zina and Vasily were arrested after a hot fight, and would be sentenced to death within a few weeks. Poor Annie Vulich, a dark-eyed young girl who had loved Andrey hopelessly in Dubravnik, had been shot in the fray. But the bearer of the news, young Vatajko, said a desperate attempt would be made to rescue them, and that they wished Andrey to be *ataman* for the undertaking, the one supreme leader of the movement. He could not refuse a request like this, and went to Dubravnik to see how the land lay. Botcharov and the Dudorov sisters had been arrested. Moreover, a traitor had loomed up, who, to save his own neck, was betraying those implicated in the attempt. Andrey returned from Dubravnik high-spirited and hopeful, but Tatiana, though acquiescing perfectly, felt that her peace had vanished.

The tribunal that tried the prisoners, against whom a common charge of conspiracy against the throne had been lodged, offered no room for any hope. The punishment was death. Most of the members of the bench had been appointed for this trial by the Governor, which was an ominous thing. In the mean time a conspirator called "the Stutterer" had prepared fifty bombs. The revolutionists were ready for extreme measures, since no others were possible to them.

The trial lasted five days. Had the usual forms been followed, it would have been three times as long. The public was excluded; but the news of the proceedings spread through the town. The day that sentence was to be pronounced, special measures were taken against an outbreak. The court was crowded with soldiers and police, and infantry and Cossacks were outside the building.

The sentence was pronounced on one prisoner after the other: Boris—death. Vasily—death. Zina—death. The last sentence shocked many who had thought the young, beautiful, modest woman would be spared. But no more would be killed; the others were too slightly implicated—no, death was the verdict for two more. Only the younger of the Dudorov sisters escaped it. Her sentence was fifteen years' penal servitude—a miserable sop to the slavish consciences of the judges.

Execution of the death sentence in Russia is rarely delayed more than a few days. On Saturday the sentence of the two Dudorov sisters was commuted to twelve years and six years respectively. But whether Zina and Botcharov would receive any leniency depended on the mood of St. Petersburg.

Andrey would know about the time of the execution two hours after orders were issued from the Governor's study, which would allow only seven or eight hours to marshal his forces. Andrey never left his room for a moment, waiting for this news. It came late Monday night. The four would be executed at ten in the morning of the next Wednesday, in Pushkarsky Field. Andrey at once sent Vatajko to the conspirators to summon them to a meeting.

He had his plan arranged. The spot for action was determined: then a retreat through the Public Garden to the river. The four condemned would be put into a boat awaiting them, while the conspirators would mingle with the crowd on the way to Pushkarsky Field. The chiefs who were to control their several parties of men had received the final instructions from Andrey at seven o'clock Friday evening. He had bidden them farewell when Vatajko burst into the room with appalling news. The bomb-maker's house had been blown out, "the Stutterer" himself taken away in an unconscious condition, in a police van, and all the bombs had been captured. No possibility of a rescue for the condemned remained. "What's to be done now?" someone asked.

"Nothing *can* be done," replied Andrey solemnly, "except to let our friends know that there is not any hope for them whatever. That at least will enable them to prepare for their fate."

He wrote the melancholy news to Zina, and she replied in the name of all, not sadly, but almost cheerfully. But her letter wrung Andrey's very soul, and he sobbed like a child; for he received it only when the great soul which spoke in its every line had already passed away.

The next day, heart-sick, his brain beating with wild rebellious thoughts, he placed himself where he could see his friends and look a last farewell. In the midst of black helmets and glistening spears, the death-car approached. The four, clad in some gray, formless garments, sat in high-backed chairs, to which they were lashed. There was Vasily's dark-brown hair, Boris's lighter locks, and Botcharov's flaxen head. But that boy with short, golden curls, at Boris's side? Zina! They had cut her hair, to hang her more easily. Boris, defiant and fierce, shouted something, which the drums drowned. But that beautiful, serene, pitying woman, her fair face flushed under the coarse, staring gaze of the crowd, was looking for some friend; and as the car passed Andrey, their searching eyes met.

A positive thirst for martyrdom then surged hotly within him. He moved forward, stretching his arms toward her. The grim car was already receding. He remained motionless. He had his message; what more was there? The great and terrible idea that shaped itself in his mind could not be uttered yet.

When he returned to St. Petersburg he waited a little while and then told Tatiana to what he had consecrated himself. He had resolved to kill the Emperor. This was agony to her love, but she came to feel that they had both consecrated themselves to something to which even the deepest, noblest human love must defer. Poor novice! She had to begin with the hardest trial that her new-born conviction and loyalty could know. She sank into her chair, pale, her eyes closed, exhausted, and waved her hand for him to go. It was harder for him to leave her so than if she had clung to him. He cast himself on his knees and clasped her, kissing her hands, face, eyes, in a whirlwind of passionate farewell, then tore himself away and rushed down the stairs as if the Furies were pursuing him. He had gone forever. Tatiana sobbed her heart out in an agony of grief. Andrey was not the only martyr.

The day arrived, one of the few spring days that St. Petersburg's hard climate knows. It was a happy augury. The Emperor would take his morning walk. He did, and he saw this stranger in his path. Instead of baring his head and standing, Andrey drew his revolver and fired. The shot failed. By a curious fatality, Andrey had broken his own pistol shortly before the hour for the attempt on the Emperor's life. There was no time to have it repaired, and he had accepted a friend's revolver, with that friend's assurance that it never missed fire.

In a frenzy he discharged the other chambers at the Emperor, who craftily zigzagged in his flight. One of the bullets pierced the cape of his overcoat; the others did no harm whatever.

George, who was watching the scene from a window, saw the spies, whose vigilance Andrey had eluded, come forward from all sides, halting somewhat until they saw he made no show of resistance, when they rushed upon him in a flock. At the sight he buried his face in his hands, unable to endure the awful futility of it all.

Arrest, imprisonment, and in quick order trial, conviction, and execution. He perished. The Emperor escaped unscathed; but the work for which Andrey had laid down his young life lost none of its vitality. Defeat after defeat does not crush out its life. That will go on until victory shall crown it, a victory that, like others in this sad world, must be bought by suffering and martyrdom.

LAURENCE STERNE

(England, 1713–1768)

TRISTRAM SHANDY (1759–1767)

The Life and Opinions of Tristram Shandy, Gentleman, Comprising the Humorous Adventures of Uncle Toby and Corporal Trim, was published in instalments of two volumes each: in 1759, January, 1761, December, 1761, 1765, and 1768 respectively, making a total of ten volumes. This was the first work of Sterne, who was forty-six years old when the first two volumes appeared. He had been an obscure country parson, a vicar at Sutton-in-the-Forest, and a prebendary of York, for twenty years, which was certainly a strange preparation for composing a book that has been characterized as the most comprehensive work of humor ever written, ranging from the highest form, that which is allied to pathos, to the lowest, which is simple pruriency. The first two volumes were published by a bookseller in York, and its local success was so great that the author had no trouble in securing a London publisher for it in Dodsley. The first edition was exhausted in three months, and Sterne became a lion of the fashionable world. A new game of cards was called "Tristram Shandy"; a "Shandy salad" was invented; and to talk in the desultory, fantastic style of the book became common in society. It was observed that the author had presented himself in the character of the Reverend Mr. Yorick, and this name was fastened upon him and accepted by him. Indeed, he followed up the success of his novel by publishing within the year *Sermons by the Reverend Mr. Yorick*. The picture of Dr. Slop, the man-midwife, Sterne intended for a thrust at a local surgeon-accoucheur named Burton, who had written a five-shilling guide to midwifery, illustrated with appalling illustrations, one of which was of a formidable pair of forceps of the writer's invention.

N the fifth day of November, 1718, was I, Tristram Shandy, Gentleman, brought forth into this scurvy and disastrous world of ours. I wish I had been born in the moon, or in any of the planets (except Jupiter or Saturn, because I never could bear cold weather), for it could not well have fared worse for me in any one of them (although I will not answer for Venus) than it has in this vile, dirty planet of ours, which o' my conscience I take to be made up of the shreds and clippings of the rest; for (since every man will speak of the fair as his own

market has gone in it) from the first hour I drew my breath in it, to this, that I can now hardly draw it at all, for an asthma I got in skating against the wind in Flanders, I have been the continual sport of the jade Fortune, who, at every turn and corner where she could get fairly at me, has pelted me with a set of as pitiful misadventures and cross-accidents as ever small hero sustained.

The records of the Yorick family inform us that it was of Danish extraction, and that one of the ancestors held a considerable post in the court of Horwendillus, King of Denmark. It has often come into my head that this post could be no other than that of the King's jester, and that Hamlet's Yorick was the progenitor of our parson.

If this is so, the Reverend Mr. Yorick came rightly by his disposition, for he was as mercurial and sublimated a composition, as heteroclite a creature in all his declensions, with as much life and whim, and *gaîté de cœur* about him as ever set table on a roar. With all this sail, poor Yorick carried not one ounce of ballast; he was utterly unpractised in the world; and at the age of twenty-six knew just about as well how to steer his course in it as a romping, unsuspicious girl of thirteen; the brisk gale of his spirits ran him foul, ten times a day, of the tackling of slow-going craft; in which entanglement, for aught I know, there may have been some design, for Yorick had an invincible dislike and opposition in his nature to gravity, or rather the affectation of it, for where gravity was wanted he would be the most serious of mortal men for days together. But as it appeared a cloak for ignorance or folly, however sheltered these might be, he seldom gave it quarter. He was fond of quoting the definition of a French wit: "Gravity is a mysterious carriage of the body to cover the defects of the mind."

Accordingly, at all times Yorick spoke his mind in plain English, without distinction of person, time, or place; if he heard of a dirty action he called its doer a dirty fellow. And as he usually ended his comments with a *bon mot*, wings were given to his indiscretion; his gibes flew far and wide and usually reached the man at whom they were pointed.

Five years before my birth, the parson who had heretofore shown himself a lover of horseflesh, much to the wonder and

amusement of the parish, appeared mounted upon a lean jack-
ass of a horse, value about one pound fifteen shillings—as sorry
a jade as Humility herself could have bestrided. As he carried
not an ounce of flesh upon his own bones, with great gravity he
would pretend that he could not bear the sight of a fat horse
without a dejection of heart, and so had made choice of a lean
one to keep himself not only in countenance but in spirits.

But the real reason was as follows: When he kept the best
horse in the parish there was hardly a week when he did not
lend the beast, upon a piteous application from a husband who
had suddenly been made a father, to ride for the nearest midwife, who lived in the village seven miles away. As the roads
were vile, the upshot was that his horse became spavined or
broken-winded, so that every nine or ten months he had a bad
horse to get rid of and a good horse to purchase in his stead.

He could ill afford this expense, especially as it limited his
charities; so, when a poor woman in the parish was left a widow
with several children to support, he took the money that a good
horse would cost that year to get her instructed in the plain principles of midwifery and accommodated himself with Rosinante.
Although this act, it seems to me, displayed as chivalric a soul
as any knight's, from Sir Guy of Warwick to him of La Mancha,
it was noised abroad to his great discredit. Every horse he had
lost and two more than ever he had lost, with all the circumstances of their destruction, were distinctly recalled. So it was
plain as the sun at noonday that he would save in the course
of his remaining lifetime many times over the expense of the new
midwife's tuition and fees. And to call this charity!

This midwife was she my mother chose to assist me into the
world. But my father, who was a philosopher in grain, speculative, systematical, desired that she procure the services of Dr.
Slop, a physician near at hand, who was a scientific obstetrician
after my father's own heart, since he had written a five-shilling
book on midwifery, in which the historical development of the
art was set forth from the days of Rebekah, and which exposed
the blunders of the whole sisterhood of midwives and suggested
several improvements upon Nature's antiquated method of
child delivery, chief among which was the use of an ingenious
pair of forceps of his own invention.

My father contended with my mother in vain upon the matter. He argued like a Christian, like a heathen, like a husband, like a father, like a patriot, like a man. My mother answered everything only like a woman. But the magnanimity of my father is shown in this that, though his arguments in these characters were as six to my mother's one, he agreed to a compromise on even terms. She was to have the old woman, and the learned physician during the operation was to drink a bottle of wine in the back parlor with my father and my Uncle Toby Shandy, for which he was to be paid five guineas.

My Uncle Toby Shandy was a retired captain who lived at our house with his faithful follower, Corporal Trim. He had been shot in the groin at the siege of Namur, and had ridden mounted ever since upon a hobby-horse. The story of his receiving the wound, told again and again with ever-increasing dilation upon the circumstances, led into the subject of investments not only in Flanders, but throughout all countries and ages, from the siege of Troy (which my uncle declared would not have lasted ten hours before modern methods of attack) down to the present. This developed into the scientific principles of fortification and assault, which finally became the whole of life and thought to my Uncle Toby and his Corporal Trim. No subject could be roused up in conversation but my Uncle Toby, assisted by his man, would run it to ground in some question of earthworks. The two had taken possession of a bowling-green back of the house, upon which Trim, under the direction of my Uncle Toby, seated near by in his wheeled chair, constructed miniature plans of the fortresses that Marlborough was then assailing on the Continent, and with all the enthusiasm of real conflict acted out the assaults of the allies as these were reported in the war-bulletins.

When Dr. Slop entered our parlor with his bag of instruments, my Uncle Toby said: "Your coming with all your implements of attack reminds me of the great Stevinus at the siege of—"

"Pish!" said my father. "I would not, brother Toby, have my head as full of sieges, of saps, mines, blinds, gabions, curtains, hornworks, and what not, for all the towns of Flanders."

"Curtains and hornworks!" quoth Dr. Slop, "that I dare say you would not," and he laughed immoderately.

Now my father blamed himself afterward that then and there he had not thrown the man-midwife and his evil instruments incontinently out of the house; for the making of a bald and trite pun he knew to be the sure sign of a shallow and clumsy intellect.

My Uncle Toby felt my father's insult keenly; but he bore it in silence, for he was of a peaceful nature and had hardly a heart to retaliate upon a fly.

"Go," says he one day at dinner, to a blue-bottle that had tormented him cruelly, buzzing about his nose, and which, after infinite attempts, he had caught, "I'll not hurt thee." And, hobbling to the window, he raised the sash and let the insect escape. "Poor devil, the world surely is wide enough to hold both thee and me."

So now, at my father's rebuff, my Uncle Toby looked up with a countenance so grieved, yet so inexpressibly tender, that it penetrated my father to the heart. He rose hastily and, seizing both my Uncle Toby's hands, said:

"Brother, I beg thy pardon; forgive, I pray thee, this rash humor which my mother gave me."

"My dear, dear brother," answered my Uncle Toby, rising by my father's help, "say no more about it."

"What have I to do, my dear Toby," returned my father, "with thy pleasures, unless it were to increase them, which, alack! I cannot."

"Brother Walter," answered my Uncle Toby, "you do increase my pleasure very much, in begetting children for the Shandy family at your time of life."

Dr. Slop opened his green baize bag of instruments to show the wonderful forceps. He fumbled so vilely in pulling them forth that the squirt popped out first.

"Good God!" cried my Uncle Toby, "are children brought into the world with a squirt?"

The old midwife entered and informed Dr. Slop that he was wanted in my mother's room. He followed her, taking his bag of instruments.

My father and my Uncle Toby waited for some time in suspense. Corporal Trim entered. "Dr. Slop is in the kitchen, please your honors, and desires—"

"What is he doing in the kitchen?" asked my father, breaking in impatiently.

"Making a bridge, your honor," answered Corporal Trim.

"'Tis very obliging in him," said my Uncle Toby, thinking of a broken drawbridge on the bowling-green, of which he had spoken to the doctor, "pray tell him I thank him heartily."

"God bless your honors," answered Trim, "'tis a bridge for young master's nose. In bringing him into the world with his vile instruments, he has crushed his nose, Susannah says, as flat as a pancake to his face, and he is making a false bridge with cotton and a thin piece of whalebone out of Susannah's stays."

"Lead me, Brother Toby," cried my father, "to my room this instant. I shall perish with sorrow."

So my father, as well as my mother, was brought to bed of my birth.

There is a tale of Herr Slawkenbergius of which my father was extravagantly fond, for it flattered two of his strangest hypotheses together, his *Names* and his *Noses*. It is as follows:

The two universities of Strasburg, the Lutheran and the Popish, were debating the question of Martin Luther's damnation. The Popish doctors had undertaken to demonstrate, *a priori*, that on October 22, 1483, five planets were in coition all at once with Scorpio in the ninth house, which the Arabians allotted to religion, whence it appeared that a child born that day must die cursing and blaspheming, with the blast whereof his soul sailed forever before the wind in the lake of hell-fire. Therefore Martin Luther was a damned man, and, by direct corollary, his doctrines were damned doctrines, too.

The little objection of the Lutheran doctors to this was, that it certainly must be the soul of another man, born October 22, 1483, that was navigating in this manner, inasmuch as it appeared from the register of Islaben, in the County of Mansfelt, that Luther was born in 1484, on November 10th. The Popish doctors cried out upon this record as a Protestant forgery, to which the Lutherans replied with the corroborative evidence that this was the eve of Martinmas, whence Luther derived his Christian name. To which the Popish doctors had no reply.

"Now you see, Brother Toby," father would say, "that Christian names are not such indifferent things; had Luther been called by any other name but Martin, he would have been damned to all eternity, or at least remained in purgatory till the doctors agreed upon the date of his birth, which was not likely to be while the world lasted."

While this dispute was raging, a stranger, mounted upon a mule, appeared at the gate of the city. He held a naked simitar before his face to defend the most enormous nose that ever had been seen on face of mortal man.

"Who goes there?" challenged the sentinel.

"A friend," answered the stranger.

"Where from?"

"From the Promontory of Noses, where I have got me one of the goodliest that ever fell to a single man's lot." And the stranger blew a blast upon that organ such as that before which the walls of Jericho tumbled down.

The sentinel was felled to the ground by the wind of it. Arising, he said: "It is a trumpet; it is an engine of war; it is contraband, and may not be taken within the city."

"It is but a nose," quoth the stranger.

"That is for the authorities to decide," responded the sentinel; "I shall report this case to them."

"Then I shall return in a month. In the mean time I shall go to Frankfort, where they have a *Juden-gasse* and know a nose when they see one," said the stranger, and turning to the north he followed his nose till it led him out of sight.

The faculties of the two universities suspended their warfare over Luther's birthday to settle the new controversy that was thrust upon them. They divided at once into Nosarians and Antinosarians. Said the Antinosarians: "A man has but one stomach and one pair of lungs, which are the organs of sanguification. They can produce just so much blood as suffices for one man, and no more, so that, if there is as much nose as man, a mortification must ensue; either the nose must fall off from the man, or the man from the nose."

"Nature accommodates herself to these emergencies," answered the Nosarians, "as in the case of half a man, when his legs have been shot off."

"Then the man dies of a plethora," said the opponents, "or spits blood to restore the equilibrium."

"It happens otherwise," said the Nosarians.

"It ought not to," said the opponents. They therefore contended, *a priori*, that despite the evidence of the sentinel, such a nose as the stranger's could not exist.

"God's power is infinite," said the Nosarians; "He can do anything."

"He can do nothing," replied the Antinosarians, "which implies contradiction."

"By God in heaven," said the Popish doctors, "He can make a nose, if he sees fit, as big as Strasburg steeple."

Now the steeple is five hundred and seventy-five feet high, and the Antinosarians denied that a nose of this length could be worn, at least by a middle-sized man. The Popish doctors swore it could.

This diverted the controversy into the extent and limitations of Divine power; which led them to Thomas Aquinas, and from the angelic Doctor to the devil.

The stranger's nose was no more heard of in the dispute. So the civil authorities decided the question for themselves. "Such a monstrous nose," they said, "if it is a true one, cannot possibly be suffered in civil society; and if false, is an imposition on it, and must have still less mercy shown it."

Accordingly, when the stranger returned, entrance was denied him. So all Strasburg went out of the gates to see him and to follow his nose. Observing this, the French, who are ever upon the catch, each followed his own nose, and marched into the city.

"Alas!" cries Slawkenbergius, "it is not the first, nor, I fear, will it be the last prize to be won and lost by a nose."

Said my father: "Fortunately the bias which good or bad Christian names irresistibly impress upon conduct affords a balance to counter the misfortune that has befallen my son in the destruction of the important organ which determines character. We shall give him the steering-oar of a beneficent name to compensate for the loss of his nasal rudder. As the greatest evil has befallen him, I must counteract and undo it with the greatest good. He shall be christened Trismegistus, brother Toby."

"This Trismegistus," continued my father, "was the greatest of all earthly beings; he was the greatest king, the greatest lawgiver, the greatest philosopher, and the greatest priest—"

"And engineer," added my Uncle Toby.

"In course," said my father.

"Then reach me my breeches off the chair," said my father to Susannah.

"There is not a moment's time to dress you, sir," cried Susannah; "the child is as black in the face as my—"

"As your what?" asked my father, for he was a dear searcher into comparisons.

"Bless me, sir," said Susannah, "the child's in a fit. The curate has the boy on his arm, waiting for the name. What is it to be?"

"*Trismegistus*—but stay, thou art a leaky vessel, Susannah; canst thou carry *Trismegistus* in thy head the length of the gallery without scratching?"

"Can I?" cried Susannah, and she was off in a huff.

"If she can, I'll be shot," said my father, bouncing out of bed in the dark and groping for his breeches.

Susannah had the start and kept it. "'Tis *Tris*-something," she said.

"There is no Christian name in the world beginning with *Tris*," said the curate, "but *Tristram*."

"Then 'tis *Tristram-gistus*," quoth Susannah.

"Nonsense," said the curate, and, dipping his hand into the basin, he said, "*Tristram*, I baptize thee," etc.; so Tristram was I called, and Tristram shall I be to the day of my death.

"I see it plainly," said my father in the most querulous monotony possible, "that either for my own sins, brother Toby, or the sins and follies of the Shandy family, Heaven has thought fit to draw forth the heaviest of its artillery against me; and that the prosperity of my child is the point upon which the whole force of it is directed to play. Unhappy Tristram! child of wrath! child of decrepitude! mistake! and discontent! What embryonic evil has not fallen on thy head ere even thou camest into the world? What evil in thy passage into it? What evil since? How we strove against misfortune after misfortune, and how have we been defeated! O Tristram, my son, my son, Tristram!"

My father, by his own computation, had lost fully three fourths of me in my unfortunate geniture, nose, and name. But one fourth was left—my education. Accordingly he sat down to compose for me, after the example of Xenophon, a *Tristra-pædia*, or system of education. He gave himself up to it with as much devotion as ever my Uncle Toby had given to his doctrine of projectiles. And with no more practical results. He proceeded so carefully and conscientiously with it that by the time he had completed the system as it related to the first year of my life, I was well into my second year, and so it would have continued to the end, and I should have grown up an ignoramus, had not Parson Yorick taken my education in hand in my tenth year.

My father proceeded on the principle of John de la Casse, the Lord Archbishop of Benevento, in composing his *Galatea*, in which his Grace spent nearly forty years, and when the book came out it was not more than half the size of a Rider's Almanac. His Grace's theory was that, when a Christian sets out to write a book that should be of service to the world, the devil attempts to prevent the beneficent work by suggesting to his mind those ideas which would ruin the souls of those that followed them. So his Grace had to exclude every one of his first thoughts, which were invariably his most brilliant ones, and scrutinize all, even the most safely dull ones, lest the devil be in them. The author's life, he contended, was not one of composition, but of resistance—a constant warfare.

By allegory my father applied this view to the *Tristrapædia*. "The multitudes of prejudices we suck in with our mother's milk are the devil and all. We are haunted with them, brother Toby, in all our lucubrations; and were a man to submit tamely to what they obtruded upon him, what would his book be? Nothing but a farrago of the clack of nurses, and the nonsense of the old women (of both sexes) throughout the kingdom."

It was decided that I should have a companion in my education. In this connection my Uncle Toby bethought himself of the son of an old comrade, Le Fèvre by name. He sent Corporal Trim to find out whether the lad were available. Trim reported that the old soldier and his son were fallen on evil times, and would be grateful if we received the boy. The father, Trim said, was very ill.

"Thou shouldst have brought him with thee," said my Uncle Toby. "Thou art an excellent nurse, and between us all we would set him on his legs. In a fortnight he might march."

"He will never march, please your honor, in this world," said the corporal.

"He will march," said my Uncle Toby, sitting up on the side of the bed with one shoe off, and marching with it, though without advancing an inch.

"He cannot stand it," said the corporal.

"He shall be supported," said my Uncle Toby.

"A-well-a-day! do what we can for him," said Trim, maintaining his point; "the poor soul will die."

"He shall not die, by G—!" cried my Uncle Toby.

The accusing spirit which flew up to Heaven's chancery with the oath, blushed as he gave it in; and the recording angel, as he wrote it down, dropped a tear upon the word, and blotted it out forever.

Le Fèvre died happy in the thought that his son had found a home with father's old comrade.

My father, my Uncle Toby, Corporal Trim, young Le Fèvre, and I, made the grand tour through Europe. My father has written a book (which I have yet to publish) of reasonings upon the characters and customs of the countries we passed over, which is so opposite to those of all other mortal men that I will not here introduce my own commonplace, nor anticipate his work by relating our conversations. Suffice it to say that I was young and full of the animal spirits that my father thought he had deprived me of in my begetting. My grand tour did not begin with Calais, but with Nannette.

'Twas in the road betwixt Nismes and Lunel, where is the best Muscatto wine in all France, that I met her. It was evening, work was done for the day, and the rustics were preparing for a carousal. My mule made a dead point.

" 'Tis the fife and tabourine," said I.

" I'm frightened to death," said he.

" They are running at the ring of pleasure," said I.

" By all the saints they curse me by," said he, " I'll not budge a step farther."

" 'Tis well," said I. " I never argue a point with one of your family."

So, leaping from his back, and kicking off one boot into this ditch and t'other into that, " I'll take a dance," said I; " so stay you here."

A sunburnt daughter of labor rose to meet me from the group. Her hair, which was of a dark chestnut, was tied up in a knot, all but a single tress.

" We want a cavalier," she said, reaching out both her hands.

" And a cavalier you shall have," said I, taking them.

A lame youth seated on the bank ran sweetly over the prelude with pipe and tabourine.

" Tie me up this tress," said Nannette, putting a string into my hand.

The whole knot fell down. By the time I had tied it up we were seven years acquainted.

The youth struck the note upon the tabourine; his pipe followed. 'Twas a Gascoigne roundelay:

> "*Viva la joia!*
> *Fidon la tristessa!*"

The nymphs joined in unison, and their swains an octave below them. Off we bounded. *Viva la joia!* was on Nannette's lips; *viva la joia!* was in her eyes. A transient spark of amity shot across the space betwixt us.

" Just Dispenser of our joys and sorrows," said I, " why could not a man sit down in the lap of content here, and say his prayers, and go to heaven with this nut-brown maid?"

Capriciously did she turn her head on one side, and dance up insiduous.

" 'Tis time to dance off," quoth I. So, changing my tune, I danced it away from Lunel to Montpellier; thence to Pesçnas, Beziers. I danced it along through Narbonne, Carcasson, and

Castle Naudairy, till at last I danced myself into Pedrillo's pavilion, where, pulling out a paper ruled in black lines, that I might go on straightforward, without any cursed digressions and parentheses, I began to write my Uncle Toby's amours. Which are another book.

A SENTIMENTAL JOURNEY THROUGH FRANCE AND ITALY (1768)

Sterne traveled more than once between England and Italy, but it was on his last journey, undertaken in 1765, that it occurred to him to write an account of his travels. The materials for the book were doubtless selected from all his journeys. He was very enthusiastic over his new project, but on his return home he postponed writing the book until he had finished the last volume of *Tristram Shandy*. Then he set to work on the *Sentimental Journey*, and when he had written enough to make two volumes, according to the methods of publication in his time, he went to London and had the matter published. He died about a month later, leaving the work unfinished, the *Sentimental Journey* as published comprising about half the work he had planned.

BEHOLD me in Calais, one-and-twenty miles from England, *en route*, or about to be (for I had paused to dine), for Paris and Italy. My landlord was conducting me to his coach-house, where I was to select my vehicle, and I was quite decided to buy one with accommodation for one person only, as conducive to economy and contemplation. He will take advantage of me, thought I, and charge me excessively in any case, and I was debating how I should best direct my discourse to the end that I should be overreached as little as possible, when I found myself face to face—did I not speak of the lady I saw talking with a monk? Indeed, I meant to do so, and here she was, proceeding also to the coach-house door. As gallantly as might be, I offered her my hand, which she took; it was gloved, and open only at the thumb and one finger; she might withdraw it, thought I, and so I held it loosely, as if it were my own intention to let go; and so we arrived at the coach-house door, where the landlord, after fumbling with the key a dozen times, discovered that he had left the right key in the house. He asked us to pardon him, he would be back in five minutes, and left us.

There we were, then, hand in hand, facing the coach-house,

475

and, lest the situation should become embarrassing by silence, I began some manner of conversation, it matters not what, but I vow it was innocuous, aye, philosophical, but naturally suggested by the event, as passers behind us might properly enough mistake us for man and wife, and of course it was such a conversation as might not have been had we faced the other way; there must have been a climax, for such is my manner of discourse, or an approach to one; at all events, when the landlord returned at the expiration of five minutes and let us into the coach-house, the lady declared with a light laugh that I had been making love to her all the time! However impossible this might have been, it was equally impossible to deny the lady's asseveration—it has ever been my lot to be deeply in love with somebody —I had already changed my plan, and was for engaging a conveyance with room for two. My mind and heart were in a furious struggle over the temptation presented, prudence saying one thing, kindly sentiment another; and the battle had not been decided when the lady's brother arrived and presently took her away toward Paris in his own vehicle.

Twice on the first stage of the journey was I obliged to dismount in the rain and pick up my portmanteau, which led me, at the first stopping-place, to engage La Fleur as my servant, a fellow whom I came to value most highly for his unfailing good nature and delicate, if sometimes mistaken, anticipation of my desires. We had hardly arrived in Amiens, when the Count de L——'s post-chaise, with his sister in it, drove hastily by; she had just time to make me a bow of recognition, and of that particular kind that told me she had not yet done with me.

She was as good as her look, for in the evening her brother's servant came with a billet, in which she said she had taken the liberty to charge me with a letter, which I was to present myself to Madame R—— the first morning I had nothing to do in Paris. There was something, she added, she wished to tell me. Then I will meet thee, said I, fair spirit! With what moral delight will it crown my journey to share the sickening incidents of a tale of misery told me by such a sufferer; for I made no doubt her revelations would be such as to move to pity. There was nothing wrong in the sentiment, and yet I instantly reproached my heart with it in the bitterest and most reprobate of expressions. For memory of my last flame came to me—I had sworn eternal fidelity, which should last at least as long as my three-months' journey; she had a right to my whole heart; to divide my affections was to lessen them, to expose them was to risk them. No! I would not go to Madame R——'s.

My first sensations, after I had settled in my chamber at my hotel in Paris, were far from being so flattering as I had prefigured them. I was such an atom in this vast place, where a man might do very well had he an imposing equipage and a retinue of servants. There seemed nothing for me but some modest alley where carriages never rolled, where perchance I might have pleasant converse with some grisette of a barber's wife. May I perish if I do! said I, pulling out the letter which I had to present to Madame R——. I'll wait upon this lady the first thing I do; and I called La Fleur to seek me a barber, and to come and brush my coat.

Now the barber was such a punctilio at his art that he was overlong in making me presentable; and when he was done, it was altogether too late to call on Madame R——; so I walked forth without any determination where to go. It occurred to me presently that I would visit the Opéra Comique, and, after casting my eyes into various shops for some face that seemed kindly enough to welcome an inquiry, I asked my way of a woman who was working at a pair of ruffles on the far side of a shop, facing the door. She willingly arose and came out to the street, the better to give me directions, which she did with great minuteness but perfect comprehensibility, repeating her instructions three times over, with the same good-natured patience the third time as the first. If tones and manners have a meaning, which certainly they have, unless to hearts which shut them out, she seemed really interested that I should not lose myself. I looked her full in the eyes as she instructed me; she was, I think, the handsomest grisette I ever saw, and I repeated my thanks as often as she had her instructions. I had not gone ten paces from the door when I discovered that I had forgotten every tittle of what she said, so I turned back to ask her whether the first turn was to the right or the left, for that I had absolutely forgotten.

"Is it possible?" said she, half laughing.

" 'Tis very possible," I replied, "when a man is thinking more of a woman than of her good advice."

As this was the real truth, she took it, as every woman takes a matter of right, with a slight curtsey. Then she called to a lad to make ready a parcel of gloves. She was about to send him, she said, to the vicinity of the Opéra Comique, and if I would but wait a moment he would attend me to the place. So I walked in with her to the far side of the shop, and took up the ruffle which she had laid upon a chair, as if I had a mind to sit; she then sat down herself on the low chair, and I instantly sat myself down beside her.

"He will be ready, Monsieur," said she, "in a moment."

"And in that moment," I replied, "most willingly would I say something very civil to you for all these courtesies. Anyone may do a casual act of good nature, but a continuation of them shows it is a part of the temperament; and certainly if it is the same blood which comes from the heart which descends to the extremes (here I touched her wrist) I am sure you must have one of the best pulses of any woman in the world."

"Feel it," said she, holding out her arm.

So, laying down my hat, I took hold of her fingers in one hand, and applied two fingers of my other to the artery, and there I sat, in my black coat and my lackadaisical manner, counting the throbs, one by one, with as much true devotion as if I had been watching the critical ebb and flow of a fever. I had counted twenty pulsations, and was going fast to the fortieth, when her husband, coming unexpected from a back parlor of the shop, put me a little out of my reckoning. " 'Tis nobody but my husband," said she, so I began a fresh score. "Monsieur is so good," quoth she, as he passed by us, "as to give himself the trouble of feeling my pulse."

The husband took off his hat and made me a bow. "Monsieur does me too much honor," said he, and walked out.

Good God! said I to myself, and can this man be the husband of this woman?

"And how does it beat, Monsieur?" said she, after an interval.

"With all the benignity," said I, looking quietly in her eyes, "that I expected."

She was going to say something civil in return, but the boy came into the shop with the gloves. I was immediately reminded that I wanted a couple of pairs for myself, and as long as possible I prolonged the endeavor to find a pair that would fit me, the beautiful grisette leaning over one side of the narrow counter, I leaning over the other. There are certain combined looks of simple subtlety where whim and sense, seriousness and nonsense, are so blended that all the languages of Babel let loose together could not express them; they are communicated and caught so instantaneously that you can hardly say which party is the infector. The beautiful grisette looked sometimes at the gloves, then sidewise toward the window; then at the gloves, and then at me. I was not disposed to break silence; I followed her example: I looked at the gloves, then toward the window; then at the gloves, and then at her, and so on alternately. I found I lost in every attack; her black eyes looked into my very heart; it may seem strange, but I could actually feel she did.

"No matter," I said at last, for the boy was waiting. I put two pairs in my pocket, paid her with a low bow, went out, and the boy with the parcel followed me.

I was going one evening to a concert in Milan, and was just entering the door of the hall when the Marquisina di F—— was coming out in an evident hurry. She was almost upon me before I saw her; so I gave a spring to one side to let her pass. She had done the same, and on the same side, too; so we ran our heads together; she instantly got to the other side to get out; I was just as unfortunate as she had been, for I too had sprung to that side, and opposed her again. We both flew to the other side, and then back, and so on—it was ridiculous; we both blushed intolerably. So at last I stood stock still, and the Marquisina had no more difficulty. I had no power to go into the concert room till I had made her so much reparation as to wait and follow her with my eye to the end of the passage. She looked back twice. The Marquisina, said I to myself, has a right to the best apology I can make her. So I ran and begged pardon for the embarrassment I had given her, saying it was my intention to have made way for her. She answered she was guided by the same intention toward me; so we reciprocally thanked each other. She was at the top of the stairs, and, seeing no attendant near her, I begged leave to hand her to her coach; so we went down the stairs, stopping at every third step to talk of the concert and the adventure.

"Upon my word, Madame," said I, when I had handed her in, "I made six different efforts to let you go out."

"And I made six efforts," replied she, "to let you enter."

"I wish to Heaven you would make a seventh," said I.

"With all my heart," said she, making room.

"Life is too short to be long about the forms of it."

I instantly stepped into her coach and she carried me home with her—and what became of the concert, St. Cecilia, who, I suppose, attended it, knows more than I.

When I got home to my hotel, La Fleur informed that a Lieutenant of Police had inquired for me, and then I remembered that I had left England without providing myself with a passport. I professed such indifference to the matter that both La Fleur and my landlord were alarmed. They were sure I should be thrown into the Bastile, and I let them think so for a time, while I entertained myself with reflecting that it could be for no more than a few weeks; and what is the Bastile but a tower, and a tower but a kind of house? and how should it be a prison to me more than many a fine mansion is to the owner who cannot go forth because of the gout? I really succeeded in reasoning myself into the conviction that a prison is troublesome only as the inmate feels it to be so, when some errand taking me to the courtyard, I heard a voice crying: "I can't get out." I supposed it was a child, and looked around me to lend assistance, but presently I discovered that the words were uttered by a starling in a cage. It kept repeating its lamentation of captivity: "I can't get out," said the starling. God help thee! said I, but I'll let thee out, cost what it may; and I tried to unfasten the cage door; but it was so inextricably bound with wires that I could not, and I had to return to my room, leaving the bird to its cry: "I can't get out."

I vow I never had my affections more tenderly awakened; nor do I remember an incident in my life where the dissipated spirits, to which my reason had been a bubble, were so suddenly called home. Mechanical as the notes were, yet so true in tune to nature were they chanted that in one moment they overthrew all my systematic reasonings upon the Bastile. Disguise thyself as thou wilt, still, Slavery, said I, still thou art a bitter draught! and though thousands in all ages have been made to drink of thee, thou art no less bitter on that account. 'Tis thou, thrice sweet and gracious goddess, addressing myself to Liberty, whom all in public or in private worship, whose taste is grateful and ever will be so till Nature herself shall change; no tint of words can spot thy snowy mantle, or chymic power turn thy scepter into iron; with thee to smile upon him as he eats his crust, the swain is happier than his monarch, from whose court thou art exiled. Gracious Heaven! I cried, grant me but health, and give me but this fair goddess as my companion, and shower down thy miters, if it seems good to thy divine providence, upon those heads which are aching for them!

The influence of such reflections as these induced me early on the following morning to take the steps necessary to procuring a passport, which I did without more delay than always attends commerce with officialdom, but which brought me in touch with interesting acquaintances, each one of whom put himself out to present me to others, so that I had much to do in accepting the engagements that were offered to me. We get forward in the world not so much by doing services as by receiving them. The nobleman who assisted me to get my passport, merely because he had done me one kindness would go on and do me another. He introduced me to the old Marquis de B——, who in his younger days had been a famous gallant. He wished he might visit England, and asked much about the English ladies. "Stay where you are, I beseech you, Monsieur le Marquis," said I; "Englishmen can scarce get a kind look from them as it is." The Marquis invited me to supper.

Monsieur P——, the farmer-general, was just as inquisitive about our taxes; they were very considerable, he had heard. "If we only knew how to collect them," said I, making him a low bow, I could never have been invited to M. P——'s concerts on any other terms.

I had been misrepresented to Madame de Q—— as a wit. Madame de Q—— was a wit herself. She burned with impatience to see me and to hear me talk. I had not taken my seat before I saw she did not care a sou whether I had any wit or no;